The Fundamentals of Aircraft Combat Survivability Analysis and Design

Robert E. Ball
Naval Postgraduate School
Monterey, California

AIAA EDUCATION SERIES
J. S. Przemieniecki
Series Editor-in-Chief
Air Force Institute of Technology
Wright-Patterson Air Force Base, Ohio

Published by
American Institute of Aeronautics and Astronautics, Inc.
1633 Broadway, New York, N.Y. 10019

American Institute of Aeronautics and Astronautics, Inc.
New York, New York

Library of Congress Cataloging in Publication Data

Ball, Robert E.
  The fundamentals of aircraft combat survivability analysis
and design.

(AIAA education series)
Includes index.
1. Airplanes, Military—United States—Combat
survivability. 2. Air warfare. I. Title. II. Series.
UG1243.B35   1985   358.4′14   85-15722
ISBN 0-930403-02-9

Foreword

The Fundamentals of Aircraft Combat Survivability Analysis and Design by Robert E. Ball—a comprehensive treatise on survivability concepts in the design of military aircraft—presents the fundamentals of the newly emerging design discipline of survivability engineering applied to tactical and strategic aircraft: both theoretical background for this new discipline and, just as important, lessons of survivability from the past military operations with various types of aircraft, both fixed- and rotary-wing.

Professor Ball developed this text from lecture notes prepared for a survivability course at the U.S. Naval Postgraduate School; he also used his notes in a similar course at the Air Force Institute of Technology. Both courses provided Dept. of Defense engineers and technical managers with the opportunity to learn the fundamentals of survivability engineering and their application in aircraft design.

Publication of *The Fundamentals of Aircraft Combat Survivability Analysis and Design*, as a formal text in the AIAA Education Series, will allow for much broader dissemination of this important material to scientists and engineers in the aerospace industry concerned with survivability of the next generation of military aircraft. Likewise, the text should also be of a great value to military analysts who plan combat operations with the objective of maximizing the survivability of the aircraft.

J. S. PRZEMIENIECKI
Editor-in-Chief
AIAA Education Series

Acknowledgment

The Joint Technical Coordinating Group on Aircraft Survivability (JTCG/AS) is chartered under the Joint Army Materiel Development and Research Command/Naval Material Command/Air Force Logistics Command/Air Force Systems Command Commanders to conduct a Joint Survivability Program and to coordinate the individual Service survivability programs. The mission of the JTCG/AS includes a long-range goal to "establish survivability as a design discipline." Professor Ball has been a leader in helping the JTCG/AS reach this goal.

In 1977, Professor Ball introduced a graduate level survivability course that has since been offered as part of the Naval Postgraduate School (NPS) Aeronautical Engineering curriculum. Professor Ball and his thesis students have made major technical contributions toward establishing survivability as a design discipline over the years. Professor Ball also developed an NPS short course on Aircraft Combat Survivability. This course has provided Department of Defense and industry engineers and managers with the opportunity to learn the fundamentals of survivability engineering and their application to actual aircraft. Both courses have gained an outstanding reputation due to Professor Ball's lecturing skills and his continuing efforts to update and improve the course material.

This book continues and extends Professor Ball's high-quality work in this field. Professor Ball has done an outstanding job of providing a comprehensive, well-written, and technically accurate book that will be useful to engineers and managers involved in all phases of aircraft design and development, as well as those involved in training engineers and program managers.

DALE B. ATKINSON, Chairman
Joint Technical Coordinating
Group on Aircraft Survivability

Table of Contents

Preface

"The survival of a military aircraft operating in a hostile environment depends upon many diverse factors, such as the design of the aircraft, the skill and experience of the crew, the armament carried, the onboard countermeasures equipment, the offboard supporting systems, and the tactics employed. The cost of modern aircraft weapon systems, coupled with the requirement that the system be *effective*, makes imperative the consideration of the aircraft's survivability throughout the life cycle of the system."

Anonymous

> In blossom today, then scattered;
> Life is so like a delicate flower.
> How can one expect the fragrance
> To last forever.

Vice-Admiral Takijiro Onishi
Kamikaze Special Attack Squad

In the book *Zero!*, by Masatake Okumiya and Jiro Horikoshi (the designer of the Zero), with Martin Caidin (E. P. Dutton & Company, New York, 1956), Mitsusa Kofukuda, Commander of the 6th Japanese Air Force during World War II, states that the ruggedness, firepower, and aggressive employment of the US B-17 and B-24 presented a serious problem to the Japanese and that the ability of these bombers to carry out their mission despite fighter opposition was the deciding factor in the final outcome of Japan's war with the United States. He further states that Japanese naval and aeronautical engineers made their greatest technical blunder by concentrating their efforts on increasing aircraft ranges and completely neglecting any attempt to improve an aircraft's ability to survive enemy firepower. According to Commander Kofukuda, this opinion was shared by many senior Japanese officers.

ix

The US 8th Air Force, operating over Germany in daylight and without fighter escort, suffered a 24% attrition rate in October 1943 in raids against the ball bearing factories in Schweinfurt. This heavy loss of aircraft led to the termination of the Air Force's daytime un-escorted, deep penetrations into Germany.

During the Korean War, US Air Force B-29's suffered a 20% loss rate during a series of daylight missions, causing the Bomber Command to cancel the daylight raids and to operate only at night.

The heavy losses of Israeli A-4 aircraft on the first day of the Yom Kippur War in 1973 resulted in cancellation of the close air support missions over the Golan Heights. When the ground situation ab-solutely required resumption of the close air missions, the tactics were changed so that A-4's operated at the outer fringes of the battle zone and were not faced with the intense Syrian air defenses.

All of the above examples, both strategic and tactical, illustrate the overwhelming requirement for the consideration of survivability in the design and utilization of military aircraft. As a result of this require-ment, a technology for enhancing survivability and a methodology for assessing survivability has evolved over the past 70 years. However, because the importance of survivability is sometimes either forgotten or neglected in the design and development of military aircraft during periods of peace, aircraft designers, program managers, and operators must be reminded that survivability considerations must be neither overlooked nor ignored. They need to be informed about the current technology for increasing survivability and about the methodology for assessing the payoffs and the penalties associated with survivability enhancement features. This text is devoted to that end. It presents the fundamentals of the maturing aircraft combat survivability design discipline. It provides the reader with the history, concepts, terminol-ogy, facts, procedures, requirements, measures, methodology, and the current technology for the nonnuclear combat survivability analysis and design of both fixed-wing and rotary-wing aircraft. It is also applicable to guided missiles. The text should be helpful to anyone involved in airborne weapons effectiveness studies or in the develop-ment of antiaircraft weapon systems for defense against hostile manned aircraft and guided missiles. Knowledge of aircraft survivability fundamentals should also be beneficial to anyone faced with the prospect of flying in a hostile environment.

This text could not have been written without the participation of several of my thesis students at the Naval Postgraduate School. In particular, R. G. Nosco and K. O. Krumbholz were early contributors to the threat and susceptibility and the vulnerability areas, respec-tively, and M. A. Boies contributed much of the material on the evolution of the survivability technology. Other thesis students who helped with various portions of the text were M. R. Etheridge Jr., P. F. Coste, J. E. Parr, C. K. Fair, and D. R. Ferrell; P. Cox assisted me in the task of putting it all together. I also want to express my deep appreciation to Dale B. Atkinson, Naval Air Systems Command, who provided continuous intellectual encouragement and financial support, and to John Morrow, Naval Weapons Center, for his tutelage. Other people I am indebted to are Capt. P. van R. Schoeffel, USN, retired, Maj. Tim Horton, USA, retired, Lieut. Col. Jim Sebolka, USAF, and John Aldridge, Vince Di Rito, George Ducker, Don Voyls, and the rest of the JTCG/AS Design Criteria and Industry Interface Subgroup for their encouragement and financial support of this effort. I especially want to thank Don Jacobs for preparing the artwork, Regina Stewart and Jo Ann Schmalz for interpreting my handwriting and typing the text, and Jim Buckner for tackling the very difficult job of editing the text.

This text is not to be interpreted as reflecting the official opinion or policy of any Government agency. The text has been written about the survivability discipline as I see it, and the views expressed are my own.

ROBERT E. BALL
Naval Postgraduate School
Monterey, California

1. INTRODUCTION

1.1 AN OVERVIEW OF THE FUNDAMENTALS

What Is Aircraft Combat Survivability?

Aircraft combat survivability (ACS) is defined here as "the capability of an aircraft to avoid and/or withstand a man-made hostile environment." The key words in this definition are "to avoid and/or withstand." The inability of an aircraft to avoid the radars, guns, ballistic projectiles, guided missiles, exploding warheads, and other elements that make up the hostile environment can be measured by P_H, the probability that the aircraft is hit by a damage-causing mechanism, and is referred to as the *susceptibility* of the aircraft. Susceptibility can be divided into three general categories: (1) threat activity; (2) aircraft detection, identification, and tracking; and (3) missile launch or gun firing, propagator flyout, and warhead impact or detonation.

These categories can be conceptually measured respectively by the probability that the threat is active and ready to engage the aircraft, P_A; by the probability that the aircraft is detected, identified, and tracked by the threat, P_{DIT}; and by the probability that a threat propagator is launched or fired, possibly guided, and either hits the aircraft or a high-explosive warhead is detonated sufficiently close to the aircraft to cause a hit by a damage mechanism, P_{LGD}. The susceptibility of an aircraft is influenced by such features as the aircraft's design (e.g., smokeless engines and small size to minimize detection, and good maneuverability to avoid the damage mechanisms); the tactics that are used (e.g., terrain masking to avoid detection, and escorts to suppress the enemy air defense); and the survivability equipment and weapons it carries (e.g., electronic countermeasures equipment to prevent detection and to spoof missiles, and antiradiation missiles to suppress tracking radars).

The inability of an aircraft to withstand the damage caused by the hostile environment is referred to as the *vulnerability* of the aircraft to the damage mechanisms. Vulnerability is determined by the aircraft's design and any survivability features that reduce the amount and the effects of damage when the aircraft takes one or more hits. Vulnerability can be measured by $P_{K/H}$, the conditional probability that the aircraft is killed given a hit by a damage mechanism. It is influenced by such things as the ability of critical components to continue to operate after taking a hit (e.g., helicopter

1

transmissions that can operate for 30 minutes after loss of lubrication) and by design features and equipment that prevent or suppress damage to critical components (e.g., two engines effectively separated so that a single hit will not destroy both engines).

The ease with which an aircraft is killed by the hostile environment is measured by the probability the aircraft is killed P_K. The probability of kill of the aircraft is the product of the probability of hit (the susceptibility) P_H and the conditional probability of kill given a hit (the vulnerability) $P_{K/H}$. Thus,

$$\text{Probability of Kill} = \text{Susceptibility} * \text{Vulnerability}$$

or

$$P_K = P_H P_{K/H} \tag{1.1}$$

The capability of the aircraft to survive the hostile environment is measured by the probability of survival P_S. Its relationship to P_K is given by

$$P_S = 1 - P_K \tag{1.2}$$

Figure 1.1 illustrates the relationships between these major concepts of survivability.

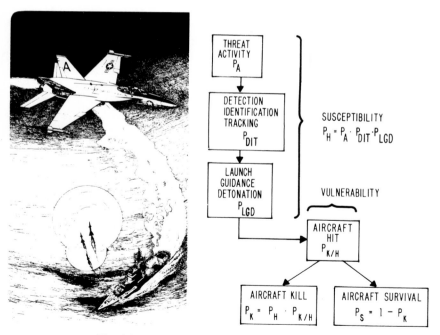

Fig. 1.1   Major concepts of aircraft survivability.

When an aircraft is hit by more than one damage mechanism in an encounter with a threat, it must survive each and every one of the individual hits if it is to survive the encounter. The probability that the aircraft survives n independent hits on the aircraft, $\overline{P}_S^{(n)}$, is given by the product

$$\overline{P}_S^{(n)} = P_S^{(1)} P_S^{(2)} \dots P_S^{(i)} \dots P_S^{(n)} \tag{1.3}$$

where $P_S^{(i)}$ denotes the probability the aircraft survives the ith hit. This equation is fundamental to the survivability problem and also applies to the probability of survival of an individual component due to n hits, to the probability of survival of a crew member after n missions, and to the probability of survival of an aircraft after encounters with n threats. If $P_S^{(i)}$ is a constant value for each of the n events, P_S, Eq. (1.3) simplifies to

$$\overline{P}_S^{(n)} = P_S^n \tag{1.4}$$

How Is Survivability Enhanced?

The survivability of an aircraft can be enhanced by a good design that does not cause weight, cost, or performance penalties, by the addition of extra elements to the design that do involve penalties, and by the proper utilization of the aircraft. Any particular characteristic of the aircraft, specific piece of equipment, design technique, armament, or tactic that reduces either the susceptibility or the vulnerability of the aircraft has the potential for increasing survivability and is referred to as a survivability enhancement feature. A survivability enhancement concept is a generic survivability enhancement feature. Table 1.1 lists the six survivability enhancement concepts for susceptibility reduction and the six for vulnerability reduction.

As shown in Table 1.1, the susceptibility of an aircraft can be reduced by the use of passive warning receivers that inform the crew of the type and location of tracking systems that are a threat to the aircraft or of a missile launch toward the aircraft. Noise jammers and deceivers, carried onboard or in supporting units, can be used to prevent tracking systems from seeing the aircraft or to send out false target signals. Signature reduction, or the

Table 1.1   Survivability Enhancement Concepts

Susceptibility Reduction	Vulnerability Reduction
Threat warning	Component redundancy (with separation)
Noise jammers and deceivers	Component location
Signature reduction	Passive damage suppression
Expendables	Active damage suppression
Threat suppression	Component shielding
Tactics	Component elimination

reduction of the observables, makes the aircraft more difficult to detect and track and is best accomplished in the original design of the aircraft. Expendables, such as chaff and infrared (i.r.) flares, can provide a screen behind which the aircraft can hide, or they can be decoys that are more attractive targets than the aircraft. Threat suppression is accomplished by using antiradiation missiles to home in on radar transmitters and by supporting fire from accompanying or ground-based units. The tactics that are developed by the operational forces attempt to reduce susceptibility by minimizing the exposure of the aircraft to the threat air defense systems. This is accomplished in part by the use of terrain and weather for masking and stand-off or launch-and-leave weapons. The performance capabilities and handling qualities of the aircraft have a major impact on the tactics that are employed, as do crew skill and experience.

The six vulnerability reduction concepts include critical component redundancy with separation, which is the use of more than one component to perform an essential function. (The redundant components must be effectively separated in order to minimize the probability of kill of more than one of the redundant components by a single hit.) Component location is the positioning of the critical components to minimize the possibility and extent of damage. Passive and active damage suppression concepts reduce vulnerability either by containing the damage or by reducing the effects of damage. Component shielding prevents the damage mechanisms from hitting the critical components, and component elimination is either the removal of a critical component or the replacement of a critical component with a less vulnerable one.

What Is the Goal of the Aircraft Survivability Discipline?

The mission of the aircraft, the supporting friendly forces, and the density and effectiveness of the threat significantly influence the relative importance of each survivability enhancement concept. Not all survivability enhancement concepts are either appropriate or necessary for any one particular aircraft on a specific mission. Furthermore, a reduction in vulnerability could lead to an increase in susceptibility (e.g., adding a lot of heavy armor could slow the aircraft down and make it easier to hit) and vice versa. Consequently, the goal of the ACS discipline is the early identification and successful incorporation of those specific survivability enhancement features that increase the effectiveness of the aircraft as a weapon system. In those circumstances where the damage will eventually lead to an aircraft kill, the survivability enhancement features should allow a graceful degradation of the system capabilities, giving the crew a chance to depart the aircraft over friendly territory.

Weapon System Effectiveness and Survivability

The combat or mission effectiveness of a particular airborne weapon system on a specific mission is influenced by many factors. These factors are associated with the threat, the weapon system itself, and the operational environment. Figure 1.2 is an illustration of a typical combat mission. In

COMBAT/MISSION EFFECTIVENESS INFLUENCED BY

- AVAILABILITY
- A/C PERFORMANCE & HANDLING QUALITIES
- TARGET ACQUISITION CAPABILITY
- TYPE, EFFECTIVENESS & NUMBER OF "WEAPONS" CARRIED ⎫ SUSCEPTIBILITY (P_H)
- C³ & OTHER SUPPORTING SYSTEMS (FE, SOJ, ETC.)
- A/C SIGNATURES & COUNTERMEASURES
- TACTICS, TERRAIN & WEATHER

- A/C VULNERABILITY ($P_{K/H}$)

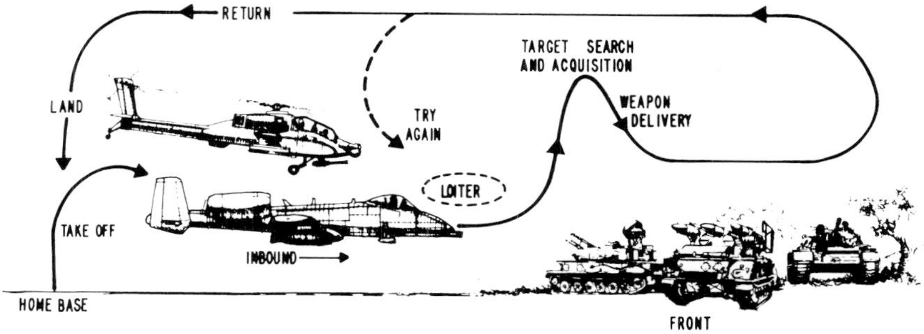

Fig. 1.2   Typical combat / mission effectiveness.

this scenario, the aircraft attempts to get to the target area, to locate the intended target, to deliver one or more weapons that kill the target, and to return home. A study of this scenario reveals that the ability of the aircraft weapon system to accomplish these tasks is dependent upon:

(1)   The availability of the weapon system for the mission.
(2)   The aircraft performance capabilities and handling qualities.
(3)   The target acquisition capability.
(4)   The type, effectiveness, and number of weapons carried.
(5)   The command, control, and communications and other supporting systems available.
(6)   The aircraft signatures and the countermeasures employed.
(7)   The tactics used and the terrain and weather conditions.
(8)   The ability of the aircraft to take a hit and survive.

Availability, or readiness, influences effectiveness because the more likely a weapon system is available to send on the mission, the more likely the target will be killed, all other factors being the same. Availability is affected by the number of systems purchased, by the reliability of the system, by the effectiveness of battle damage repair, by the availability of spare parts, and by the required turnaround time between sorties. It is also affected by the survivability of the aircraft. Aircraft with more survivability will return from a mission more often, and consequently more aircraft will be available for subsequent missions.

Aircraft performance capabilities affect effectiveness by limiting the combat radius, cruise speed, dash speed, maneuverability, payload, and loiter time on station. Undesirable handling qualities affect effectiveness by increasing the pilot workload and by limiting the flight envelope (e.g., flying "close to the deck" to avoid detection may be too difficult to accomplish).

The ability to rapidly acquire the target has a very strong influence on effectiveness, for it is in this phase that the aircraft could be the most susceptible. Target acquisition capability depends upon the navigation and targeting aids, the visual field of view from the cockpit, and assistance from an onboard radar and electro-optics, such as a forward-looking infrared (FLIR) sight. Flight vectoring assistance from airborne platforms or ground-based forward-area controllers (FAC) also helps the crew to locate the target rapidly.

The type, effectiveness, and number of weapons carried influence weapon delivery tactics and the number of sorties required to kill the target. The more sorties required to get the job done, the more likely the loss of aircraft. The use of launch-and-leave or fire-and-forget weapons can allow the aircraft to quickly exit or remain outside of the threat envelope. Any self-protection or antiradiation missiles carried by an aircraft to defend itself from enemy interceptors and radars reduce the payload carried.

Supporting systems, like command, communications, and control (C^3), fighter escorts (FE), threat-suppression aircraft, stand-off jamming (SOJ) aircraft, target locators/designators, and electronic signal monitoring/missile launch warning aircraft, reduce the susceptibility of the aircraft and hence increase the likelihood that the aircraft will get to the target and return home.

The aircraft signatures and the countermeasures employed influence the probability that the aircraft is detected, tracked, and fired upon before it gets to the target to deliver its weapon and hence influence effectiveness. They also affect the performance and payload capabilities of the aircraft.

The tactics used can significantly affect the susceptibility of the aircraft. Low-level or nap-of-the-Earth flight, terrain masking, bad weather, and nighttime operations are often used to reduce exposure to the threats.

Note that all of the above categories strongly influence the susceptibility of the attacking aircraft. Combining these categories with the aircraft vulnerability leads to the inescapable conclusion that weapon system effectiveness and aircraft survivability are neither incompatible nor exclusive, but instead are inextricably related, one to the other.*

The importance of survivability to effectiveness can be assessed quantitatively by considering the mission of the aircraft from two points of view: an offensive point of view in which the aircraft attempts to conduct its mission (e.g., deliver troops, locate submarines, destroy enemy bombers), and a defensive point of view in which the aircraft operates in a hostile environment. Figure 1.3 illustrates a breakdown of a war-at-sea (WAS) attack

*This conclusion is based upon the assumption that the return of the aircraft is desirable. However, even in those situations where no return is expected, as in the case of the Japanese Kamikaze Special Attack Corps in World War II, the aircraft must be sufficiently survivable to reach the target.

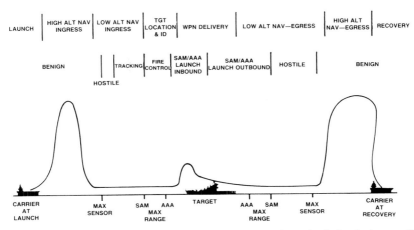

Fig. 1.3 **Offensive and defensive views of a mission; hypothetical mission profile, single plane, day, WAS strike.**

mission into a chain of events or mission elements for each point of view. Note that although these two chains are separate, they are subtly intertwined. The demands of the offensive elements will affect survivability and vice versa (e.g., the crew workload required to operate a countermeasures set can degrade their operation of the weapon delivery system and low-level, high-speed ingress to reduce the enemy's detection range and tracking accuracy will adversely affect performance). The effectiveness of the aircraft in the offensive view of the mission can be quantified by the mission attainment measure (MAM), which ranges from 0 to 1. When evaluating the MAM for a specific mission, the aircraft operates as if the threat were present (e.g., appropriate countermeasures and tactics are employed), but the damaging effects of the threat are not considered. Thus, the MAM is a relative measure of the ability of the aircraft to accomplish its objectives in the presence of the threat without the consideration of the threat effects. The effectiveness of the aircraft in the defensive view of the mission can be measured by the survival rate S, defined as the ratio of the number of aircraft that return to the number of aircraft launched. The more survivable the aircraft is, the closer S is to unity.

A combined measure of effectiveness of an aircraft in a particular scenario is the measure of mission success (MOMS), which is given by

$$MOMS = S\,MAM \tag{1.5}$$

Given a total mission goal G, then $L = G/MOMS$ aircraft must be launched to achieve that goal. Hence, the larger the value of the MOMS, the fewer aircraft that must be launched to accomplish the goal. In essence, the MOMS is a measure of the efficiency of the aircraft. Note that the MOMS is directly proportional to the survival rate. The aircraft must survive in order to accomplish its mission. Aircraft that are very effective from an offensive point of view will have a large MAM. If those same aircraft have a low survival rate, the MOMS will be significantly reduced. Consequently, more aircraft must be launched to accomplish the total goal in a campaign, such as the delivery of a total number of troops or bombs, and many aircraft will be lost. The number of aircraft lost in accomplishing the goal is $L(1 - S)$, or $(G/\text{MAM})(1 - S)/S$. In some circumstances, the MAM may have to be reduced to gain an increase in S, and the more survivable aircraft could possibly have a smaller MOMS. In this case, more sorties will have to be flown by the more survivable aircraft in order to accomplish the total goal. However, there will most likely be more of the more survivable aircraft available to sustain the operations, and fewer replacement aircraft and aircrews will be needed. This reduced demand for replacements could be of paramount importance in an intense conflict because of the long times required to build aircraft and train aircrews.

For a number of good reasons, there are other measures of combat/campaign effectiveness that have been used in the past. Some of them involve costs, such as hardware, research, development, test and evaluation, and peacetime operational and supply costs. It is inevitable that cost considerations will be taken into consideration when evaluating the contribution of any survivability enhancement feature to the weapon system effectiveness.

Survivability Enhancement Feature Selection Methodology

In order to determine which survivability features increase the effectiveness of an airborne weapon system, a survivability program must be conducted to determine the change in the offensive and defensive effectiveness measures. The flow of the program task is illustrated in Fig. 1.4. Because an aircraft's survivability is directly dependent upon the intensity and the lethality of the threat, the methodology begins with a mission-threat analysis. This analysis consists of the definition of the mission and the aircraft operational mode throughout the mission. The operational mode includes the aircraft configuration factors, such as weight, fuel status, armament loading, etc., and the proposed operational concepts and tactics. The threats to the aircraft, based on the aircraft operational mode, are identified, and their characteristics and capabilities are estimated. The interaction between the threat coverage and the aircraft operational mode is analyzed to determine the encounter conditions for the threat and the aircraft.

The second step in the methodology consists of obtaining the most detailed technical description of the aircraft that is available. This should include information on the location, construction, and operation of all of the systems, subsystems, and components of the aircraft.

The assessment of the susceptibility of the aircraft at this stage of the methodology usually consists of the determination of the level of the

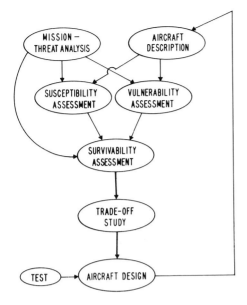

Fig. 1.4 Flow of the survivability enhancement feature selection methodology.

signatures of the aircraft, such as the radar signature and the infrared signature, that are used by the threats for detection and tracking.

The assessment of the vulnerability of the aircraft to the predicted threats consists of the following:

(1) The identification of the flight and mission essential functions and the critical components required to perform these functions.

(2) The determination of the damage-caused failure (kill) modes and the kill criteria or $P_{K/H}$ for each critical component.

(3) The computation of the numerical values for the measures of vulnerability of the aircraft. The computation of the vulnerability measures can be carried out manually or with the assistance of digital computer programs.

In the survivability assessment, the encounter conditions and threat capabilities identified in the mission-threat analysis are combined with the results of the susceptibility and vulnerability assessments to determine the probability of survival of the aircraft in a selected scenario. Of interest is the survivability of the aircraft in an encounter with a single threat platform (one-on-one P_S) and the survivability rate S for the mission. The prediction of aircraft P_S in the scenario can be accomplished through the use of digital computer programs that mathematically model:

(1) The physical and electromagnetic aspects of aircraft detection and tracking.

(2) Missile launch, or gun firing, and propagator flyout.

(3) The endgame, which consists of the warhead impact or proximity detonation and the terminal effects.

In order to determine the payoffs and the penalties associated with each survivability enhancement feature, a trade-off study is performed. In this study, the modified vulnerability and susceptibility measures and the new P_S and S are computed for each feature, or combination of features, considered. The impact of these features on aircraft weight, performance, reliability, maintainability, safety, repairability, and the MAM is evaluated, and the associated costs are estimated for a postulated wartime-peacetime lifetime of the aircraft. A campaign measure of effectiveness, or figure of merit, is then determined, such as the cost of the number of aircraft saved during combat by the survivability features minus the cost associated with incorporating the features on all of the aircraft.

Topical Fields

It should be obvious to the reader by now that the discipline of ACS spans a large number of widely varying activities. In order to minimize the communication problems that confront survivability practitioners and workers in allied disciplines in Government and industry, the military standard MIL-STD-2089, "Aircraft Nonnuclear Survivability Terms," has been prepared. This standard contains definitions and examples of usage of many aircraft survivability terms. All of the terms in the standard have been grouped into the six topical fields shown in Table 1.2. For example, the threat topical field contains those elements and activities that relate to the estimation of the nature and capabilities of the threats to aircraft.

Table 1.2   Survivability Topical Fields

Topical Field	Associated Activities/Elements
Threats	Threat analysis, threat characteristics, threat operations, and threat lethality
Assessment methodology	Computational methods and measures of aircraft susceptibility, vulnerability, and survivability
System response	System/subsystem response to damage mechanism impact, component kill criteria, kill levels, and system kill modes
Survivability enhancement	Vulnerability reduction (hardening) and susceptibility reduction (self-defense, electronic countermeasures, and reduction of detection)
Survivability enhancement trade-offs	Benefits and penalties from survivability enhancements, trade-off studies
Survivability test and combat data	Test data, experimental methods, combat data analysis

Points to Remember

In closing this brief overview of the fundamentals of ACS, two very important points should be emphasized. First, survivability must be seriously considered by everyone during the early design phase of the aircraft. It is at this stage that survivability enhancement features can best be incorporated. Retrofitting survivability enhancement features into existing aircraft, or adding them in the full-scale development phase, usually creates weight and cost penalties that could have been avoided if the features had been included in the early design. The second point is that the people who are responsible for survivability analysis and design of aircraft weapon systems must not work in a vacuum. They must have contact with the aircraft designers, the program managers, and the operators on a continuing basis, pointing out the importance of those features of the aircraft design and utilization that contribute to the reduction of the susceptibility and the vulnerability of the aircraft.

1.2 HISTORICAL PERSPECTIVE

World Wars I and II

Survivability enhancement of military aircraft began in World War I with makeshift efforts by the pilots to provide themselves with some form of ballistic armor protection against surface and aircraft guns. This progressed from steel infantry helmets and stove lids nailed to the pilot seats to 0.8-in.-thick all-steel pilot seats. In 1917, Germany designed a twin-engined bomber with 880 lb of 0.20-in. steel plate armor located in critical areas. The British also installed steel seats and 0.50- to 0.625-in.-thick nickel-chrome steel armor around radiators, fuel tanks, and the aircrew in some of their aircraft.

In the 1930's, although the United States began to install armor in some of their fighter aircraft, the main emphasis in aircraft design was on ruggedness and on the improvement of performance, such as maximum range and top speed. Then, on May 10, 1940, Germany invaded Holland, Belgium, and France. The British and French air units on the Continent conducted air strikes on the advancing German armor columns. On the first day of the invasion, the Royal Air Force Advanced Air Striking Force in France, equipped with Fairey Battle light bombers and Blenheim bombers, lost 23 out of the 64 Fairey Battles sent into action. By the second day, two squadrons of Blenheim bombers had been destroyed. On May 14, 1940, 63 Fairey Battles were sent against the advancing German columns, and 35 of these aircraft were destroyed.

FAIREY BATTLE III

On June 22, 1941, Germany invaded Russia. The Russians met the German onslaught with I-16 and I-153 fighters. By noon on June 22, 800 Russian aircraft had been destroyed, and by nightfall, 1489 aircraft had been destroyed, most of them before they took off. The Germans lost 35 aircraft during that first day.

SOVIET I-16

During the first months of the war in the Pacific, the Japanese Zero clearly showed its superiority over the Allied aircraft. In the battle for Java, which ended on March 8, 1942, over 550 Allied aircraft were destroyed, including large numbers of fighters such as the Brewster Buffalo, the Curtiss Hawk, the Curtiss P-40, and the Hawker Hurricane. The Brewster Buffalo was also used by the US Marines in the defense of Midway in June 1942. In one raid, 20 Buffalo fighters took off to intercept incoming Japanese aircraft. The Buffalos were overwhelmed by the far superior Japanese Zero. Thirteen of the 20 Buffalos were shot down, and the rest were badly damaged.

BREWSTER BUFFALO

The primary carrier-based fighter for the US Navy during the early part of World War II was the Grumman Wildcat. It, too, was inferior to the Zero in almost all respects. The Wildcat was, however, capable of absorbing much battle damage. Nevertheless, only a very experienced pilot was capable of surviving in combat with the Japanese fighters.

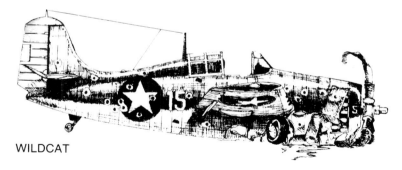

WILDCAT

Clearly, the Fairey Battle, the Russian I-16, the Brewster Buffalo, and the Grumman Wildcat were no match for the fighters introduced by the Axis at the start of the war. New aircraft had to be produced and modifications made to existing aircraft if there was to be any hope of gaining control of the skies. The US aircraft industry was able to meet this challenge, and a large number of excellent combat aircraft were eventually produced. The Army Air Corps developed the Lockheed P-38 Lightning, the Republic P-47 Thunderbolt, and the North American P-51 Mustang fighters. The main Air Corps bombers included the Boeing B-17 Flying Fortress, the Consolidated B-24 Liberator, the North American B-25 Mitchell, and the Douglas A-26 Invader. The Navy developed the Grumman F6F Hellcat and the Chance-Vought F4U Corsair fighters and the Grumman TBF/TBM Avenger torpedo bomber. A presentation of the specific survivability features of several of the most famous aircraft of World War II is given in Appendix A.

The survivability enhancement features that were incorporated on the aircraft of World War II were, for the most part, added components necessitated by combat experiences. Studies indicate that the critical components leading to aircraft losses in World War II were, in order of magnitude: (1) engines, (2) lubrication systems, (3) fuel systems, and (4) flight controls.

Liquid-cooled engines were vulnerable mainly due to their exposed cooling systems. Modifications were made on numerous aircraft, such as routing the cooling lines away from the underside of the aircraft or relocating vulnerable cooling components. An emergency boost in engine power was provided by water injection systems. The power boost gave the pilot a chance to outrun chasing aircraft. Some of the multiengined bomber aircraft had a backup system for feathering the propellers on an engine that had to be shut down. If the propellers could not be feathered, the added drag on the aircraft could slow it down and cause it to drop out of formation, making it an easy target for the enemy fighters. Fuel systems were self-sealing to a degree, except in most Japanese aircraft. Some attention was also directed to the suppression of fuel fires. A few aircraft had fuel tank inerting systems, and some had a fuel tank depressurization switch. Venting of fuel vapors from void areas was also done. Balsa wood was installed around some of the voids in wing fuel tanks to prevent fuel leakage and fires in those areas. Fire extinguishers were stowed in some crew compartments and in engine nacelles. The British experimented with fire-extinguishing systems in the fuel tank areas of some of their multiengined aircraft.

The use of armor plate was a common practice, except in the Japanese aircraft. Most aircraft had armor plate behind the pilot, and several had side and bottom cockpit armor as well. The available body armor in 1942 was awkward and heavy and thus was seldom used. The need for lightweight armor led to the development in 1943 of fiberglass bonded into a laminate and called Doron, after Col. G. F. Doriot. The introduction and use of flak suits significantly reduced casualties. None of the armor of this period was effective against armor-piercing-incendiary (API) bullets, however. Flat plate laminated-armor glass was incorporated into the windshields of some combat aircraft as an added protection for the pilot, and some aircraft had armor shielding around such components as radiators and oil reservoirs.

One of the major contributors to the improvement in US aircraft effectiveness was the development of more powerful engines. These engines allowed the weight of the aircraft to be increased, as well as providing a significant improvement in performance. The rugged construction of the successful aircraft of World War II was based more on the desire of the manufacturer to produce an aircraft capable of withstanding large aerodynamic forces than to produce an invulnerable aircraft. Fortunately, this construction also contributed greatly to the survivability of many aircraft. It is important to note that rugged construction, by itself, was not enough to guarantee survival. The Buffalo and the Wildcat are prime examples of rugged, but inferior, fighters.

The susceptibility of World War II aircraft was reduced mainly by the introduction of more powerful engines, by the use of lethal armament, and by the tactics employed. The massed bomber formations, with their self-protection armament and fighter escorts, provided a formidable shield against the enemy fighters. Many bombers were lost, but the fighters paid a high price. The bomber flight paths were routed around the areas where the flak was the heaviest whenever possible, and decoy formations were often used to draw the enemy fighters away from the main force. Countermeasures, such as chaff and electronic noise jammers, were used to confuse the enemy air-defense radar operators. Camouflage was used to hide aircraft, and contrails were suppressed to make early detection more difficult. A few aircraft had radar tail-warning devices to alert the pilot that an aircraft was approaching from behind.

Looking back at all of the attempts during World War II to make aircraft more survivable, and hence more effective, we can see that all six concepts for reducing vulnerability and all six concepts for reducing susceptibility were used. In general, it took combinations of these concepts to make a good weapon system.

Post-World War II and the Korean Conflict

In 1948, the First Working Conference on Aircraft Vulnerability was held at the US Army Ballistic Research Laboratory at the Aberdeen Proving Ground, Md. The participants were from the Air Force Air Material Command, the Army Ballistic Research Laboratory, Johns Hopkins University Applied Physics Laboratory, University of Chicago Ordnance Research, General Electric Engine Company, New Mexico School of Mines, the Navy Ordnance Explosive Group, and the Rand Corporation. The purpose of this meeting was to define the problems of military aircraft vulnerability and to identify the technology required to develop design improvements. Unfortunately, the excellent beginning initiated by this group was curtailed by the emerging philosophy that all future wars would be fought with nuclear weapons.

During the Korean conflict, there was a limited revival of interest in nonnuclear survivability. The emphasis was primarily directed to fighter and attack aircraft. The major survivability enhancement techniques were mainly improvements in armor and self-sealing fuel tank designs. The use of coordinated tactics in air-to-air combat with fighter aircraft became an area of interest to the Air Force and the Navy and proved to be an important factor in the one-sided kill ratios enjoyed by the United States. After this conflict, the emphasis of military aircraft design was again directed to general nuclear war considerations, and little attention was paid to nonnuclear survivability during the 1950's and early 1960's. The conflict in Southeast Asia in the mid-1960's changed this attitude.

The Southeast Asia Conflict

Helicopters. The employment of large numbers of US helicopters in Southeast Asia in the mid-1960's resulted in a painful awareness of their susceptibility and vulnerability to hostile, nonnuclear weapon systems. This was the first time US helicopters were used in large numbers in combat roles where exposure to enemy fire was commonplace. Introduced in limited numbers during World War II, the helicopter was employed in its first major combat-support roles during the Korean War, where it was used primarily for observation and as an air ambulance. The major problem facing the helicopter designers in the 1950's was not how to make the helicopter more survivable, but how to make it more practical in terms of lift capability and efficiency. Consequently, pilots sat on stove lids for vital protection, much the same as their ancestors did in World War I. The reciprocating engines were able to absorb a fair amount of small arms fire and continue to operate, and the transmissions on these early models, such as the H-21 and the H-34, could run for 30–60 min after complete loss of oil. The plywood and fabric rotor blades could also withstand hits by small arms fire as long as the blade spar was not damaged. The flight controls consisted of a simple cable and pulley system with no redundancy.

The first operational use of the helicopter for offensive combat was by the French in Algeria between 1956 and 1959. From their experiences, the French concluded that suppressive fire delivered from the helicopter was a necessary requirement for reducing combat losses, and that the helicopter had a relatively low vulnerability to 7.62-mm projectiles.

The Army recognized the threat of small arms and light antiaircraft weapons to aircraft operating in direct support of forward area units and, in the late 1950's, initiated action to develop protective measures for the aircrew and critical aircraft components against these threats. The Air Vehicle Environmental Research Team, consisting of technical representatives from the user and the appropriate technical service laboratories, was

V. C. WITH AP-47

formed, and they developed the original concepts for ballistic protection systems that were later employed in all Army combat aircraft. These concepts were also used in varying degrees by the Air Force and Navy. These efforts led to the development of a new family of lightweight armor materials, damage-tolerant components, and major advances in fuel system protection.

In order to increase the performance and efficiency of the helicopter, the heavy, rugged reciprocating engine was replaced with the lighter turboshaft engine. Introduction of the turboshaft engine, however, did not contribute to an increase in survivability. On the contrary, the turboshaft engine ran at high speeds and was constructed of lightweight materials, thus increasing its vulnerability to small arms fire. The high-speed transmissions associated with the turboshaft engines were also more vulnerable than the earlier ones, and loss of lubrication was almost always catastrophic.

Turboshaft helicopters were first used in combat in South Vietnam in 1962, with armed Bell UH-1A and UH-1B aircraft flying escort for H-21 troop-transport helicopters. The primary threats were 7.62- and 12.7-mm projectiles. The casualties in this period were relatively few, and, as expected, flight at the low altitudes and slow airspeeds used during troop insertions were the prime reasons for aircraft damage and loss.

The euphoria resulting from the low damage and loss rates associated with the early missions in South Vietnam was short-lived. After 1962, the level and caliber of weapons fire directed against helicopters significantly increased. By 1970, over 1500 US helicopters had been lost, pilot survivability had become a severe problem, and steps were taken to improve survivability. Redundancy was achieved in the utility helicopters by using two pilots. If one pilot was incapacitated, the copilot could usually fly the helicopter, provided the pilot did not bind the controls and the helicopter was not hovering at the time. In the single-piloted scout aircraft, losses resulting from pilot incapacitation were significant. Lightweight composite armor was installed around the pilot's seat, but it only protected the torso.

Many pilots placed personnel-type flak jackets in the cockpit for added protection.

In the early 1970's, a large number of helicopters were downed by 12.7- and 23-mm projectiles. The flight controls, rotor blades, fuel systems, engines, and transmissions were found to be highly vulnerable to the 23-mm antiaircraft fire. It was at about this time that the Soviet-built, man-portable SA-7 infrared seeking missile was introduced in Vietnam. A hit by an SA-7 missile, normally just behind the helicopter's engine exhaust, would completely sever the tail boom, causing an immediate crash. The heavy losses due to the shift from a low-level threat environment to higher intensities indicated the need for more advances in survivability technology.

Fixed-wing aircraft. While the Army and Marines were losing helicopters, the Air Force, Navy, and Marines were experiencing significant fixed-wing aircraft losses. Both the F-100 Super Sabre and the A-1 Skyraider were restricted from operating in North Vietnam due to high loss rates. As a consequence, the Services embarked on programs to analyze the problems and to develop retrofit modifications to existing aircraft and additional requirements for new models to make them more survivable. The development of a flexible, reticulated foam for insertion inside fuel tanks to suppress fires and explosions was one of the major improvements. This orange foam was installed in many Air Force aircraft. Additional backup flight controls (differential flaps) were added to one aircraft, and existing

A-1 SKYRAIDER

INFANTRY AA MISSILE

redundant, but adjacent, hydraulic systems were replumbed/rerouted on another aircraft so that one hit would not kill all systems. A stabilator lock and auxiliary power unit were added to two aircraft to eliminate loss due to an inability to control the stabilator. Bomb bay fire extinguishers, improved self-sealing fuel tanks, and independent, self-sealing engine fuel feed systems were also installed. Armor was added around engines, hydraulic actuators, and flight control components on several aircraft. On another aircraft, fuel vapors in voids were eliminated by the addition of a vent, and a fuel depressurization switch was added.

Later in the conflict, when the sophistication of hostile weapon systems was raised to a level never before experienced, many new survivability enhancement features were developed and employed. These included radar homing and warning systems, onboard and stand-off electronic countermeasures, infrared emission suppression devices for aircraft engines, evasive

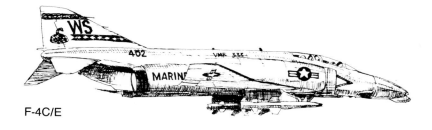

F-4C/E

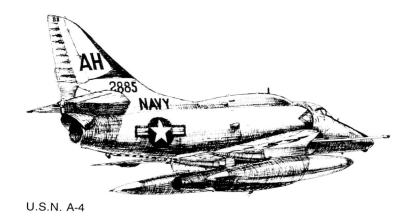

U.S.N. A-4

RNAF HARRIER

maneuvers against surface-to-air missiles, aural and visual signature reduction, special tactics, and antiradiation missiles.

The Past Decade

Several conflicts have taken place around the globe during the past ten years, such as Iran vs Iraq, Great Britain vs Argentina, the Soviet Union vs Afghanistan, etc. Israel fought the Yom Kippur War in 1973 and has had a continuing, low-intensity battle with Syria ever since. Its most recent

FRENCH-BUILT MIRAGE

experience was the confrontation with the PLO and Syria in Lebanon in 1982. Most of these conflicts have been either intense and short-lived or relatively quiet and long term. Each side has essentially fought with the supplies at hand. There has not been much change in the hardware.

In spite of this empirical data, the question, "What is the survivability of today's aircraft against a sophisticated air-defense system?" has not really been answered. The 1973 Yom Kippur War in the Middle East provides one example. On the first day of the war, Israeli aircraft provided accurate ground support for Israeli tank units. These aircraft were equipped to jam the Syrian SA-2 surface-to-air missiles, but were completely susceptible to the semiactive homing SA-6. Consequently, losses on the first day were heavy. During the first afternoon, many aircraft were lost to either the SA-6 or to the radar-directed 23-mm cannon fire of the Soviet-built ZSU-23-4. The ZSU-23-4 was particularly deadly to aircraft flying at low altitudes in an attempt to avoid the SA-6 coverage. These early losses were so severe that subsequent air strikes were canceled over the Golan Heights. However, owing to the rapidly deteriorating ground situation, the strikes were eventually resumed but the tactics were changed such that the aircraft operated on the perimeter of the battle zones, thus avoiding the concentration of the air defenses.

On the other hand, the Israeli aircraft losses suffered in the 1982 war in Lebanon were negligible compared to those in the 1973 war. The air defenses were directly attacked from the beginning with coordinated threat suppression tactics. Both the SA-6 and the mobile SA-8 were rendered ineffective. The combined use of electronic countermeasures, drones, anti-radiation missiles, and ordnance were apparently too much for the defenses. Whether the same situation will hold true in another theater under different conditions remains to be seen.

Lessons Learned

History has shown that when an aircraft has not been designed to survive in the environment it must operate in, it will not be able to accomplish its mission with any regularity. The operational commanders will be forced to cancel raids, or to change tactics, or even to remove the aircraft from the area. Morale will become low, and the ability to conduct sustained air operations will be significantly reduced due to the lack of capable aircraft and crews. The increasing intensity and sophistication of air-defense systems will exacerbate this situation. Survivability cannot be ignored—its importance will not go away.

1.3   US MILITARY POLICIES, PROCEDURES, AND ORGANIZATIONS

The fundamental objective of the US military survivability policy is to require that a thorough and systematic survivability program be conducted in order to ensure that effective survivability enhancement features are incorporated in current and future US airborne weapon systems. This is accomplished in different ways by each of the three Services.

Army

The US Army Materiel Command (AMC) regulation 70-3, "Survivability" (Feb. 17, 1976), prescribes policies, responsibilities, and procedures for improving the survivability of AMC items and systems.† The objectives of the AMC survivability program are to:

(1)   Allow forces to avoid detection, acquisition, and attacks by hostile forces during all phases of combat operations.

(2)   Permit absorption of unavoidable attacks with a minimum loss of human resources while maintaining sufficient combat power and efficiency to ensure continued participation in combat.

(3)   Facilitate rapid battlefield recovery and recuperation with assets and skills available in the forward areas and common to organizational and direct-support maintenance units.

(4)   Enhance the repair of low-density/high-cost or high-density items in theaters of operation.

The Deputy Commanding General for Materiel Development (DCGMD) has primary responsibility for survivability within AMC. The US Army Materiel Systems Analysis Activity (AMSAA), Aberdeen Proving Ground, Md., is designated as the lead activity within AMC. In this role, the Director, AMSAA, is to:

(1)   Provide the central expertise for directing the AMC survivability program and for issuing guidance. In this regard, the Director will maintain, improve, and disseminate methodologies needed to carry out survivability studies (including methodologies developed in Joint Service programs), and ensure that data having application to a number of commodity classes are exchanged within the AMC community.

(2)   Review letters of agreement (LOAs), required operational capabilities (ROCs), development plans (DPs), and, when requested, engineering

---

†AMC regulation 70-53, "Nonnuclear Vulnerability and Vulnerability Reduction" (June 16, 1971), sets forth the policies and responsibilities for the development, integration, and application of nonnuclear vulnerability and vulnerability reduction efforts within the US Army Materiel Command and is still in effect. AVSCOM regulation 70-6, "Vulnerability Analysis and Investigations" (Nov. 12, 1975), is primarily concerned with procedures for conducting vulnerability analyses on aircraft.

change proposals (ECPs), and product improvement proposals (PIPs) for AMC's major and designated nonmajor systems to determine that survivability aspects are quantified, if possible, in these documents. Further, the Director will ensure that survivability is balanced properly in trade-off studies and that adequate baseline data are obtained in test programs to permit assessing survivability aspects in a total evaluation of major and nonmajor systems.

(3)   Develop and maintain the capability to perform independent studies of survivability concepts and options, as requested or as associated with the AMSAA mission for low-cost, quick-response solutions, and assist, through coordination and joint studies, in developing a similar capability at each development center.

(4)   Continually assess the survivability efforts of AMC and periodically make recommendations to the DCGMD on areas needing increased emphasis and allocation of funds.

(5)   Through coordination with the US Army Training and Doctrine Command (TRADOC), identify tactical variations in deployment and use of materiel and quantify the survivability benefits when possible.

Commanders of AMC research and development commands, materiel readiness commands, and project/product managers responsibilities are defined as follows:

(1)   Include appropriate survivability requirements in each LOA, ROC, DP, development contract, and PIP.

(2)   Develop and maintain a capability to conduct feasibility studies and experiments of potential survivability modifications to fielded materiel, as well as materiel undergoing development. (Note: This applies only to the command or center, not *normally* to a project manager.)

(3)   Include survivability testing and evaluation in the developmental test process.

(4)   Inform the Director of the AMSAA of any potential survivability improvements that involve TRADOC responsibilities for doctrine, tactics, and training.

There are several other AMC organizations with assigned collateral survivability responsibilities that will continue to be responsible for particular areas. The major organizations are:

(1)   Project Manager, Aircraft Survivability Equipment (ASE).

(2)   Vulnerability assessment teams in the several research and development commands.

(3)   Ballistic Research Laboratory, nonnuclear vulnerability.

(4)   Mobility Equipment Research and Development Command, camouflage and countermine.

(5)   Harry Diamond Laboratory, nuclear vulnerability.

(6)   US Army Communications and Electronics Command, electronic warfare.

AMC has designated a project manager (PM) for aircraft survivability equipment (ASE), located at the US Army Aviation Systems Command (AVSCOM), St. Louis, Mo. The ASE Project Manager is responsible for the centralized management of aircraft survivability within the Army. The current Project Manager charter was approved by the Secretary of the Army on May 11, 1982. The mission is as follows:

The PM is responsible in accordance with Department of Defense (DoD) Directives 5000.1, 5000.39, and 5000.40; Army Regulations (AR) 1000-1, 702-3, 700-127, 70-17, and 11-18; AMC-R 715-2, 70-1, and 11-16; and other pertinent regulations for the development, acquisition, and life cycle management of ASE. Program objectives are to provide self-protection for the current Army aircraft fleet on the modern battlefield; contingency protection equipment and plans as required; vulnerability analysis and development of survivability techniques and equipment for aircraft project, product and weapon system managers; and a viable technical data base within AMC to interface with future aircraft development programs.

The ASE Project Manager is supported by the following organizations: US Army Aviation Systems Command; US Army Training and Doctrine Command; US Army Communications and Electronics Command; US Army Missile Command; US Army Armament Command; US Army Test and Evaluation Command; US Army Laboratory Command, agencies, and subordinate activities; US Army Operational Test and Evaluation Agency; US Army Logistics Evaluation Agency; US Army Materiel Systems Analysis Activity; Central DA TMDE activity; US Army Safety Center; Project Manager training devices; and aircraft project/product managers.

Navy

In May 1974, the Chief of Naval Material (CNM), Adm. I. C. Kidd, issued a policy statement that established CNM policy for survivability requirements in naval weapon systems. This policy memorandum stated:

Survivability should be treated as follows during the Weapon System Acquisition process:
- Threat analyses should be conducted and firm survivability objectives established during the conceptual phase of the acquisition process.
- It is essential that both survivability requirements and measurement and validation criteria be specified upon entry into full-scale development; these requirements must be included in the contract.
- The request for authorization to proceed into production must specify the survivability requirements to be imposed and the means for measuring their attainment.
- Weapon systems should be tested against expected threat weapons whenever practicable.

Operational weapon systems should be assessed regularly to ensure that changes to the threat environment are considered and advantage is taken of state-of-the-art advances in survivability enhancement.

I expect each of you to ensure that survivability is fully considered in development proposals and that they are properly reflected in contracts.

NAVMAT instruction 3900.16, "Combat Survivability of Naval Weapon Systems" (Nov. 27, 1979), establishes policies, procedures, and responsibilities within the Naval Material Command (NMC) to improve achievement of combat survivability in naval weapons systems and directs a vigorous program of research and development to develop concepts, procedures, materials, designs, and hardware and software for survivability enhancement of mission essential weapons systems (MEWS). It directs that survivability requirements be included during the earliest conceptual formulation of MEWS and become increasingly specific and comprehensive as the acquisition process progresses.

NAVAIR instruction 3920.1, CH-1, "Establishment of Naval Air Survivability Program (NASP)" (May 28, 1976), provides the procedures, responsibilities, and organizational relationships for the NASP (now known as the Naval Air Combat Survivability Program, or NACSP) within the Naval Air Systems Command. The deputy commander, assistant commanders, command special assistants, and designated project managers are to be responsible for implementing the following NAVAIR policies:

(1) Threat analyses will be conducted and firm survivability objectives established during the conceptual phase of the acquisition process.

(2) Both the survivability requirements and the measurement and validation criteria will be specified upon entry into full-scale development; these requirements will be included in appropriate development plans and properly reflected in contracts.

(3) The request for authorization to proceed into production must specify the survivability requirements to be imposed and the means for measuring their attainment.

(4) Weapon systems and the survivability enhancement technology utilized in these systems should be tested against expected threat weapons when, in the judgment of NAVAIR, the capability to test exists and it is technically sound and economically feasible.

(5) Operational weapon systems should be assessed regularly to ensure that changes to the threat environment are considered and advantage is taken of state-of-the-art advances in survivability enhancement technology.

The major goal of the NACSP is to establish aircraft survivability as a design discipline within the Navy. It includes:

(1) Development of improved techniques to analyze and predict aircraft subsystems failure modes.

(2) Development of improved techniques to analyze and predict aircraft survivability in the combat threat environment.

(3) Development, testing, and evaluation of prototype survivability hardware directed toward Navy aircraft and threat environments.

(4) Development of engineering design techniques and criteria for the use in the design of survivable aircraft.

The responsibility for air combat survivability is assigned within NAVAIR to code AIR-5164, the Naval air combat survivability branch. AIR-5164 manages and administers the NACSP, provides the interface between the NACSP with its supporting laboratories and the air system program managers (PMAs), represents AIR-05 as the responsible organization for the development of air combat survivability requirements, the evaluation of survivability in proposed and developmental systems, the monitoring of survivability in operational systems, and the liaison with the Joint Technical

Coordinating Group for Aircraft Survivability and the survivability focal points in the Army, Air Force, and in allied nations.

AIR-5164 is supported in the NACSP by several Navy laboratories. The Naval Weapons Center (NAVWPNCEN) is designated as the lead laboratory for nonnuclear air combat survivability. The NAVWPNCEN conducts survivability assessments and trade-offs and participates in the development of methodologies for both, supports AIR-5164 in the development and implementation of survivability requirements, conducts research and development of hardware technology to enhance survivability, and conducts extensive testing. Other laboratories that support nonnuclear survivability include the Naval Air Development Center, with involvement in aircraft technology development; the Naval Air Propulsion Center, which supports propulsion system survivability; the Naval Surface Weapons Center, which supports armor development at Dahlgren; the Naval Weapons Support Center, which is involved in the development of assessment simulations; and the Naval Research Laboratory, which is involved in vulnerability to laser threats. Nuclear survivability is supported by the Naval Surface Weapons Center at White Oak, Md.

Air Force

Air Force regulation 80-38, "Management of the Air Force Systems Survivability Program" (Aug. 2, 1982), is the current document that establishes the policy and procedures for the Air Force Survivability Program. The purpose of the program is to identify those US Air Force systems that must operate in and survive man-made hostile environments and to make sure that:

(1) Air Force systems and mission equipment are capable of surviving the effects of man-made hostile environments.

(2) Survivability is adequately considered in each US Air Force system program during its life cycle.

(3) System survivability is reevaluated throughout the life cycle of each system when the hostile environment, the system, or the mission is altered.

(4) System survivability is maintained throughout the life cycle of each system.

The policy of the program is as follows:

(1) Sufficient numbers of each US Air Force system must be capable of surviving man-made hostile environments to carry out their designated mission.

(2) The need for a level of desired system survivability for new systems to be developed should begin with the identification of the required capability in the statement of operational need (SON) or the justification for major system new start (JMSNS). The SON, as validated by the requirements assessment group (RAG), must state the requirements in quantitative terms from which quantitative levels can be derived. The program management directive (PMD), as the implementing document, must state survivability requirements in quantitative terms. If survivability is not a factor in the operation of the system, a statement to this effect must be included and a justification provided.

(3)   Survivability must be considered in developing the requirements for, and the trade-offs leading to, the basic design of a US Air Force system. Survivability is a function of system design hardness, components, operating conditions during its employment, and the types and intensities of the man-made hostile environments. Survivability warrants management attention throughout the system life cycle.

(4)   The impact of survivability requirements on system cost, performance, reliability, maintainability, logistics support, and other system requirements must be carefully considered to ensure maximum operational effectiveness consistent with program constraints as stipulated in the PMD. It is not intended that every US Air Force system should meet the same set of survivability criteria. If possible, the SON should prioritize the survivability requirements with respect to other requirements to show how trade-offs might be made. Specific criteria must be established for each system based on its requirement to function in the man-made hostile environments.

To achieve acceptable survivability with the minimum impact on the performance of each system, survivability must be balanced with the other performance parameters of the system. The threat estimate, the threat weapon allocation, and the scenarios must be defined and evaluated during all phases of the system life cycle. The following steps are required:

(1)   During the concept exploration phase, verify, refine, or further define survivability requirements as stated in the SON and establish appropriate criteria based on the validated threat estimate.

(2)   During the demonstration and validation phase, the system's survivability is considered and discussed in the decision coordinating paper (DCP) and the integrated program summary. Trade-offs between various hardness levels and other characteristics (such as weight, speed, range, cost, operational effectiveness, etc.) will be described in quantitative terms. The justification for the release of funds for full-scale development should acknowledge that the necessary survivability technology is attainable, thus stating the requisite hardness levels of inclusion in the request for proposal (RFP). The trade-offs between hardness, cost, performance, reliability, operability, and maintainability should be further refined when the final system specifications are released for full-scale development and production.

(3)   During full-scale development, there must be adequate analyses and testing of systems to evaluate and affirm that the system will meet the survivability requirements and hardness specifications and to determine, where practical, the hardness levels that have been achieved.

(4)   During the production phase, an active hardness assurance program will be employed to ensure system survivability for those systems with hardness requirements. Survivability must be reassessed before any retrofit changes to survivable systems are made.

(5)   During the operational phase, active hardness maintenance and hardness surveillance programs will be employed to ensure system survivability for those systems with survivability requirements. The hardness maintenance and hardness surveillance programs should identify any further evaluation, testing, or retrofit changes that may be required to ensure system survivability throughout the system's life cycle. Survivability must be reassessed when there are operational experiences, changes in the threat, or

other circumstances that have, as determined by the system manager or as directed by higher headquarters, invalidated the prior assessments.

AFR 80-38 designates responsibility for directing survivability activities within HQ USAF to the director of operational requirements and development plans (HQ USAF/RDQ). For the nuclear survivability areas, an Air Force nuclear criteria group (NCG) with general officer membership was set up to establish nuclear criteria for USAF systems.

Within the major commands, the Air Force Logistics Command (AFLC) and the Air Force Systems Command (AFSC) are required to perform an independent engineering audit or review at each critical point in the acquisition life cycle (at least annually) for the designated systems for which they have engineering responsibility. The major operating commands are to support AFLC and AFSC in implementing their responsibilities. The Air Training Command is to ensure that appropriate survivability considerations are included in system training programs. The Air Force Test and Evaluation Center makes sure that appropriate operational test and evaluation (OT&E) is conducted on weapon systems in a realistic operational environment to estimate the survivability of each system.

The Joint Technical Coordinating Group on Aircraft Survivability

As the attrition rates of US aircraft increased in the Southeast Asia conflict, the Joint Logistics Commanders decided to establish a tri-Service organization to bring together the best expertise in each of the Services to plan and execute a program to reduce the vulnerability of current fleet aircraft and to develop design criteria and improved technology to increase the survivability of future aircraft. The organization formed to conduct this program was designated the Joint Technical Coordinating Group on Aircraft Survivability (JTCG/AS). The JTCG/AS charter was signed by the Joint Logistics Commanders on June 25, 1971. The charter was revised and renewed on June 22, 1977.

The purpose of the JTCG/AS is to provide a mechanism to:

(1)   Coordinate the individual Service programs to increase the combat survivability of aeronautical systems in a nonnuclear threat environment.

(2)   Implement efforts to complement the Service survivability programs.

(3)   Maintain close liaison with Service levels to ensure that all survivability research and development data and systems criteria are made available to the developers of new aircraft.

The mission of the JTCG/AS is to:

(1)   Establish survivability as a design discipline.

(2)   Provide technical data and inputs for survivability improvements to cognizant Aircraft Program Managers (Army), Project Managers (Navy), and System Program Directors and System Managers (USAF), and to assist these offices in the use and implementation of current survivability technology for the design and production of new aircraft and retrofittings of in-service aircraft where warranted.

(3)   Revise, coordinate, and update design manuals oriented toward nonnuclear survivability.

(4) Coordinate research and advanced development efforts contributing to the reduction of vulnerability for aeronautical systems in a nonnuclear threat environment.

(5) Plan and propose joint technology programs contributing to the improvement of survivability in aeronautical systems.

(6) Interface with the Joint Technical Coordinating Group for Munitions Effectiveness (JTCG/ME) on advancements in weapons technology to determine the long-range effects on aircraft survivability and on current weapons effectiveness against aircraft for their use in developing improved attrition models.

(7) Review and analyze data on the combat damage of aeronautical systems.

(8) Conduct studies of future threat environments to determine systems survivability requirements.

(9) Conduct studies to assess enhanced survivability design features in a combat environment.

(10) Plan and coordinate joint Service tests and maintain cognizance over single Service tests designed to validate improved survivability design features.

(11) Serve as the Joint Logistics Commanders' point of contact for the office of the Secretary of Defense, the Services, and industry for aircraft survivability matters.

(12) Determine and update the best procedures to dispense the latest survivability data to the Services and industry.

(13) Determine and implement methods of instruction to the using commands to provide quantified survivability direction in the required operational capabilities (ROC), operational requirements (OR), and general operational requirements (GOR).

In order to function in all areas of survivability, the following subgroups have been established: Technology Research and Development, Methodology, Design Criteria and Industry Interface, and Countermeasures.

Two special committees have also been formed: the Vulnerability to Directed Energy Weapons (VUDEW) committee and the Threat Review Advisory Committee (TRAC).

The current address and phone number of the JTCG/AS central office is AIR-5164J, Naval Air Systems Command, Washington, D.C. 20361; telephone: (202) 692-1730/2120 or AV 222-1730/2120.

1.4   SURVIVABILITY REQUIREMENTS FOR US MILITARY AIRCRAFT

Survivability requirements for aircraft have been specified in different ways by the three Services. The Navy developed Aeronautical Requirement AR-107, "Navy Aircraft Survivability/Vulnerability (Nuclear and Nonnuclear)," in 1974. This document was superseded by MIL-STD-2072(AS), "Military Standard: Survivability, Aircraft; Establishment and Conduct of Programs for," in 1977. In 1981, the Department of Defense issued MIL-STD-2069, "Requirements for Aircraft Nonnuclear Survivability Program." These documents were prepared in recognition of the need for a standardized systems approach to improving the survivability of military aircraft.

DoD MIL-STD-2069 provides the requirements and guidelines for establishing and conducting aircraft survivability programs while maintaining the flexibility required by acquisition program managers in the development of a survivability program compatible with the needs of the procuring Service and the scope of the acquisition program. It is applicable to major system acquisitions of all DoD combat and combat-support aircraft, including remotely piloted vehicles (RPV), but excluding aircraft designated solely for research and training. This Standard is to be applied to aircraft as they enter the concept definition, validation, full-scale engineering development (FSD), production, and operational phases. It may also be applied selectively to existing aircraft programs where it appears likely that significant survivability enhancement can be achieved at acceptable cost and weight or performance penalties.

The Standard is to be used when preparing survivability requirements and will be invoked in requests for proposals, contract statements of work, survivability program plans, and other contractual documents. Prior to FSD, the Standard requires studies, threat definitions, and trade-offs to generate designs that will meet survivability requirements and data to be used in the FSD specifications. In FSD, the Standard will be invoked in whole or in part in the aircraft detail specification.

The general requirements of MIL-STD-2069 are included in the following paragraphs owing to their applicability to any survivability program.

Survivability Program

The contractor shall develop, propose, implement, and maintain an effective survivability program that is planned for and integrated into all phases of aircraft design, development, and production.

Organization

The contractor shall provide adequate staff for managing and accomplishing the survivability program. The responsibilities and functions of those personnel directly involved with implementation of the program shall be clearly defined. The responsibility and authority of the survivability organization and its relationships with all levels of management shall be identified. The survivability organization shall be involved with all relevant design, support, and program management activities so that the survivability requirements are effectively incorporated into the aircraft. The relationships to each relevant activity shall be defined.

Program Plan

The contractor shall develop, propose, obtain Government approval of, and implement a survivability program plan. It shall outline the procedures by which the contractor proposes to conduct the program tasks, incorporate the design requirements, and conduct the demonstrations and tests for which the contractor is responsible. The functional relationship with other program tasks and events shall be clearly shown and described. Each task in the plan shall be identified with the work breakdown structure so that traceability and monitoring of funding may be accomplished. The contractor shall conduct the survivability program in accordance with this Standard and the approved program plan. The plan shall describe:

(1) The tasks, schedules, manpower requirements, special facilities, and significant milestones of the program. Planned use of subcontractors to supplement in-house capabilities must be indicated and the subcontractors identified when possible.

(2) The organizational structure, with survivability personnel at a level such that survivability design techniques are effectively implemented.

(3) A procedure for conveying to subsystem and component designers the latest survivability design techniques applicable to their particular design areas. This procedure might be in the form of periodic briefings, internal information bulletins, personal contact between survivability and design engineers on a regular basis, and shall include active participation by survivability personnel in making design decisions.

(4) A procedure for designers to provide current design information to survivability analysis personnel so that survivability assessments and trade-off studies reflect the status of the weapon system design as it actually exists.

(5) The plan and schedule for survivability program reviews.

(6) The anticipated design support tests in all areas of survivability (vulnerability reduction, detectables, etc.).

(7) The methodologies for the specific requirements of this Standard where procuring agency approval is required.

Program Reviews

Program reviews shall be planned and scheduled to permit the contractor and Government representatives to periodically examine the status of the survivability program. These reviews shall be coordinated with the aircraft system design reviews and identified in the survivability program plan. The contractor shall document all survivability actions that have taken place on the aircraft systems during the period covered by the program review.

Program Tasks

The survivability program shall consist of the following tasks:
(1) Mission-threat analysis.
(2) Aircraft geometric description.
(3) Flight and mission essential function identification.
(4) Failure mode, effects, and criticality analysis (FMECA).
(5) Aircraft vulnerability assessments.
(6) Susceptibility assessments.
(7) Survivability assessments.
(8) System cost-effectiveness analyses.
(9) Survivability enhancement trade-off studies.
(10) Combat damage repair assessment.
Most of these tasks will be described in detail in the following chapters.

Program Guides

The document "Guidebook for Preparation of Aircraft System Survivability Requirements for Procurement Documents," report JTCG/AS-77-D-001, has been prepared to assist program/project officers and other agencies that must prepare procurement specifications for aircraft survivability enhancement equipment, for the survivability tasks associated with the procurement of a total aircraft system or related subsystems, and also for the modification of current fleet aircraft and their related subsystems. The guidelines include general requirements statements for the establishment of a survivability program, requirements statements for reducing the susceptibility of the system to the threat weapons, and requirements for the reduction of vulnerability to nonnuclear, nuclear, and laser weapon effects. Requirements for survivability assessments and the verification of vulnerability levels and survivability enhancement features are also included. Although nuclear and laser weapon effects are included, the major emphasis is on the reduction of susceptibility and vulnerability to conventional weapons and the establishment of the survivability program. Another JTCG/AS report, "Documentation of Survivability/Vulnerability Related Aircraft Military Specifications and Standards," report JTCG/AS-74-D-003, identifies and documents those military specifications and standards that impact the survivability of military aircraft.

1.5   A TYPICAL AIRCRAFT SURVIVABILITY PROGRAM

Survivability engineering has been firmly established as a system engineering specialty. It has been integrated into the system engineering process as defined in MIL-STD-449A, "Engineering Management." This places survivability engineering into a position of primary consideration in aircraft system development. Management of survivability programs must conform to the objectives required by MIL-STD-449A, which defines engineering management as:

> The management of the engineering and technical effort required to transform a military requirement into an operational system. It includes the system engineering required to define the system performance parameters and preferred system configuration to satisfy the requirement, the planning and control of technical program tasks, integration of the engineering specialties, and the management of a totally integrated effort of design engineering, specialty engineering, test engineering, logistics engineering, and production engineering to meet cost, technical performance and schedule objectives.

Life Cycle Survivability

To develop a survivable, combat-effective aircraft requires a systematic survivability program beginning with the conceptual phase and continuing throughout the life cycle of the aircraft. The life cycle of a typical survivability program is shown in Fig. 1.5. The requirement for survivability will be stated in the operational requirement (OR) along with the expected threat.

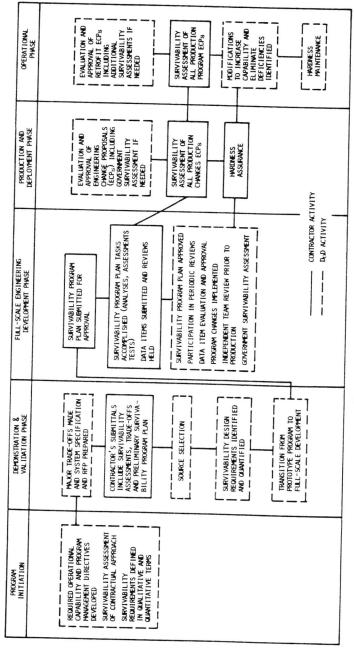

Fig. 1.5 Survivability life cycle.

It is essential that survivability criteria be established early in the conceptual phase and that alternative design and utilization solutions be developed. The relationships between the aircraft's mission and performance, the hostile threat system capabilities, the hostile weapons effects, and the essential aircraft system functions must be analyzed to identify those areas where survivability enhancement techniques will provide the most payoff in combat effectiveness. By developing this information before the design configuration is established, the most effective survivability enhancement techniques can be identified. Significant survivability benefits can be achieved for little or no penalty if survivability is considered early in the program. Trade-off studies should be conducted to select the most effective combinations, and these should be reflected in the decision coordinating paper (DCP) for the Defense System Acquisition Review Council (DSARC).

During the validation phase, the design alternatives should be verified by analyses, trade-off studies, and selected testing. There are numerous testing options available. Ballistic and laser testing can be conducted on material specimens, components, and realistic mock-ups of subsystems. Radar cross-section measurements can be made on models of different configurations. If the aircraft is being prototyped, actual radar and infrared signature measurements can be made in flight. The refined survivability criteria should be specified as requirements in the request for proposal for the full-scale development (FSD) phase.

During the FSD, a continuous and strong survivability engineering interface must be provided with all the design areas involved, not only in the detailed design, but also in reliability, maintainability, and the other engineering specialties. The individual subsystem designer must be provided the survivability design data and information necessary for the design requirements to be met. Feedback must be provided from analyses and trade-off studies at both the subsystem and total system levels. This is a continuing, iterative process. There must be sufficient analyses and testing to verify that the design meets the survivability requirements at the total system level before proceeding to DSARC III.

During the production phase and the remainder of the life cycle, there must be a continuous monitoring of engineering change proposals (ECPs) and retrofit programs to evaluate their impact on total system survivability. The threat must be periodically assessed to determine if the aircraft is still capable of operating effectively in the hostile environment. Modification programs should be undertaken to eliminate any deficiencies identified.

Contractor Organization

The successful implementation and conduct of an effective survivability program for an aircraft system by a contractor requires a survivability engineering organization that is properly integrated into the contractor's management system. It must have the capability to perform the functions required to support the design process, perform analyses and trade-off studies, conduct development programs and tests, and carry out verification programs. The survivability engineering organization must also be in a

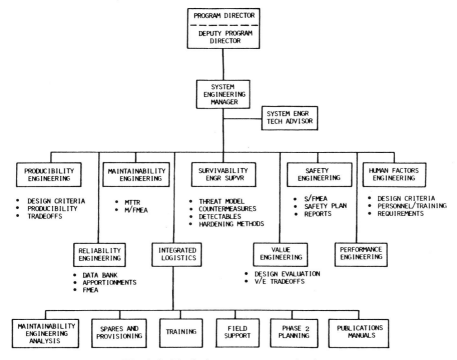

Fig. 1.6   Typical contractor organization.

position to provide system design management with the necessary information and recommendations to influence the proper recognition and
acceptance of survivability requirements. It must also identify effective
survivability enhancement methods for implementation into the design
concept. An example of a typical contractor organization is shown in Fig.
1.6. The survivability engineering function is under the system engineering
manager, who in turn reports directly to the program director's office. The
survivability engineering group is on the same management level as produci-
bility, maintainability, safety, reliability, human factors, integrated logistics,
and value engineering. This arrangement also permits effective interface and
cooperation with all of the system engineering disciplines.

1.6   SURVIVABILITY HANDBOOKS

Several handbooks have been prepared to provide military and industrial
planners and designers with the information and guidance needed for
retrofitting survivability into existing aircraft and for incorporating survivability in future aircraft designs from the conceptual to the final stage.

The Air Force Systems Command has published design handbooks DH-1
through DH-3 for use in support of Air Force acquisition programs. They

are a principal source of design criteria and guidance in technical areas of Air Force systems and equipment design.

The Army has published the "Survivability Design Guide for US Army Aircraft," USAAMRDL TR-71-41. This guide contains pertinent design data related to aircraft vulnerability reduction and aircrew protection from small arms or ballistic threats. Rotary-wing aircraft design features have been emphasized, since they represent the greatest portion of the Army aircraft inventory. The Army's "Aircraft Crash Survival Design Guide," USARTL TR-79-22, contains information, data, and design criteria for the crashworthy design of aircraft. Much of this material is also pertinent to the survivability design.

The Navy has published the military handbook MIL-HDBK-268(AS), entitled "Survivability Enhancement, Aircraft Conventional Weapon Threats, Design and Evaluation Guidelines." This handbook provides uniform design and evaluation guidelines for the survivability enhancement of Navy aircraft mission essential weapon systems (MEWS). The design guidelines encompass signature reduction and vulnerability reduction because these are the two survivability areas that are most strongly affected by the aircraft design. The evaluation guidelines relate to the quantification and evaluation of the measures of survivability and include the mission scenario, threat environment, vulnerability, encounter survivability, and survivability enhancement trade-offs.

A DoD military handbook, "Survivability/Vulnerability, Aircraft, Nonnuclear," MIL-HDBK-336, has been developed under the sponsorship of the JTCG/AS. The handbook is applicable to all three Services and addresses all vehicle subsystems. Both vulnerability and susceptibility features are included. The handbook has been prepared in several functional volumes. Volume 1, "General Information and Survivability Assessment Methodology," contains general information pertaining to survivability assessment techniques, weapon terminal effects, computer program descriptions, and basic subsystem design concepts. Volume 2, "Airframe and Subsystem Design," contains specific subsystem design concepts, procedures, and other pertinent information. Volume 3, "Engine Propulsion System Design," is concerned with the design of aircraft engines for enhanced survivability.

Selected Bibliography

American Defense Preparedness Association, *Proceedings of the Symposium on Vulnerability and Survivability*, National Headquarters, Washington, D.C., Vol. I, Oct. 21–23, 1975.

American Defense Preparedness Association, *Proceedings of the Second Symposium on Vulnerability and Survivability*, National Headquarters, Washington, D.C., Vol. I, Oct. 26–28, 1976.

Atkinson, D. B., "Aircraft Survivability," *The Shock and Vibration Bulletin*, No. 53, Part 1, May 1983, pp. 33–38.

Atkinson, D. B., "An Analysis of Current Survivability Policies and Procedures Which Impact the Systems Acquisition Process," Study Project Report PMC 76-1, May 1976, Defense Systems Management School, Fort Belvoir, Va.

Borgart, P., "The Vulnerability of the Manned Airborne Weapon System, Part 1, Probability of Detection," *International Defense Review*, Vol. 10, No. 4, August 1977, pp. 667–671.

Borgart, P., "The Vulnerability of the Manned Airborne Weapon System, Part 2, Probability of Kill," *International Defense Review*, Vol. 10, No. 5, Oct. 1977, pp. 860–866.

Defense Helicopter World, Vol. 2, No. 4, Dec. 1983–Feb. 1984 (a special issue devoted to survivability).

Dotseth, W. D. and Nickel, R. W., "Documentation of Survivability/Vulnerability Related Aircraft Military Specifications and Standards," JTCG/AS-74-D-003, April 1975.

Insight Team of the London Sunday Times, *The Yom Kippur War*, Doubleday and Co., New York, 1974.

Leary, F., "Tactical Aircraft Survivability," *Space/Aeronautics*, Vol. 4, No. 6, June 1967, pp. 68–81.

Sapp, C. N. Jr., "Survivability—A Science Whose Time Has Come," *U.S. Naval Institute Proceedings*, U.S. Naval Institute, Annapolis, Md., Dec. 1978, pp. 59–67.

STUBBY ATTACK AIRCRAFT, PRODIGIOUS
WARLOADS, LONG LOITER TIME

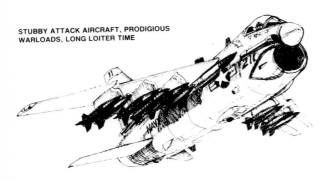

HIGH-SPEED INTERCEPTORS, THIN WINGS,
HUGE, THIRSTY ENGINES

LARGE AND BULKY, HEAVY CARGO CARRIER

THIN AND ANGULAR, AGILE, ATTACK ROLE SPEED

2. AIRCRAFT ANATOMY

2.1 GENERAL FEATURES

Aircraft come in many different shapes, sizes, and configurations that are determined by the intended role or roles of the aircraft. There are the sleek, high-speed interceptors with their thin, delta-shaped wings and huge, thirsty engines; and then there are the slower, stubby attack aircraft that must carry prodigious warloads over long ranges or loiter for long periods of time near the battle zone. The helicopter, valued for its vertical takeoff and landing capability, can be large and bulky in order to carry large amounts of cargo, or thin and angular for agility and speed in the attack role.

Regardless of the roles or missions for which the aircraft was designed, the final product will have surfaces (fixed or rotary) that provide lift, a powerplant that provides thrust, and a means for controlling the direction of flight. These three essential functions (lift, thrust, and control) are usually provided by the following five major aircraft systems: (1) structural, (2) propulsion, (3) flight control, (4) fuel, and (5) crew.

There are several other systems that appear on most aircraft. These include (1) avionics, (2) armament, (3) environmental control, (4) electrical, and (5) launch and recovery.

The relative importance of each of the systems listed above to the survivability of the aircraft depends upon the particular aircraft design. In order to give the reader an understanding of the part each system plays in the survivability of aircraft, a brief description of each system is given for both fixed- and rotary-wing aircraft. In the presentation that follows, a system is assumed to be made up of a group of subsystems, and a component is a particular part of a subsystem. For example, a fuel tank is one component of the fuel storage subsystem, which is one subsystem of the fuel system.

2.2 FIXED-WING AIRCRAFT

General Arrangement

An illustration of a current fixed-wing, tactical aircraft is given in Fig. 2.1. Note the location of the various components. The forward part of the aircraft typically contains the crew and many of the avionics components.

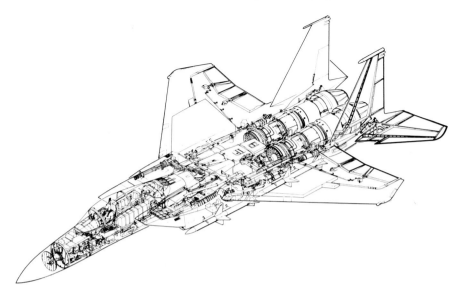

Fig. 2.1   General arrangement.

The center portion of the aircraft, including the wings, usually contains the fuel tanks and the armament. The fuel and armament are located here, close to the center of mass of the aircraft, because they will change drastically in weight as the mission progresses. The fuel will be consumed, and the armament will be expended. Locating these items close to the center of mass will cause the center to remain essentially in the same location during the entire mission. Thus, the flying qualities will not change significantly during the mission. The engines and part of the flight control system often make up the aft portion of the aircraft, although the engines are sometimes supported by the wings.

The Structural System

Illustrations of the major structural assemblies and structural arrangement of our fixed-wing aircraft are given in Figs. 2.2a and 2.2b. The major functions of the structural system are to provide structural integrity, rapid access to all internal compartments, and pressurized compartments. The major structural subsystems or groups are the wings, the fuselage, and the tail, or empennage.

Materials used in the structure typically include aluminum, steel, and titanium alloys, alclad sheets, sandwich construction, and graphite- and boron-epoxy advanced composites.

Wing structure.   The wing consists of one or more major beams called spars that run spanwise (root to tip) along the wing and several formers or

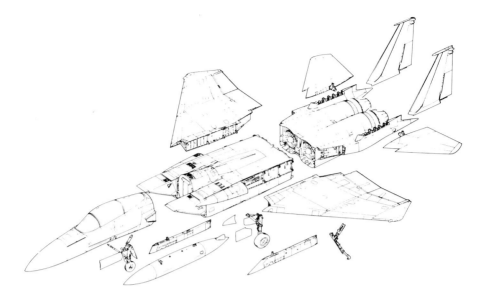

Fig. 2.2a   Major structural assemblies.

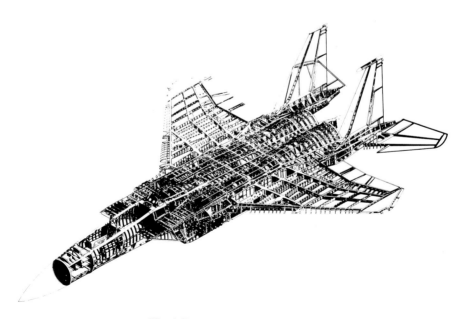

Fig. 2.2b   Structural assemblies.

ribs that run chordwise (leading edge to trailing edge). A spar has upper and lower flanges connected by a solid web or struts. The ribs form the aerodynamic shape or airfoil of the wing and may be built up as a rigid frame or truss or may be made solid, like a bulkhead. The wing skin over the spars and ribs provides the major lifting surface of the aircraft. The skin, when thin, may be stiffened by lightweight, spanwise members called stringers. The combination of spars, ribs, and stiffened skin form a box beam or torque box. The box beam may be cantilevered from the fuselage, or it may be continuous from wing tip to wing tip. Naval aircraft carried on ships usually require a folding wing. The skin over the leading and trailing edges of the wing is usually nonstructural and serves to direct the flow of air over the wing.

Fuselage structure.   The fuselage structure is typically of semimonocoque construction and is usually divided into three sections: forward, center, and aft. In semimonocoque construction, sometimes referred to as stressed skin, the fuselage skin is stiffened by several members running lengthwise called stringers, if they are light, or longerons, if they are heavy. The skin shape is maintained by several lateral frames or bulkheads. A major fuselage beam running lengthwise is referred to as a keel.

Tail structure.   The tail group is attached to the aft fuselage and usually consists of one or more fins or vertical stabilizers and a horizontal stabilizer or tail plane. When the trailing edge of the wings extends back to the aft end of the fuselage, the horizontal stabilizer is either removed entirely or replaced by small stabilizers on each side of the forward fuselage know as canards. The construction of the vertical and horizontal stabilizers is similar to that of the wings. The stabilizers may be rigidly attached to the fuselage, or they may be attached by means of a torque tube and bearing arrangement that allows the entire stabilizer to rotate. The purpose of the stabilizers is to provide lifting surfaces that can develop the necessary aerodynamic forces to control the flight of the aircraft.

The Propulsion System

The major functions of the propulsion system are to provide controlled thrust, air to and from the engine, and power for the accessory equipment. The main subsystems of the propulsion system are the engine, any propellers, the engine air inlets and exhausts, the lubrication subsystem, and the engine controls, accessory drives, and gear boxes. If the aircraft has propellers, the transmission or reduction gears and shafting between the high revolutions per minute (rpm) engine shaft and the lower rpm propellers are referred to as the power train. Figures 2.3a and 2.3b illustrate the location of the main propulsion subsystems of our example aircraft.

Engines.   The engines in fixed-wing aircraft are either buried within the airframe or podded. The thrust necessary for flight can be provided by

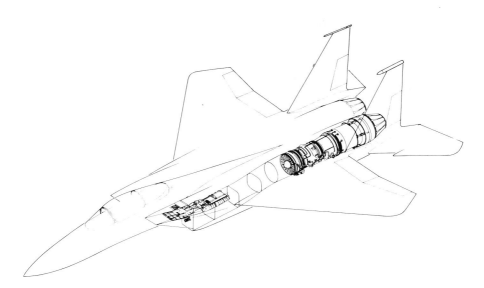

Fig. 2.3a Propulsion system.

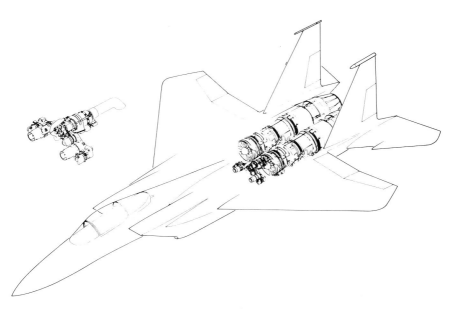

Fig. 2.3b Accessory drive for secondary power.

engine-driven propellers or internal fans, or by the jet exhaust from one or more engines, or by a combination of these two methods. Engine types are the piston, the ramjet, and the gas turbine.

(1) Piston engines. Piston engines, also know as reciprocating, internal combustion engines, drive a propeller or airscrew to produce a thrust. These engines are cooled either with air or with a liquid. The air-cooled engines have the cylinders arranged either in a radial fashion around the axis of the engine or in one or more rows along the axis of the engine. The liquid-cooled engines nearly always have one or more rows of cylinders along the axis of the engine. The liquid-cooled engines require a radiator or heat exchanger to dissipate the heat of the coolant. When operating at high altitude, piston engines usually require a supercharger to increase the amount of air entering the engine and thus obtain an adequate amount of power.

(2) Ramjets and gas turbines. The air-breathing ramjet engine takes in, slows down, and compresses atmospheric air through an inlet duct, heats the air in a combustion chamber or combustor by burning fuel, and directs it out an exhaust duct or nozzle. The hot, accelerated exhaust gas provides the thrust. If the inlet air is compressed with the aid of a high-pressure compressor that is driven by a turbine that is turned by the exhaust gas, the engine is a type of gas turbine called a turbojet. If the power developed by the turbine also turns a propeller, the engine is called a turboprop. If a low-pressure compressor, called a ducted fan, is added and if some of the inlet air is bypassed around the high-pressure compressor, the engine is called a bypass turbojet or turbofan. The fan may compress all of the air entering the engine or only the bypass air. The total thrust from the turbofan engine is made up of the thrust from the hot exhaust gas that passes through the primary duct consisting of the high-pressure compressor, the combustor, the turbine, and the exhaust nozzle, and the thrust on the fan caused by the acceleration of the inlet air. (In the turbofan engine, the fan acts like an internal propeller.) The hot exhaust gas and the bypass air may be mixed and flow out of one exhaust nozzle, or they may exit through separate ducts, with the cooler bypass air usually surrounding the hot exhaust gas. Additional thrust in gas turbines can be obtained by burning fuel in the exhaust duct or augmenter. This is referred to as afterburning or reheat.

Gas turbines are typically built with several spools, each spool containing a portion of the total turbine and fan wheels. For example, in a two-spool engine, the high-pressure turbine (the first turbine after the combustor) may drive the high-pressure compressor on one spool, and the following low-pressure turbine may drive the inlet fan on the other spool.

Turbofan engines usually are most efficient at low and medium subsonic flight speeds. However, the addition of afterburning extends the utility of turbofans to the supersonic region. The turbojet is usually most efficient at transonic and supersonic speeds, and the ramjet operates at relatively high supersonic speeds.

Engine air. Piston engines are used only on subsonic aircraft, and the air required for their operation is taken in through small scoops on the cowling around the engine.

The inlets to gas turbines, on the other hand, must capture air from the freestream and possibly decelerate it to provide uniform, subsonic airflow to the engine face throughout the aircraft flight envelope at various attitude conditions. The inlet opening may be located and shaped to take in air over a wide range of angles of attack and is often positioned away from the surface of the aircraft so that it is out of the surface boundary layer. The inlet opening may be of a fixed size, or it may have a variable opening geometry provided by one or more hinged ramps or movable bodies that adjust and contour the amount of air entering the engine when the aircraft is traveling at high subsonic speeds and above. Bypass doors in the inlet duct that open to allow excess, high-velocity inlet air to escape are some-times used, and sometimes inlet doors that take air in at low velocity are employed.

The exhaust duct provides the path for the engine exhaust gas. The duct must be shaped to minimize losses. The nozzles on supersonic aircraft are usually built with a variable area throat and exit opening for improved performance at all flight speeds and altitudes, and some aircraft have exhaust nozzles that can pivot and change the direction of thrust. The nozzle is usually circular or axisymmetric; however, the use of rectangular or two-dimensional nozzles is expected in future aircraft.

Engine lubrication, cooling, control, and accessory drives. The lubrication subsystem is usually a self-contained, pressurized oil subsystem that provides pressure lubrication to the engine bearings and accessory drives. It has a storage tank, pressure and temperature indicators, pumps, lines, and coolers. The coolers typically use air or fuel for the heat dissipation.

The engine cooling subsystem may consist of a closed, pressurized liquid subsystem with pumps, lines, and a radiator, or it may use the freestream air for cooling. The requirement for the cooling of turbofan engines is mini-mized by the availability of the bypass air for cooling. Typically, air scoops or inlet duct slots gather and direct boundary layer or inlet air through the length of the engine compartment, thus cooling the engine as well as venting the compartment of any fuel vapors. The cooling air is usually expelled near the tail of the aircraft so as to minimize drag.

The major engine control consists of a power setting (rpm) or throttle lever and linkage to the fuel control on the engine for regulating thrust. Detents usually exist at the off, idle, military, and maximum positions. The engine indicators for a gas turbine typically consist of engine rpm, turbine inlet temperature, engine fuel flow, and the exhaust nozzle setting for aircraft with variable exhaust nozzles.

The accessory drives provide power to such things as fuel pumps and controls, an overspeed governor, a tachometer, one or more electrical generators, a lubrication pump, one or more hydraulic pumps, and perhaps a variable exhaust area power unit.

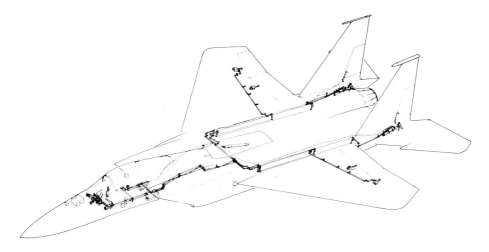

Fig. 2.4a   Flight controls, control surfaces, and surface actuators.

The Flight Control System

The control of the flight path of an aircraft is accomplished using devices called controls that position movable surfaces on the aircraft called control surfaces. The force required to position a control surface is usually provided by a hydraulic power unit called a servoactuator. Consequently, the flight controls, control surfaces, and hydraulic subsystems make up the flight control system. Figure 2.4a shows the location of the controls, surfaces, and actuators on our example aircraft. The major function of this system is to provide control about the three axes of motion, as commanded by the pilot, throughout the flight envelope.

The three axes of an aircraft about which motion can take place are (1) the longitudinal or rolling axis that runs from the tail to the nose, (2) the lateral or pitching axis that runs from the left wing tip to the right wing tip, and (3) the vertical or yawing axis that is normal to the plane containing the other two axes. The motion of the aircraft about these three axes is dependent upon the flight characteristics of the aircraft and the ability of the pilot to control the motion.

Aircraft stability.   Aircraft may be statically and dynamically stable, or neutral, or unstable. A statically stable aircraft will develop aerodynamic forces and moments that tend to return the aircraft to its original position after its equilibrium has been slightly disturbed by a gust of wind or a change in load. If the aircraft is also dynamically stable, the return path will be either in the form of damped oscillations about the original position or a nonoscillatory or deadbeat return, depending upon the damping characteristics of the aircraft. When the aircraft oscillations following a disturbance are divergent, the statically stable aircraft is said to be dynamically unstable. When the oscillations neither decay nor diverge, the aircraft has neutral dynamic stability.

A statically unstable aircraft will develop aerodynamic forces and moments that increase the initial disturbance. For example, if a gust causes a change in the angle of attack, the ensuing motion of the aircraft will be such as to increase the change. Neutral static stability exists when the aircraft neither returns to the original position nor departs in the direction of the disturbance.

The longitudinal stability of an aircraft about the pitch axis is provided mainly by the horizontal stabilizer. Directional stability about the yaw axis is provided by the vertical stabilizers and any ventral fins, and lateral stability about the roll axis is provided by a combination of wing slope (upward is dihedral and downward is anhedral), wing location, and wing sweep.

The more stable an aircraft is, the more difficulty the pilot has when attempting to change its direction. Very stable aircraft are sluggish and hard to maneuver. On the other hand, as the aircraft becomes less stable, the pilot's ability to maneuver the aircraft increases, but precise control of the aircraft flight path decreases. Controllability continues to decrease as the aircraft approaches neutral stability, and the aircraft eventually becomes uncontrollable when a certain level of static instability or negative static stability is reached. Consequently, most aircraft have been designed to be slightly stable, with the degree of stability depending upon the stability axis and the role of the aircraft. However, the advent of computer-controlled flight has allowed new aircraft to be designed with relaxed static stability. The computer can continuously provide all of the fine adjustments of the various control surface positions that are required to maintain the flight path selected by the pilot. Without the computer, the pilot may or may not be able to control the aircraft, depending upon the particular design.

Control surfaces.   Conventional control surfaces are basically panels that are hinged to portions of the wings, the fuselage, and the vertical and horizontal stabilizers. Movement of the panel changes the airflow over the supporting member and hence changes the aerodynamic force on the local structure. If the control surface reaction is felt by the pilot as a feedback through the control system, the system is called reversible. If the forces required to position the surfaces are too large for the pilot, servoactuators are used, and an artificial-feel subsystem is added to provide the pilot with a responsive feel when flying the aircraft. This type of system is called irreversible.

The conventional control panels or surfaces are the ailerons, the elevators, and the rudder. In general, the ailerons and rudder are used together to roll and turn the aircraft, and the elevators are used to change the climb angle or angle of attack. One aileron is usually located along an outer portion of the trailing edge of each wing. They can be counterrotated either up or down. When the left aileron pivots upward, the right aileron pivots downward. The lift force on the left wing will decrease, and that on the right wing will increase, causing the aircraft to roll counterclockwise about the roll axis. (The aircraft will also tend to yaw during a roll due to unbalanced forces.) Directional motion about the yaw axis is controlled by the rudder, a panel that is hinged to the vertical stabilizer and that can rotate in both directions. The elevators are panels hinged to the horizontal stabilizers. They affect the pitching motion of the aircraft. For example, rotating the elevators upward causes the nose of the aircraft to pitch upward due to the reduction in the aerodynamic lift force on the horizontal tail.

There are many deviations from these three basic surfaces, particularly with respect to the elevators. For example, allowing both horizontal stabilizers to pivot symmetrically as a unit slab called a stabilator can eliminate the need for the elevators. Allowing the horizontal stabilizers to pivot independently or asymmetrically provides both pitch and roll control and can eliminate the need for the ailerons. This type of control is sometimes used on aircraft with variable geometry wings because the ailerons can become ineffective when the wings are fully swept back. A mixer assembly is required to convert the pilot's control inputs into the proper surface movement. On tailless aircraft, there may be no stabilators or elevators. Their functions may be provided by the ailerons, which are called elevons in this application.

Two other hinged surfaces that can be used for control are spoilers and speed brakes. Spoilers, sometimes called flaperons, are usually panels hinged to the upper surface of the wings. They only rotate in one direction and serve to reduce the lift on the wings. They can assist in the roll control of aircraft with and without ailerons. Speed brakes are panels hinged to the fuselage or wings that are extended into the airflow to slow the aircraft down. They can also be used to control the motion of the aircraft in an emergency. Split ailerons can also be used as a speed brake by rotating the upper half upward and the lower half downward.

Other movable surfaces that are primarily intended to provide extra lift, such as wing leading- and trailing-edge flaps and leading-edge slats can also be used as supplementing or backup control surfaces.

A small tab is often located at the trailing edge of a control surface. This tab is called a trim tab and is used to finely balance or trim the aircraft. A deviation of the trim tab position will cause an opposing deviation in the position of the control surface. The trim tab reduces the magnitude of the hinge moment required to position the control surface and, hence, reduces the required control forces.

The flight controls.   The aircraft flight controls that move the control surfaces include the control column (a stick or wheel) for moving the elevator and ailerons and the control pedals for moving the rudder. The column and pedals can be mechanically linked to the surfaces or to the controlling servoactuators by cables, push-pull rods, torque tubes, bell cranks, and quadrants, or electrically linked by wires from the column and pedals through a computer and on to the servoactuators. The use of electrical wiring to carry the control signals is referred to as fly-by-wire.

Artificial-feel devices or packages are inserted in the linkage or control path to provide force cues and feedback to the pilot.

The automatic flight control system.   The pilot may be assisted in the flying of the aircraft by an automatic flight control system (AFCS). The AFCS normally provides two functions: (1) It augments the aircraft's natural damping characteristics, and (2) it provides automatic commands to the controls for holding the attitude, altitude, and heading selected by the pilot. The first function, the modification of the aircraft damping characteristics, decreases the tendency of the aircraft to oscillate and is carried out by the stability augmentation subsystem (SAS) or the control augmentation subsystem (CAS). A computer is used to process inputs from the pilot's controls and from aircraft motion sensors. It then generates the necessary control surface commands for roll, pitch, and yaw to reduce oscillations and maintain stability. Aircraft that are designed with relaxed static stability may not be controllable without the SAS. The second function of the AFCS is provided by the autopilot. The autopilot relieves the pilot of much of the work load required to fly the aircraft by maintaining a hold on the selected attitude, altitude, and heading.

The hydraulics.   On small aircraft that fly at slow speeds, the control surfaces can be moved physically by the pilot directly through the mechanical linkage from the cockpit controls to the control surfaces. However, the forces required to position the control surfaces on high speed or large aircraft can be excessive. Consequently, either a power-boosted or a power-operated control system is used. A power-boosted system employs a servoactuator in parallel with a mechanical linkage to assist the pilot in positioning the surface. A power-operated system uses the servoactuator to supply all of the force required to position the surface.

Most powered systems use servoactuators that contain a hydraulic fluid under very high pressure, typically 3000 psi. The servoactuator contains a control or servovalve that receives the input control signal and accordingly meters the hydraulic fluid to one or more power cylinders that make up the actuator. The servoactuator is usually located close to the surface to be moved. The pressurized hydraulic fluid is supplied to all of the actuators as well as other hydraulically operated components, such as flaps and landing gear, by hydraulic lines from an engine-driven, hydraulic pump, accumulator, and reservoir configuration. Figure 2.4b shows the location of many hydraulic subsystem components.

Aircraft that rely totally on hydraulic power for the control forces may become uncontrollable when a hydraulic failure occurs. The pilot may be simply unable to move the control surfaces. Consequently, most aircraft employ more than one hydraulic subsystem for safety of flight. Each one is usually independent and typically operates a portion of the control system. These subsystems are usually referred to as the power control (PC) and utility subsystems. Each subsystem may have more than one circuit. Normally, each servoactuator is pressurized by two or more subsystems. A

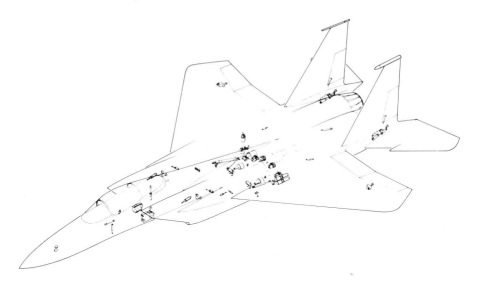

Fig. 2.4b   Hydraulic subsystem.

backup electrohydraulic power module or hand pump may be provided for emergency operation of selected components.

The Fuel System

The major function of the fuel system is to provide the fuel for combustion in the powerplant. The fuel can also be used for cooling and hydraulic power. The system consists of the internal and external storage tanks, the distribution subsystem, the refueling/dumping subsystem, and the indicating subsystem. The internal storage and distribution subsystems of our example aircraft are shown in Fig. 2.5.

Storage.   Most of the fuel carried by an aircraft is usually stored internally in the fuselage and/or wings in one or more closed tanks or cells located near the center of mass of the aircraft. The tanks may be "leak-proof" metal boxes or metal cavities formed by the structural elements of the aircraft, such as the skin, spars, ribs, and bulkheads. The latter are known as integral or wet tanks. The fuel may also be stored in semiflexible bags or bladders that fit inside the tank. The bladders, typically made of rubber and nylon fabric, may require a special supporting structure or backing board that separates the bladder from the external skin or other structural elements of the aircraft. Wet tanks are seldom used in the fuselage due to leakage problems, but most wing tanks are wet.

The external storage consists of expendable metallic or nonmetallic tanks carried under the fuselage and/or under the wings on pylons. These tanks

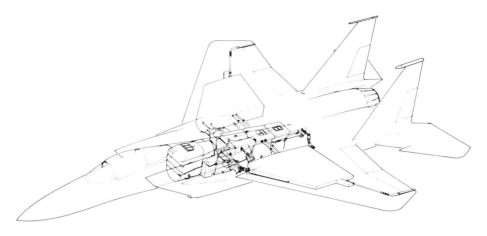

Fig. 2.5   Fuel system.

are referred to as drop tanks although they are usually jettisoned only in an emergency.

Distribution. Typically, several internal and external tanks are used, and the fuel is continuously transferred between the tanks to maintain an even balance of the fuel load. Any external fuel is usually transferred to the wing tanks as the wing tanks transfer their fuel to the fuselage tanks. When the external fuel is totally transferred, the wing tanks begin to empty. If the fuel is used to absorb the heat from engine accessory drives, lubrication oil, or hydraulic fluid, the hot fuel may be recirculated back to the wing tanks for cooling. Thus, the wing tanks may always contain a certain amount of fuel.

The fuel can be transferred between tanks by several methods. It can be moved from one tank to another by one or more electric boost pumps, by motive flow, or by gravity flow. (Motive flow works on the Venturi principle.) A net positive pressure in the tank ullage (the internal space above the fuel surface) is usually provided by a combination of air vents and a pressure air supply (usually bleed air from the engine) to assist in the fuel transfer and to prevent the fuel from boiling when the aircraft is at high altitudes. The ullage pressure is regulated to prevent both a relatively large net internal pressure buildup during aircraft ascent and a net external pressure buildup during descent.

The tank that supplies the fuel to the engine is called the feed or sump tank. It is usually the lowest fuselage tank. The fuel is pumped or flows from the feed tank through the feed line to the engine. If the fuel is not pressurized in the feed line, vaporization or vapor lock may occur, causing engine flameout. A compartment or baffles in the feed tank may provide a limited fuel supply during negative *g* or inverted flight. The pump that supplies high-pressure fuel to the engine combustor is the main fuel pump and is typically located with the engine accessories.

In addition to supplying the engine and cooling the accessories, the fuel is sometimes used as a hydraulic fluid to operate components such as a variable area engine exhaust nozzle.

The other subsystems.   The refueling/dumping subsystem consists of the piping and valves required to fill the storage tanks with fuel and to dump excess fuel from the tanks. An in-flight refueling probe is installed on some aircraft, and nearly all aircraft have the capability to dump fuel overboard from the tanks. The indicating subsystem consists mainly of the fuel quantity in the various tanks.

The fuel.   Aviation fuel is currently obtained from petroleum. There are several grades of fuel available. Because the fuel used by piston engines is pressurized in a hot cylinder prior to ignition, a relatively light fuel, known as gasoline or AVGAS, is used that contains additives to prevent premature detonation or knocking. In a gas turbine, on the other hand, the combustion process is continuous at a constant pressure, and the antiknock requirement does not exist. Consequently, the choice of fuel for gas turbines is based upon efficiency, safety, operation at low temperatures, cost, and availability. Kerosene, a heavy fuel called JP-1, would be a good fuel, except for its poor performance at low temperatures. Consequently, a lighter fuel must be used for cold weather or very-high-altitude operations. The US Air Force currently uses JP-4, and the US Navy uses JP-5. These are mixtures of various grades of fuel extractable during the refining process. JP-4 is a blend of gasoline and kerosene, and JP-5 is a less volatile, heavier kerosene-based fuel. Other fuels sometimes used are the commercial aviation fuels Jet A and A-1, which are similar to JP-5, and Jet B, which is similar to JP-4.

The Other Systems

The other systems include a crew, avionics, armament, environmental control, electrical, and launch and recovery. The location of some of the components of these systems is shown in Figs. 2.6a–2.6d for our example aircraft.

The crew obviously operates the aircraft and can range in size from one to many members.

The avionics system may include the automatic flight control system previously discussed and the stores management, fire-control, navigation, motion sensors, and internal and external communications subsystems.

The armament system consists of the bombs, guns and ammunition drums, rockets, missiles, mines, and torpedoes carried by the aircraft for offensive and defensive purposes.

The environmental control system (ECS) includes the air-conditioning, oxygen, and air-pressurization subsystems. The air-conditioning subsystem provides ventilation, heating, cooling, moisture control, and pressurization for the crew stations and equipment bays. The oxygen subsystem typically

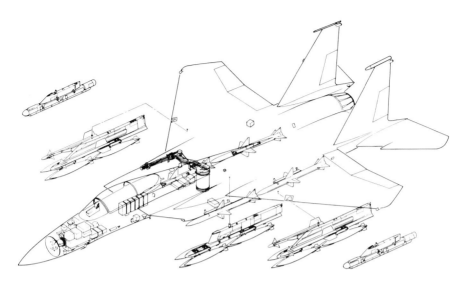

Fig. 2.6a   Avionics and armament systems.

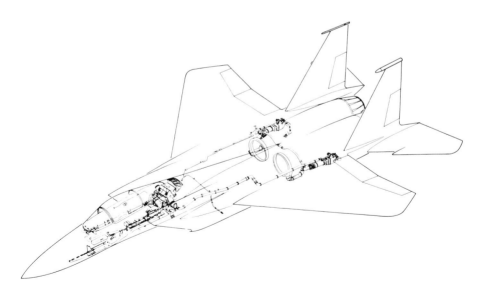

Fig. 2.6b   Environmental control system.

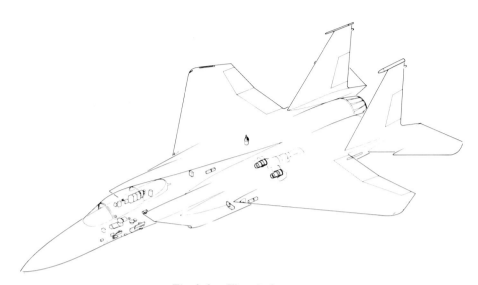

Fig. 2.6c   Electrical system.

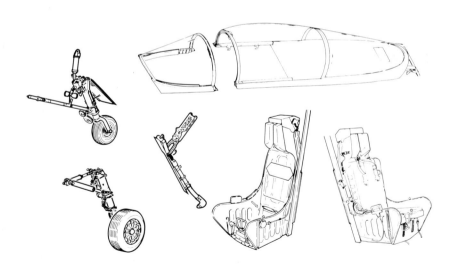

Fig. 2.6d   Landing gear and escape subsystems.

consists of a liquid oxygen (LOX) storage container and the controls, valves, and piping to the crew stations. The air-pressurization subsystem typically uses a mixture of hot bleed air from the gas turbine high-pressure compressor section and freestream ram air. This high-pressure air is supplied to the air-conditioning subsystem, the gun bay for purging the gun gas, the rain repellent subsystem for cleaning the windscreen, the deicing subsystem, and to the fuel tanks for internal pressurization.

The electrical system consists of ac and dc subsystems that include generators, batteries, controls, and distribution components. This system provides the electrical power throughout the aircraft.

The launch and recovery system includes the landing gear and sometimes a drag chute or arresting hook for quicker stops.

2.3 ROTARY-WING AIRCRAFT

Rotary-wing aircraft require lift, thrust, and control to fly, just like fixed-wing aircraft. They have the same five major systems that provide these functions as fixed-wing aircraft, except the power train and rotating blades are usually identified as a separate system. The major lifting surfaces are the main rotor blades. However, some rotary-wing aircraft have wings that provide lift during forward flight, thus reducing the load on the rotor. The thrust is also provided by the main rotor, and the aerodynamic forces required to control the direction of flight are provided by a combination of rotors.

General Arrangement

A typical rotary-wing aircraft is the helicopter illustrated in Figs. 2.7a and 2.7b. The forward portion of the aircraft usually contains some of the crew and avionics components. The center portion of the aircraft contains the

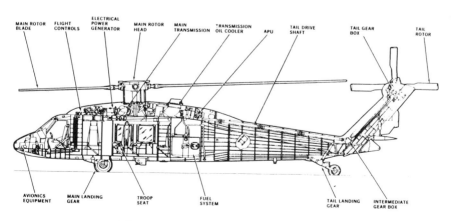

Fig. 2.7a   General arrangement: elevation.

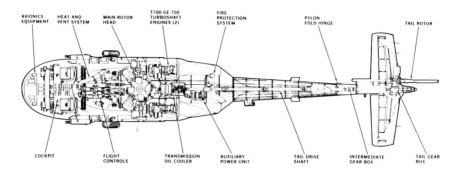

Fig. 2.7b   General arrangement: plan.

main rotor, the engines, usually on top, the fuel tanks, usually on the bottom, any wings, and the payload. The aft portion contains the tail rotor, and any vertical and horizontal tail planes. Other rotor arrangements are two coaxial main rotors that rotate in the opposite direction, two main rotors in tandem, and two main rotors side by side.

The Structural System

Helicopters typically use the same kind of construction as fixed-wing aircraft. The fuselage is semimonocoque, and any wings and vertical and horizontal stabilizers are single- or multiple-spar box beams. The tubular semimonocoque or trussed portion of the fuselage that runs from the center bay back to the tail rotor is called the tail cone or boom.

Much of the helicopter structure is designed to be crash-resistant for reasons of safety. In particular, the fuel tanks should be designed to retain their integrity during a crash.

Currently, aluminum is the most common material used in helicopters, but the use of advanced, lightweight composites may be predominant in future designs.

The Propulsion System

Helicopter powerplants usually consist of air-cooled gas turbines that turn shafts in the power train system that eventually turn the rotor blades. These engines are called turboshaft engines. The main objective of the turboshaft engine is to convert as much of the output power into the shaft power as possible. The engines are either buried within the fuselage or are carried externally in pods or nacelles. Air for the engine operation enters through the inlet in the cowling. This inlet air may also be used for cooling purposes, and a scheme for preventing foreign object damage (FOD) to the engine is usually included in the inlet duct or engine inlet. The engine installation is shown in Fig. 2.8 for our example helicopter.

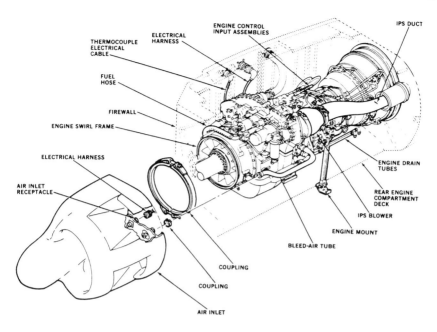

Fig. 2.8   Engine installation.

The Power Train and Rotor Blade System

The power or drive train typically consists of gearboxes that connect the engine drive shaft(s) with the engine-to-transmission drive shaft(s), a main transmission, a main rotor drive shaft, and tail rotor and pylon drive shafts with intermediate and tail rotor reduction gearboxes. (The rotor drive power does not always come from the main transmission; sometimes the rotor drive comes directly from an engine output gearbox.) Figure 2.9a shows many of the power train components for the example helicopter. The transmission converts the high speed of the input shaft to the much lower speed of the main and tail rotor drive shafts. The gearboxes also allow a change in direction and speed between the input and output rotating shafts. Some form of lubrication and cooling of the transmission and gearboxes is usually required.

The main rotor drive shaft is supported by a rotor support structure. The tail rotor drive shaft is supported along its length by hanger bearings, dampers, and antiflail sleeves. The rotor hub is at the top or end of the rotor drive shaft and connects the rotor blades to the shaft. Figure 2.9b shows the main rotor shaft, the rotor hub, and the connections to the main transmission.

The rotor blades are beamlike structures that are built in the shape of an airfoil. They can be attached to the hub in a variety of ways. The pitch of

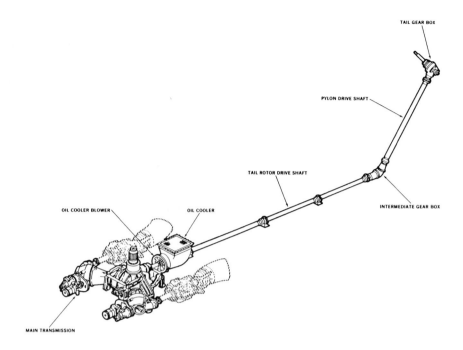

Fig. 2.9a   Power train.

the blades, which governs the amount of lift, is usually set by pitch links (shown in Fig. 2.9b) that are attached to a swashplate (also shown in Fig. 2.9b) that rotates with the rotor. The rotating swashplate turns on or within a stationary swashplate whose position is governed by the flight control system. Displacement of the stationary swashplate changes the pitch of the blades.

The Flight Control System

The major control surfaces of a helicopter are the rotor blades. The lateral, longitudinal, and directional control of the helicopter is provided by a collective stick, a cyclic stick, and either two foot pedals or one bar. The collective mostly affects the total main rotor lift. The cyclic mostly affects the direction of the main rotor lift vector by varying the pitch of each blade as it rotates and, hence, provides the lateral and longitudinal control. The pedals, sometimes referred to as rudder pedals, provide directional control by positioning the pitch of the tail rotor blades, which affects the lateral force on the tail of the helicopter. This lateral force is required at all times on single rotor aircraft under powered flight to counteract the torque caused by the main rotor powered rotation. A cambered vertical tail plane is

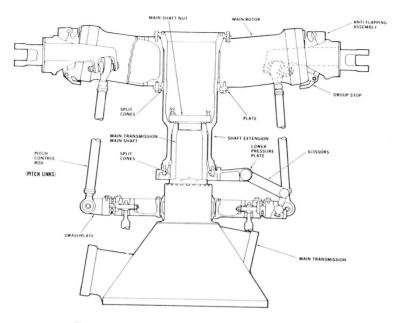

Fig. 2.9b   Transmission and main rotor head.

sometimes used to provide this counteracting force during forward flight, and a horizontal stabilator may be used to assist in the longitudinal control.

The sticks and pedals are connected to servoactuators that serve to position the pitch links. The connection may be mechanically, through push-pull rods, cables, bell cranks, and quadrants, or electrically through wires. A mechanical mixer assembly provides interconnections between the controls and the rotor blades to account for such things as the required increase in tail rotor pitch due to an increased collective command.

An automatic flight control subsystem may assist the pilot in flying the aircraft. The AFCS may have both stability augmentation and autopilot capabilities.

The hydraulic subsystem typically consists of one or more pumping and distribution subsystems that provide hydraulic power to operate the flight controls, an auxiliary power unit (APU) start motor, the rotor brake, and weapons.

The Fuel System

The fuel system on rotary-wing aircraft usually includes the same subsystems used by fixed-wing aircraft. However, in most helicopters, the fuel is usually stored below the engines, often outside the fuselage, and gravity flow cannot be used. Consequently, the fuel must be transferred either by positive boost pressure or by suction up to the engines. If suction transfer is used, a scheme for priming the fuel lines must be provided.

The fuel used by rotary-wing aircraft is typically JP-4 or JP-5.

The Other Systems

Rotary-wing aircraft require crew, avionics, armament, ECS, electrical, and launch and recovery systems, just like fixed-wing aircraft, and they operate in much the same way as those on the fixed-wing aircraft. Perhaps the major difference between the two lies in the launch and recovery system. This system supports special takeoff and landing procedures that differ considerably from those of fixed-wing aircraft. The normal takeoff and landing procedure is vertical. However, environmental and load conditions may require a horizontal run to build up sufficient lift for vertical flight. A unique feature of the helicopter is its ability to land relatively slowly with no engine power, using the autorotational feature where the rotor blades are turned by the upward motion of the air passing through the rotor (thus generating lift) as the helicopter descends.

Selected Bibliography

Desoutter, D. M., *Aircraft and Missiles, What They Are, What They Do, and How They Work*, John Degraff Inc., New York.

Stinton, D., *The Anatomy of the Aeroplane*, American Elsevier Publishing Company, New York, 1966.

Zhemchuzhin, N. A. et al., *Soviet Aircraft and Rockets* (translated from Russian), Amerind Publishing Co. Pvt. Ltd., New Dehli, NASA TT 74-52007, 1977 (available from the U.S. Dept. of Commerce, National Technical Information Service, Springfield, Va.).

Don Jacobs -85

3. THE MISSIONS, THE THREATS, AND THE THREAT EFFECTS

3.1 MILITARY MISSIONS

The survival of a military aircraft on a particular mission is related to the type of mission being conducted, to the amount of support from friendly forces, and to the intensity and effectiveness of any hostile environment encountered during the execution of that mission. Almost all combat missions, such as close air support, interdiction, fighter escort, fighter sweep, combat air patrol, defense suppression, photoreconnaissance, and forward air control will involve encounters with air-defense systems of one form or another. Aircraft that conduct utility missions near the forward line of own troops (FLOT, formerly known as the forward edge of the battle area, or FEBA) or in the vicinity of combat zones, such as transport of supplies, equipment, and personnel, search and rescue operations, early warning, communications, strike and traffic control, long-range targeting, submarine detection and prosecution, and electronic support and countermeasures, could very likely encounter a threat to their survival. This section presents a brief description of these missions and of a strike in Vietnam in 1965 in order to give the reader an understanding of the operational aspects of military aircraft and of the potential interaction between the aircraft and the threat. The specific encounter conditions between the aircraft and any threats for a particular scenario are determined in the mission-threat analysis, which is described in Sec. 3.7 of this chapter.

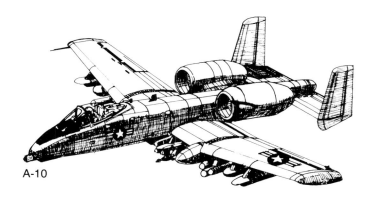

A-10

61

Close Air Support (CAS)

The close air support mission involves air action against hostile targets that are in close proximity to friendly forces and requires detailed integration of each air mission with the fire and movement of those forces. Some of the US fixed-wing aircraft that might conduct this mission are the A-4 Skyhawk, the A-6 Intruder, the A-7 Corsair II, the F-4 Phantom II, the F/A-18 Hornet, and the A-10 Thunderbolt II. The A-10 has been designed specifically for this role. Helicopters, such as the AH-1 Cobra and the AH-64 Apache, can also be used for close air support.

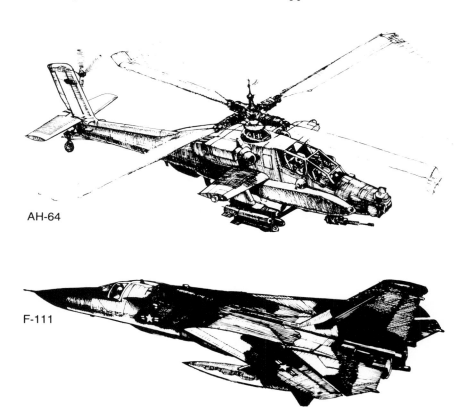

AH-64

F-111

Interdiction

Interdiction or strike missions are designed to destroy, neutralize, or delay the enemy's military potential before it can be brought to bear effectively against friendly forces. These missions are conducted at such distances from friendly forces that detailed integration with the fire and movement of the friendly forces is not required. The US aircraft that may conduct this

B-52

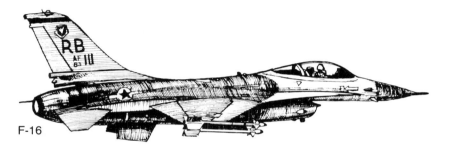

F-16

mission are essentially the same ones that can conduct the close air support mission and the F-111 and the B-52.

Fighter Escort (FE) and Fighter Sweep

The fighter escort mission is the dedication of fighter aircraft to protect or defend other aircraft during the mission, and the fighter sweep is an offensive mission by fighter aircraft to seek out and destroy enemy aircraft or targets of opportunity in an allotted area of operation. Some US aircraft that may be employed on these missions are the F-4, the F-14 Tomcat, the F-15 Eagle, the F-16 Fighting Falcon, and the F/A-18.

Combat Air Patrol (CAP)

This mission consists of an aircraft patrol that is provided over a specific area for the purpose of intercepting and destroying hostile aircraft or missiles before they reach their target. Many of the aircraft that perform the fighter missions can also perform the CAP mission. In particular, the F-14 with the Phoenix missile system was designed to deliver multiple shots at multiple incoming targets at long ranges.

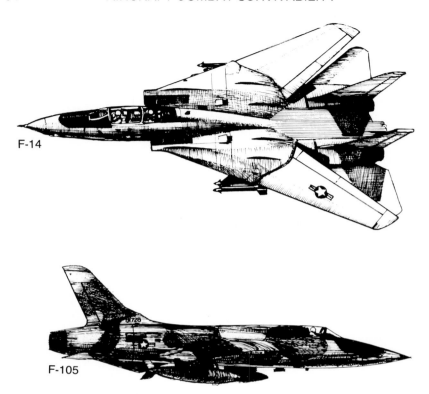

F-14

F-105

Defense Suppression

The defense suppression mission is usually conducted by special purpose aircraft such as the Wild Weasel, a modified F-4 or F-105 Thunderchief, and Iron Hand. Wild Weasel aircraft have been given equipment that allows them to locate, identify, and either jam or physically destroy ground-based enemy air-defense systems that employ sensors that radiate electromagnetic waves (e.g., radar). The primary job of Iron Hand aircraft, such as the F-105, is to seek out and destroy missile sites.

RF-101 "VOODOO"

Photoreconnaissance

The objective of this mission is to obtain photographs for the purpose of making maps or charts or for information on the results of bombing or on enemy concentrations and movements. The mission is usually conducted by a special purpose aircraft, such as the RF-101 Voodoo and the RF-4, sometimes with, and sometimes without, an escort. The "recce" is usually the last one over the target after a bombing strike for bomb damage assessment (BDA), and the mission is successful only if the aircraft returns with the film.

OV-10

Forward Air Control (FAC)

Aircraft on a FAC mission control other aircraft in close air support of ground troops from an airborne position. The OV-10 Bronco aircraft was specifically designed for this mission.

C-130

Transport of Supplies, Equipment, and Personnel

This mission can consist of the pickup or delivery of cargo and/or troops in an area that may be within range of some form of enemy fire. The Marines refer to this mission as either amphibious or land assault, depending upon the origin of the mission. Both large fixed-wing aircraft, such as the C-130 Hercules and the C-5 Galaxy, and helicopters, such as the CH-47 Chinook, H-46 Sea Knight, and UH-60 Blackhawk, may be used for this mission.

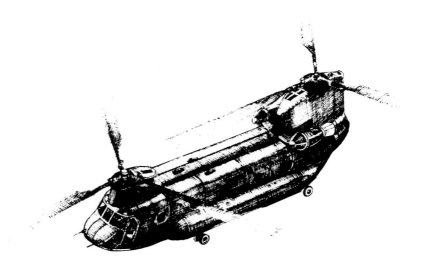

CH-47 CHINOOK

Search and Rescue (SAR)

This mission involves the search for and rescue of personnel in distress on land or at sea. If this mission is conducted in a hostile area, it is referred to as combat SAR (CSAR). The mission is often conducted by fixed-wing aircraft, such as the A-1 Skyraider, and helicopters, such as the HH-3 Jolly Green Giant, working together, with the fixed-wing aircraft providing an air cover for the searching helicopter.

Early Warning, Communications, and Strike and Traffic Control

These missions are conducted by aircraft that are located in a position where they can observe and notify friendly forces of the launch or approach of unknown weapons or weapons carriers. They may also direct air interceptors toward the incoming threats. They are usually on station for long periods of time and may be a high-priority target in the event of a surprise attack. US aircraft employed in this role are the E-2 Hawkeye and the E-3 airborne warning and control system (AWACS).

Long-Range Targeting

This mission, also known as over-the-horizon targeting (OHT), involves the location and identification of potential hostile targets and the subsequent relay of position information to a friendly command center.

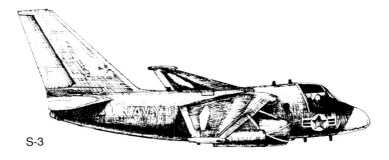

S-3

Submarine Detection and Prosecution

This mission consists of a systematic search of a particular area for the purpose of locating and destroying a submarine known or suspected to be somewhere in the area. Aircraft that conduct this mission are known as antisubmarine warfare (ASW) aircraft and include the fixed-wing land-based P-3 Orion and carrier-based S-3 Viking, and the H-2 Seasprite and H-3 Sea King helicopters.

Electronic Support and Countermeasures

Special purpose aircraft whose mission is to search for, detect, locate, and identify sources of radiated electromagnetic waves are known as electronic support measures (ESM), signal intelligence (SIGINT), or special electronic mission (SEMA) aircraft. Special purpose aircraft whose role is to radiate electromagnetic energy that degrades or deceives hostile electronic equipment are referred to as electronic countermeasures (ECM) aircraft. Examples of ECM aircraft are the Navy's EA-6B Prowler and the Air Force's EF-111.

EA-6B

A Strike in Vietnam in 1965

The first major strike against a bridge in North Vietnam known as the Dragon's Jaw is a vivid illustration of the vast amount of operational resources that have been dedicated in the past to enhancing the survivability of strike aircraft. Shortly after noon on April 3, 1965, 79 US Air Force aircraft took off for Thanh Hoa in North Vietnam. Forty-six were F-105's, 21 were F-100 Super Sabres, 2 were RF-101's, and 10 were KC-135 tankers. Fifteen of the F-105's and seven of the F-100's were to provide flak

KC-135 AND F-105

suppression; that is, they were to destroy the enemy's ground-based air defenses using 750-lb bombs and 2.75-in. rockets. Two F-100's were dedicated to weather reconnaissance, four F-100's were for fighter escort or MIG CAP, and eight were for SAR or RESCAP, if required. The remainder of the 79 aircraft, only 31 F-105's, were scheduled to strike the bridge with Bullpup missiles and 750-lb bombs. (Each F-105 bomber carried 6000 lb of bombs, which was about the same bomb load as that carried by a B-17 in World War II.) The strike was not totally successful. The bridge was damaged, but not destroyed, and the antiaircraft fire was considerably more intense than anticipated. Two of the aircraft were lost, and several were damaged on this first of many strikes on the Dragon's Jaw bridge. [*Airwar-Vietnam* (see Bibliography) contains a detailed description of this strike and many of the other major air actions in Vietnam.]

3.2   THREAT TERMINOLOGY

The threats to aircraft have been defined as those elements of a man-made environment designed to reduce the ability of an aircraft to perform mission-related functions by inflicting damaging effects, forcing undesirable maneuvers, or degrading system effectiveness. The hostile environment can be made up of numerous threat elements, each having a distinct set of characteristics and capabilities. Assurance that all of the threat elements and their effects are completely and accurately considered in the survivability analysis, design, and operation of an aircraft requires more than a casual knowledge of current and anticipated hostile air defense systems.

In order to become proficient in the discipline of survivability analysis and design, one must become familiar not only with the specific threats to the aircraft, but also with the proper usage of generic threat terms and the various terminology concepts and distinctions. The major subfields that

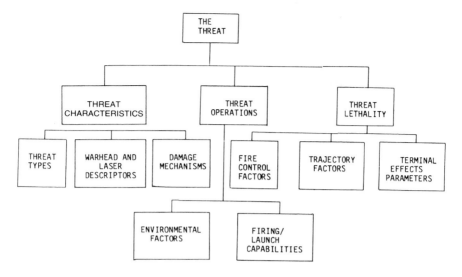

Fig. 3.1   Threat topical field.

make up the threat topical field are shown in Fig. 3.1. This topical field contains those subfields that are used to describe the threat characteristics, the threat operations, and the threat lethality. Threat characteristics refer to the type of threat, such as antiaircraft artillery or surface-to-air missiles; the warhead descriptors, such as armor-piercing or shaped charge; and the associated threat or damage mechanisms, such as blast or fragments. Threat operations refers to those inherent capabilities and environmental factors that relate to the ability of the threat to perform its basic firing/launch functions. For example, environmental factors include threat mobility, locational adaptability, and weather capability. The firing and launch capabilities include slew rate, rate of fire, and intercept envelope. Threat lethality refers to those factors related to the fire control, trajectory, and terminal effects of the threat in the process of directing, projecting, and activating threat mechanisms designed to cause damage to a target. Fire-control factors consist of items such as aiming error, lead angle prediction, and tracking error. Trajectory factors include ballistic dispersion, gravity drop, and thermal blooming; and among the terminal effects parameters are projectile caliber, equivalent weight of TNT, and fragment density.

It is important to note that none of the threat terms given above reflects any interaction between the damage mechanisms and the aircraft or target. Rather, these descriptors relate to the inherent or possessed capabilities of the threats themselves. The system response topical field, shown in Fig. 3.2, is the field that contains those terms that are used to describe the interactions of the damage mechanisms and the target, i.e., the damage processes. Damage processes are phenomena such as penetration and blast loading.

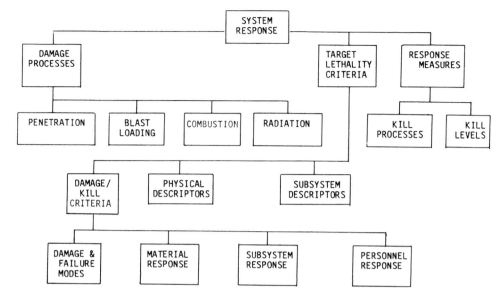

Fig. 3.2   System-response topical field.

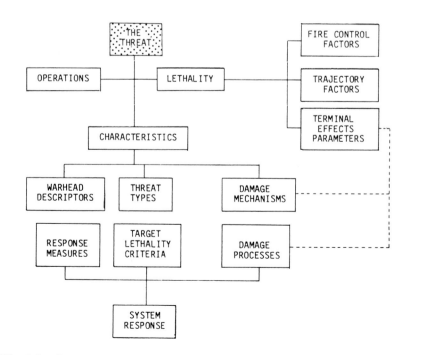

Fig. 3.3   Connections between the threat and the system-response topical fields.

Subfield	Key Concepts of Definition	Example Terms
Damage mechanisms	Nature of the warhead output	•Penetrator •Incendiary particles •Electromagnetic flux •Blast •Accelerated electron
Terminal effects parameters	Intensity of the damage mechanism output	•Projectile caliber •Incen. flash duration •Energy beam intensity •Equiv. weight of TNT •Electron-volts
Damage processes	Interactions between damage mechanism and target	•Penetration •Combustion •Temperature rise •Blast loading •Vaporization

Fig. 3.4   Comparison of example terms.

This field also contains the target lethality criteria, which define the conditional response of the target to the damage processes, and the response measures, which are quantitative measures of the final results of the interaction of the damage mechanisms with the target.

The connection between the threat topical field and the system response topical field is often difficult to grasp because of the misuse of many of the terms and concepts. The dotted line in Fig. 3.3 connecting the damage mechanisms, the terminal effects parameters, and the damage processes subfields illustrates one of the more confusing connections. Figure 3.4 gives a comparison of example terms in these three subfields that in the past have been commonly, but erroneously, interchanged, with resulting ambiguity.

3.3   THREAT CHARACTERISTICS

The threat characteristics of interest here are those descriptions that relate to the threat type, the warhead type, and the damage mechanisms.

Threat Type

Threat type denotes the general classification of the threat element in terms of firing platform and site type. In general, threat elements can be grouped into two types: terminal and nonterminal, as shown in Fig. 3.5.

The nonterminal threats do not in themselves possess a capability to inflict damage. They are the electronic and/or optical systems used by enemy forces to support the terminal threat elements. These elements normally consist of detection and early warning, target identification, target tracking, electronic counter-countermeasure (ECCM), fire or weapon con-

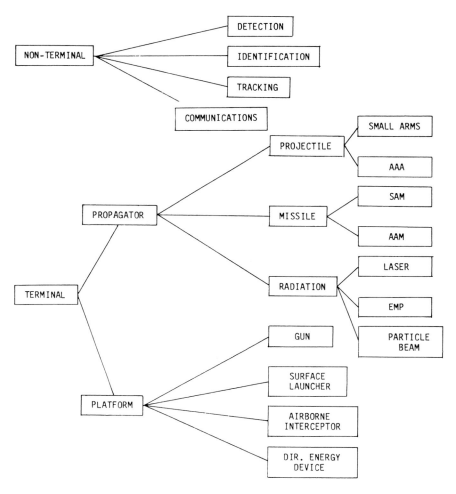

Fig. 3.5 Threat types.

trol, and communication systems. They can be land-, sea-, or air-based and are normally an integrated part of the enemy's offensive and defensive forces. Their purpose is to supply target position, speed, and heading information to the terminal threat units.

Terminal threat elements have the capability to cause damage to an airborne target. They consist of the firing platform and the threat propagator.

Threat platforms. Terminal threat platforms are divided into four categories: guns, missile launchers, airborne interceptors, and directed energy devices.

(1) Gun. A gun is a device, including any stock, carriage, or attachment from which projectiles are propelled by the force of an explosive reaction. It includes threats of various sizes, ranging from hand-held small arms to much larger transportable or stationary antiaircraft artillery (AAA).

(2) Surface-to-air missile (SAM) launch and guidance equipment. This surface platform is used to launch and guide SAMs to an intercept point. SAM launch and guidance equipment varies in size from a single hand-held launch tube to a semipermanent complex containing numerous trailers, vans, and launch units. The system may employ both optical and radar target tracking in conjunction with special missile tracking and guidance computers.

(3) Airborne interceptor (AI). This is a high-performance, highly maneuverable aircraft designed to engage and destroy airborne targets. Weapons systems employed by the airborne interceptor include air-to-air guns, missiles, and the associated equipment for identifying, tracking, and firing the weapons.

(4) Directed energy device. Weapon systems that produce a beam of electromagnetic radiation with intensity sufficient to damage a target are called directed high-energy weapons (DHEW). In addition to melting or thermally degrading portions of the target, these weapons may do more subtle damage by overloading or blinding the various electromagnetic and optical sensors on the target.

Threat propagators. Threat propagators are divided into three categories: projectiles, guided missiles, and radiation.

(1) Projectiles. A projectile is an object initially propelled by an applied exterior force and continuing in motion by virtue of its own inertia, as a bullet, bomb, or shell. The term projectile is generally used to represent the device containing the warhead. This propagator is usually associated with guns, such as small arms and AAA, although grenades and mortors are also projectiles that have been used against aircraft at low altitude or on the ground.

Small arms are guns that fire projectiles up to and including 20 mm in diameter. The term small arms is generally used to denote guns with calibers of 7.62, 12.7, 14.5, and 20 mm. These weapons usually employ visual or optical tracking and are fabricated in differing barrel configurations, usually one to four. Most projectiles fired by these weapons are of the ball (B), armor-piercing (AP), or armor-piercing-incendiary (AP-I) type, except for the 14.5-mm machine gun, which is also capable of firing a high-explosive incendiary (HE-I) and an incendiary tracer (I-T) projectile. Figure 3.6 shows a typical AP-I projectile.

AAA denotes that category of guns that fires projectiles greater than 20 mm in size. (The entire group of automatic weapons larger than 12.7 mm is also referred to as antiaircraft or AA guns.) AAA is generally standardized

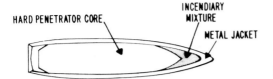

Fig. 3.6   Typical AP-I projectile.

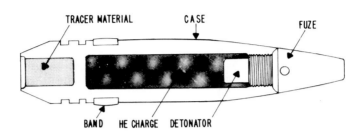

Fig. 3.7   Typical HE-T projectile.

to calibers 23, 30, 37, 57, 85, and 100 mm, although there are some types with calibers greater than 100 mm. The projectiles are either high-explosive (HE) or armor-piercing (AP), and they may contain incendiary (I) and/or tracer (T) material. Figure 3.7 shows a 23-mm HE-T projectile. The guns that fire these projectiles may be land-, sea-, or air-based and may employ either optical or radar tracking, or both. Like small arms, AAA may have either single- or multiple-barrel configurations.

(2)   Guided missiles.   A guided missile is an aerospace vehicle, with varying guidance capabilities, that is self-propelled through space for the purpose of inflicting damage on a designated target. (An unguided missile is called a rocket and is normally not a threat to airborne aircraft.) These propagators contain a propulsion system, a warhead section, a guidance system, and one or more sensors. Movable control surfaces are deflected by commands from the guidance section to direct the missile in flight. Some missiles are dependent on offboard equipment for guidance commands, while others are able to guide themselves independently after launch. The various kinds of missile guidance are described in Sec. 3.5 of this chapter. A sketch of a typical missile configuration is given in Fig. 3.8. The two types of missiles that pose a threat to airborne aircraft are the air-to-air or air-intercept missile (AAM or AIM) and the surface-to-air missile (SAM).

Air-to-air missiles are launched from interceptor aircraft. Although they may employ various guidance techniques, some form of homing is the primary type of guidance used due to weight constraints in the launch platform. Weight constraints in the missile itself dictate the use of relatively small warheads.

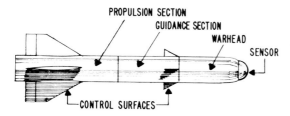

Fig. 3.8   Typical missile configuration.

Surface-to-air missiles are those launched from land- or sea-based platforms. They have varying guidance and propulsion capabilities that influence their launch envelopes relative to the target. They employ various, and in many cases sophisticated, electronic counter-countermeasure schemes to enhance their effectiveness. Because weight is not as much of a problem for the SAMs, these missiles are often much larger than their air-to-air counterparts, and they can have larger warheads and longer ranges.

(3) Radiation.   Radiation is energy transmitted as either particles or waves through space at the speed of light. Radiation is capable of inflicting damage when it is transmitted toward the target either in a continuous beam or as one or more high-intensity, short-duration pulses. Weapons utilizing radiation as the propagator are referred to as directed high-energy weapons and are predicted to become operational within the next decade. These weapons present a new and a significant problem to the science of aircraft survivability.

There are three types of radiation that are propagated by the DHEW. They are the coherent electromagnetic flux, the noncoherent electromagnetic pulse (EMP), and charged nuclear particles. The coherent electromagnetic flux is produced by the high-energy laser (HEL). The HEL generates and focuses electromagnetic energy into an intense concentration or beam of coherent waves that is pointed at the target. This beam of energy is then held on the target until the absorbed energy causes sufficient damage to the target to result in its eventual destruction. Radiation from a laser that is delivered in a very short period of time with a high intensity is referred to as a pulse-laser beam. The acronym laser stands for light amplification by stimulated emission of radiation.

A noncoherent electromagnetic pulse consists of an intense electronic signal of very short duration that travels through space like a radio signal. When an EMP strikes an aircraft, the electronic devices in the aircraft can be totally disabled or destroyed. The effects of EMP were first observed and measured during the high-altitude nuclear testing that took place in the early 1960's, and since that time, EMP has generated considerable interest and concern. In the past, EMP of sufficient energy to qualify as a threat has been generated only by nuclear detonations. Aside from that very real threat, however, present technology trends indicate that nonnuclear weapons capable of sufficient power to generate a real EMP threat to aircraft may become operational within the next decade.

The charged particle beam weapon is the newest of the developing threats and utilizes radiation in the form of accelerated subatomic particles. These particles, or bunches of particles, may be focused on the target by means of magnetic fields. Considerable target damage can result. This type of weapon has the advantage that it will propagate through visible moisture, which tends to absorb energy generated by the HEL.

Warhead Descriptors

Another characteristic of the threat is the type of ordnance package carried by the propagator. The ordnance package consists of the warhead and possibly a fuze. The purpose of the warhead is to provide or generate the damage mechanisms, and the different types of warheads can be described in terms of their configuration and ingredients. In conventional warheads in projectiles and missiles, the warhead consists of a core or filler and a casing. A fuze package is included when a high-explosive core is employed. The counterpart of the conventional warhead for directed energy weapons is the delivered energy distribution (DED).

Fuzing.   Warheads come in two basic categories, fuzed and nonfuzed. Fuzed warheads contain a high-explosive charge and are detonated at or in the vicinity of the target. The fuze package consists of a safety and arming device to keep the weapon safe until it is deployed and clear of friendly forces, a detonator to initiate the HE charge detonation, a device that senses the presence of a target, known as the target detection device (TDD), and a logic circuit that initiates detonation at the proper time. Fuzing or charge detonation may be accomplished by several methods. The simplest of these methods are the time- and contact-fuzed warheads normally associated with light AAA. Time-fuzed warheads are set to detonate at a predetermined elapsed time after launch. Contact fuzes may detonate the charge either instantaneously upon target contact (superquick) or after a short delay, depending upon whether the detonation is desired on the external surface or within the target. High-explosive projectiles used by light AAA are normally designed to be contact-fuzed with a preset detonation delay because the small amount of explosive used can only be effective when the warhead is detonated inside the aircraft.

Proximity fuzing, sometimes referred to as VT fuzing (a code name used during World War II to imply variable time fuzing), is normally used in conjunction with heavy AAA and missile warheads. With proximity fuzing, the warhead is detonated at some distance from the aircraft based upon the fuze logic and the relative location and motion of the target. The fuze TDD may be active, semiactive, or passive. The active TDD radiates an electromagnetic signal, a portion of which is reflected by the target and detected by the TDD. A semiactive TDD detects electromagnetic energy reflected from a target that is being illuminated by another source. A passive TDD detects electromagnetic energy radiated by the aircraft itself. Most proximity-fuzed warheads also have time- and contact-fuzing capabilities for self-destruction and for detonation due to a direct hit; and some missile warheads can be command detonated by radio signals from the missile controller when the nonterminal tracking and guidance equipment displays indicate sufficient proximity to the target.

Nonfuzed warheads are referred to as penetrator warheads or kinetic energy penetrators and only cause damage when direct contact is made with the target. (Note that this group does not include contact-fuzed weapons, since no enhancement of the damage processes, either by the charge detonation or by a change in the damage mechanisms, occurs when non-fuzed warheads strike the target.) Warheads of this type are employed almost exclusively by small arms and light AAA weapons. The delivered energy distribution should also be considered in the nonfuzed category of warhead descriptors.

Penetrator warheads. The penetrator warheads include the following:

(1) Ball-type projectiles (B). These are penetrators with relatively soft metal cores designed to be used in small arms weapons against personnel and unarmored targets. The soft core flattens on impact, creating a larger hole than would normally be made by a harder substance of similar size and shape.

(2) Armor-piercing projectiles (AP). The armor-piercing projectile is composed of a hardened steel core encased in a metal jacket. It is shaped in such a manner to give it maximum penetrability through the target. This type of projectile is normally associated with small arms and light AAA.

(3) Armor-piercing incendiary projectiles (AP-I). This type of projectile is the same as the armor-piercing projectile, except that an incendiary mixture has been installed inside the nose of the metal casing. The metal jacket is supposed to peel off upon impact with the aircraft skin. The heat generated on impact ignites the mixture, causing an intense and prolonged fireball which may burn for several seconds. This increases the probability of inducing a fire or explosion. These projectiles are also normally associated with small arms and light AAA.

High-explosive (HE) warheads. A high-explosive warhead consists of a metal casing around a high-explosive core. All high-explosive warhead types are fuzed, and some may contain incendiary materials that are ignited upon warhead impact or detonation. They may be used either in projectiles or in missiles and may be detonated by any of the fuzes previously discussed.

There are four major types of HE warheads used against aircraft. They are the blast or pressure warhead, the fragmentation warhead, the continuous rod warhead, and the shaped charge warhead.

(1) Blast or pressure warheads. In the blast warhead, the case surrounding the HE charge is relatively thin, and the primary damage mechanism is

the expanding, spherically shaped blast wave produced by the detonation of the HE charge. Although this type of warhead is relatively inexpensive, it has a small radius of effectiveness due to the small amount of charge weight in the warhead and to the rapid reduction in the blast pressure with distance from the detonation. Consequently, in most aerial target HE warheads the charge is used primarily to break the case into many high velocity fragments, rods, or penetrators, and these become the primary damage mechanisms.

(2)   Fragmentation warheads.   Many of the current air target warheads are designed to kill the target with fragments. In this type of warhead, the case around the high-explosive core is designed to break into hundreds or thousands of high-velocity fragments upon charge detonation. The frag-

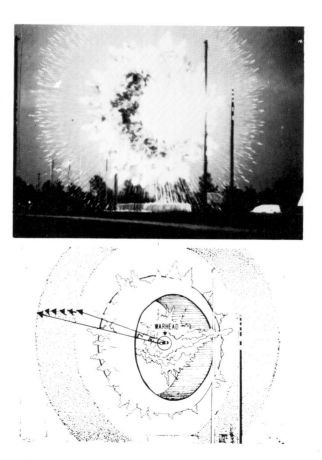

Fig. 3.9a   Fragment spray pattern from a stationary HE warhead detonation.

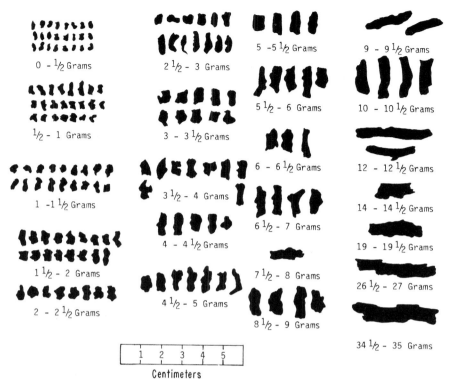

Fig. 3.9b   Fragments from a natural fragmentation case (1 pound = 7000 grains; 1 ounce = 28.4 grams; 1 gram = 15.4 grains).

ments are ejected as a narrow spray band with a pattern that is roughly spherical in shape, as shown in Fig. 3.9a. Natural fragmentation of a smooth case is random in size, with the structural configuration and material of the casing and the core contributing to the size variation of the fragments. An example of the fragments from a natural fragmentation case is given in Fig. 3.9b. The fragment weight is usually expressed in grains. The fragment distribution for this case will usually contain a few fragments that are quite big and very destructive if they hit the target and many fragments that are too small to cause much damage even if they do hit the target. Consequently, fragmenting cases are often designed to break up into fragments of a particular size and shape in order to optimize the effectiveness of the warhead against a particular type of target. These cases are called controlled fragmentation cases. The desired fragment dimensions and shape can be obtained by scoring or grooving the inner and/or outer surface of the case or by wrapping the case with wire. Some cases are composed of preformed fragments, such as steel cubes, blocks, or small rods, that are buried in a

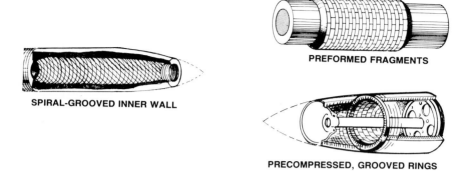

Fig. 3.10a   Several examples of controlled fragmentation warheads.

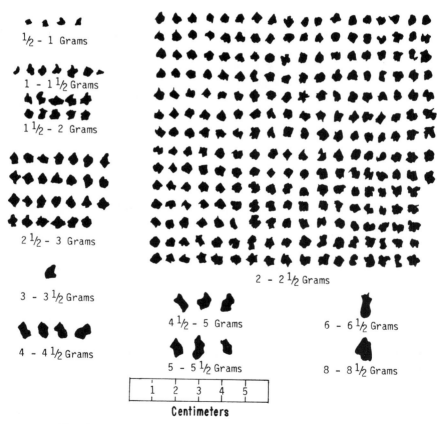

Fig. 3.10b   Fragments from a controlled fragmentation case.

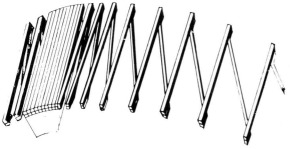

ROD EXPANSION ACTION

Fig. 3.11a   Continuous rod warhead.

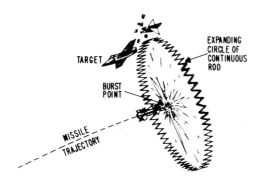

Fig. 3.11b   Expanding rods.

plastic matrix. Three examples of controlled fragmentation cases are shown in Fig. 3.10a, and the fragments from a controlled fragmentation case are shown in Fig. 3.10b.

(3) Continuous rod warheads.   The continuous rod warhead consists of a bundle of rods running lengthwise around the circumference of the case, as illustrated in Fig. 3.11a. The rods are welded together at alternate ends so that upon detonation of the explosive core the rod bundle expands away from the blast center, creating the large jagged ring shown in Fig. 3.11b. The rods are the damage mechanism, and they have been likened to the blade of a knife that cuts deeply through target skin and structural members on contact.

(4) Shaped charge warheads.   These are specially constructed warheads that utilize a special geometry of the explosive charge and liner to focus the

energy of the explosion in one or more desired directions. Such focusing of the detonation pressure on the liner can hydrodynamically create one or more very high-velocity jets and slugs of molten liner material that can cause much deeper target penetration than would be realized by a uniform detonation of the same mass of explosive in a fragmentation warhead. This energy can be focused along the warhead axis (a conical shaped charge) or in a desired array around the weapon (a linear shaped charge or a multi-shaped charge) to increase the number of jets. Air target shaped charge warheads are usually multishaped. Figure 3.12a illustrates a multishaped charge warhead with hemispherical liner inserts and the detonation pattern from this warhead. The multi-P-charge warhead is a variation of the shaped charge warhead. This warhead typically has many saucer-shaped inserts, as illustrated in Fig. 3.12b. The detonation pressure does not hydrodynamically compress the insert, but instead inverts the saucer. This type of penetrator is referred to as an explosively formed penetrator or a self-forging fragment.

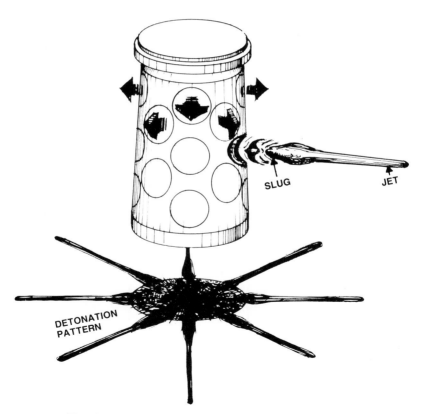

Fig. 3.12a   Example of a multishaped charge warhead.

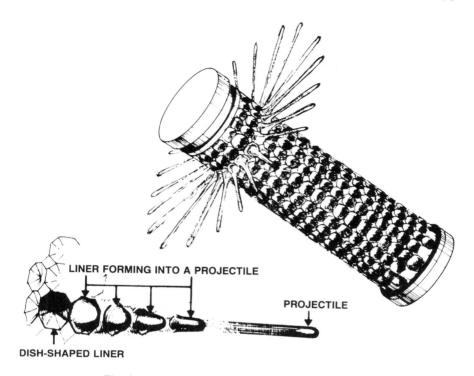

LINER FORMING INTO A PROJECTILE

PROJECTILE

DISH-SHAPED LINER

Fig. 3.12b   Example of a multi-P-charge warhead.

Delivered energy distributions.   Delivered energy distribution (DED) describes both the total radiation energy incident on a target, the energy pile, and the rate of energy addition, the power or flux. The term energy pile is a general definition of the amount and spatial distribution of energy incident on a target surface. It is the integral or sum of the power applied over the time of weapon-target interaction. Electromagnetic flux is the rate of flow of electromagnetic energy through a reference plane. This time rate of energy flow is a measure of the power either passing through or applied to a surface, depending upon the transparency of the surface to the radiation.

EMP parameters.   The warhead parameters that influence the damage processes of an electromagnetic pulse are the frequency spectrum/rise time and the peak intensity. Frequency spectrum and rise time are linked closely together in that those pulses with larger frequency spectra will generally have shorter rise times. The peak intensity of the pulse determines whether permanent or temporary damage results.

Particle beam parameters. The warhead descriptors for the particle beam weapon are the particle type (charge and mass) and the particle velocity (potential). These two parameters define the kinetic energy, and thus the ionizing ability of the particles. A third important factor is the particle density or population of particles in the beam. These accelerated particles are merely a directed form of radiation, and therefore the number of particles, or the radiation level, has a large bearing on the destructiveness of the weapon.

Damage Mechanisms, Damage Processes, and Terminal Effects

A damage mechanism is the output of the warhead that causes damage to the target. It is the physical description of the tangible instrument or measurable quantity designed to inflict damage upon the target. Damage mechanisms are also referred to in the literature as threat or kill mechanisms. The conventional damage mechanisms are penetrators, fragments, incendiary particles, and blast. The difference between a penetrator and a fragment is the relative size, shape, and number produced. For example, AP cores, continuous rods, and shaped charge jets are penetrators; whereas small cubes and diamond-shaped chunks of metal are fragments. The difference between the two terms is not always distinct. The damage mechanisms associated with the DHEW are coherent electromagnetic flux, electromagnetic pulse, and charged nuclear particles. Certain threat types may utilize more than one damage mechanism in attempting to destroy a target. For example, a proximity-fuzed surface-to-air missile can have blast, fragments, and incendiary particles as its primary damage mechanisms. The missile debris caused by the warhead detonation, such as the broken control surfaces, motor case, and other miscellaneous parts, are secondary penetrator-type damage mechanisms.

A damage process refers to the interaction between the damage mechanism and the target. The conventional damage processes are ballistic impact, penetration, combustion (leading to a fire or explosion), hydraulic ram, and blast loading. Some radiation damage processes are combustion, thermal weakening, and burn-through. One damage mechanism may initiate several damage processes. For example, Fig. 3.13 shows the relationship between the conventional damage mechanisms and the damage processes for the proximity-fuzed SAM.

The terminal or threat effects refer to the response or reaction of the various materials, components, and personnel in the aircraft when subjected to the damage processes. In order to make the design decisions required to enhance the survivability of an aircraft, the engineer must be aware not only of the particular type of weapons that constitute the threat, but also of the nature of the damage processes and the terminal effects that are caused by the damage mechanisms.

Penetrators. A penetrator can be the core of an AP projectile, or a rod, or a shaped charge jet. The damage processes associated with the penetrator are ballistic impact, penetration, hydraulic ram, and combustion. Combus-

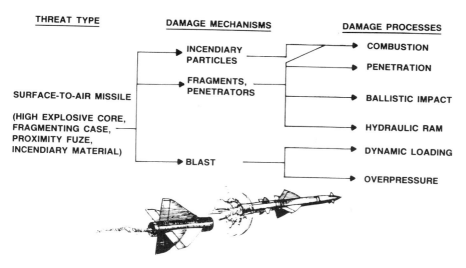

Fig. 3.13   Damage process generation for a surface-to-air missile.

tion can occur due to the fact that there may be an incendiary flash when a high-velocity metal penetrator strikes a metal surface. Hydraulic ram occurs when the penetrator passes through a fluid container. The amount of penetration of a penetrator through aircraft structure, components, and fluid is proportional to its momentum; therefore penetrator velocity and mass are important parameters.

(1)   Ballistic impact and penetration.   The primary damage processes caused by penetrators are, not too surprisingly, called ballistic impact and penetration. Initial penetration upon impact usually involves piercing the skin of the target. Penetrators with soft cores generally flatten on impact and create larger holes than their initial diameter. When the penetration produces a clean hole, the section of the structure sheared out by the penetrator is called a plug, and this type of penetration is called plugging or punching. For slightly harder material, the penetrator must tear the surface during entry, and a crown-shaped protrusion surrounded by radial cracks is formed, as shown in Fig. 3.14. This type of penetration is called petalling.

The velocity required for penetration is called the ballistic limit or V_{50} ballistic limit and is that velocity at which 50% of the impactors penetrate and 50% do not penetrate. The specific definition of "penetration" varies with the three Services. After penetration, the penetrator will have a new or residual velocity, possibly a new direction, and possibly a new mass. Several sets of penetration equations have been developed for the residual velocity, direction, and mass of penetrators and fragments impacting the various materials found in aircraft. The two most often used are the THOR equations and the DRI equations.

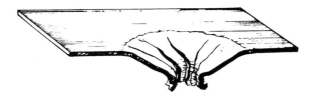

Fig. 3.14   Petalling damage.

The terminal effects of impact and penetration depend upon the element that is penetrated. In the case of structural members (e.g., spars, ribs, skin, and longerons), penetration can lead to a loss of load-carrying ability. Aerodynamic surfaces (e.g., ailerons and rudders) can fail to perform their aerodynamic function after penetration. Mechanical components (e.g., hydraulic actuators, control rods, and drive shafts) can crack, jam, or sever. Penetrated engine components (e.g., combustor case, turbine blade, and fuel valve) can lead to catastrophic engine failure, fuel leakage, and engine fire. Penetration through fluid or pressure containers (e.g., fuel tanks and hydraulic reservoirs) can result in leakage, hydraulic ram damage, fuel leakage into an inlet duct and subsequent ingestion by an engine, and possibly fires and explosions. Penetration through avionics components (e.g., computers and radar equipment) can cause a loss of signal or function and possibly a fire or explosion. When penetrated, crew members tend to lose their ability to function, and penetration through explosives or propellants can result in a fire or explosion.

When a penetrator impacts armor or very hard structural material, a damage process called spallation can result. In spallation, fragments are spalled off the rear suface of the structural material. These fragments then become a damage mechanism themselves. This special damage process will be discussed in the section on fragments.

(2)   Penetration through fluids (hydraulic ram).   When a penetrator enters a compartment containing a fluid, a damage process called hydraulic or hydrodynamic ram is generated. Hydraulic ram can be divided into three phases: the early shock phase, the later drag phase, and the final cavity phase, as illustrated in Fig. 3.15a. The shock phase is initiated when the projectile penetrates the wall of the container or tank and impacts the fluid. As energy is transferred to the fluid, a strong hemispherical shock wave centered at the point of impact is formed. This creates an impulsive load on the inside of the entry wall in the vicinity of the entry hole that may cause the entry wall to crack and petal. As the penetrator travels through the fluid, it usually tumbles, and its energy is transformed into kinetic energy of fluid motion as the projectile is slowed by viscous drag. An outwardly propagating pressure field is generated as fluid is displaced from the projectile path. In contrast to the pressures developed in the shock phase, the fluid in the drag phase is accelerated relatively gradually, rather than impulsively, so

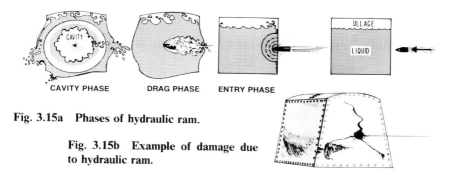

CAVITY PHASE   DRAG PHASE   ENTRY PHASE

Fig. 3.15a Phases of hydraulic ram.

Fig. 3.15b Example of damage due to hydraulic ram.

that the peak pressure is much lower; however, the duration of the pressure pulse is considerably longer. A cavity develops behind the projectile as it passes through the fluid, which is filled with liquid vapor evaporated from the cavity surface and with air which has entered the cavity through the entry hole. As the fluid seeks to regain its undisturbed condition, the cavity will oscillate. The concomitant pressures will pump fluid from any holes in the tank, and they may be sufficient to damage other system components. This cavity oscillation is called the cavity phase.

The hydraulic ram loading on all of the wet walls of the tank can cause large-scale tearing and petalling, with openings very much larger than those made by the actual penetrator. The hydraulic ram loading can also be transmitted through attached lines, causing failure at fittings or other discontinuities in the lines. Figure 3.15b depicts a typical example of the damage caused by hydraulic ram.

(3) Combustion.   A metal penetrator that impacts a metal target at high velocity may generate incandescent metal particles or vapors that are a source for ignition of nearby flammable gases or combustible materials. This phenomenon is known as vaporific flash.

Fragments.   Fragments are a damage mechanism that can be described as irregular metal particles varying in weight, shape, and velocity. Their weight is usually expressed in grains. They may be produced either by the detonation of an explosive warhead (blast-generated or fire-formed fragments) or by ballistic impact (impact-generated fragments). Figures 3.9b and 3.10b are examples of the fragments from a natural fragmentation case and a controlled fragmentation case, respectively.

(1) Blast-generated fragments.   Blast-generated fragments result from the detonation of a high-explosive AAA, SAM, or AAM warhead. They are usually steel or tungsten and typically weigh between 30 and 200 grains. Their shape may be cubic, diamond, parallelepiped, or irregular. Their total initial velocity can vary from 4000 to as high as 10,000 ft/s, depending

upon the type of HE charge, the ratio of case weight to charge weight, and the missile velocity. (For comparison, 7.62- and 12.7-mm projectiles weigh about 150 and 750 grains, respectively, and have a muzzle velocity between 2500 and 3000 ft/s.) Depending upon the fuzing technique employed, the warhead detonation may occur either inside or outside the aircraft. The size, momentum, and pattern of blast-generated fragments can be controlled by the warhead design to most effectively damage a specific type of target. The damage processes and terminal effects associated with blast-generated fragments are the same as, or similar to, those associated with a penetrator, i.e., ballistic impact and penetration, hydraulic ram, and combustion. However, the damage caused by fragments can be more severe than that caused by penetrators when a multitude of closely spaced fragments strike the target. Cracks can occur between the holes caused by the individual fragments, compounding the extent of damage.

(2)   Impact-generated fragments.   Impact-generated fragments may occur either as spallation of the target material or by a breakup of the weapon at the impact point. Spallation is a characteristic of hard materials that resist penetration. High-speed impact by a damage mechanism, such as a penetrator or fragment, generates an internal compression stress wave in both the damage mechanism and in the target. Interaction internally within the target material between the initial compression wave and any reflected tensile stress waves off of a free surface can cause high tensile stresses, which may result in pieces of the target material being ejected from the rear surface of the target material at high (lethal) velocities. If the damage mechanism is brittle, stresses within the mechanism itself can reach values sufficient to shatter the mechanism after striking a hard surface. In both cases, high-velocity fragments can be ejected inside the aircraft with the capability of generating the same damage processes as a penetrator. Impact-generated fragments also tend to disperse randomly from the point of impact, and therefore cause damage over a greater area than does a single penetrating round.

Incendiary particles.   This damage mechanism includes those chemical agents designed to cause combustion and which are added as a filler agent to certain projectile and missile warheads. Figures 3.6 and 3.7 show the location of the incendiary filler in a small arms projectile (AP-I) and of the tracer material, also a source of incendiary particles, in a high-explosive AAA round (HE-T), respectively. In the small arms projectile, the incendiary material is located in front of the passive core and is initiated upon contact with the target. In a high-explosive warhead, any incendiary material is ignited when the warhead is detonated and is dispersed by the explosion. Incendiary particles may also be generated by the high-speed impact of a metal penetrator or fragment on the metal surfaces of the target. The damage process associated with incendiaries is combustion in the form of a fire or an explosion.

(1)   Fire.   The effectiveness and wide use of incendiaries in antiaircraft weapons systems stems from the vulnerability of the aircraft fuel system to fire. Ignition and subsequent fire may take place within the ullage or vapor space of a fuel tank. Fires can also occur in conjunction with a penetration damage process in which fuel spills out of holes punched in the tanks by penetrators or fragments and into adjacent void areas or dry bays. Incendiary particles igniting the vapors from these spilled fuels can lead to eventual loss of the aircraft due to the fire burning through structure, control rods, etc. It should be noted, however, that fuel is not the only combustible material onboard an aircraft. Incendiary particles can initiate fires in any flammable material or gas, such as air and vaporized liquid oxygen, and in other fluids, such as hydraulic fluid.

(2)   Explosion.   Under certain conditions, an explosion or detonation of a fuel-air mixture by incendiary particles can occur. This depends primarily on the composition of the fuel-air mixture and the intensity of the ignition source. Fuel vapors detonated within a fuel tank ullage can cause tank rupture, can damage the surrounding structure, or can result in complete aircraft disintegration. The phenomena of fire and explosion are discussed in more detail in the section on suppression and prevention of fires and explosions in Chapter 5.

Blast.   Blast is the rapid movement of a spherically shaped pressure wave away from a center of high pressure, as in an explosion. It is one of the damage mechanisms associated with high-explosive warheads used in missiles and antiaircraft artillery larger than 20-mm in caliber. The pressure in the blast above the ambient pressure is called the overpressure, and the peak overpressure occurs at the leading edge of the wave. A typical pressure wave is shown in Fig. 3.16 for several values of time after detonation. The important parameters of the wave are the peak overpressure and the duration of the positive overpressure phase of the blast.

The pressure loading on a target caused by the blast from an explosion is called the blast loading. It is the damage process associated with blast, and is the combined effect of the dynamic pressure loading (drag) and the overpressure loading. In most warheads, the blast is a secondary damage mechanism. The blast is usually the last damage mechanism to reach the target, except for close detonations, and compounds or enhances the damage caused by the other damage mechanisms. If the pressure loading is sufficiently intense to significantly damage the aircraft, the other damage mechanisms probably have killed the target, provided they hit the target.

(1)   Dynamic loading.   This loading is produced by the velocity of the air in the blast with respect to the aircraft. It's a drag loading on the target. The dynamic loading damage process causes structural deformation, bending and tearing of cantilevered structures (wings), and dynamic removal of any loosely secured attachments (e.g., canopy, panels, and antennae).

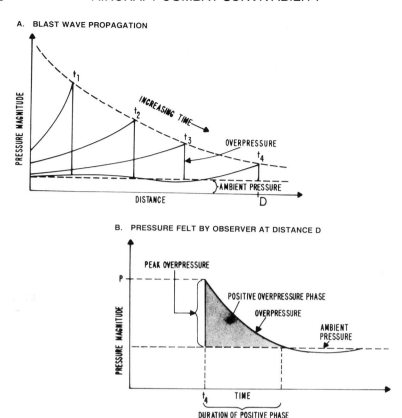

Fig. 3.16   Blast from an HE warhead.

(2) Overpressure loading.   This damage process is the one that results from the effects of the overpressure in the blast striking and moving over the surfaces of the target. Note from the overpressure profile shown in Fig. 3.16 that the initial overpressure is eventually followed by a period of underpressure. Any semiclosed structures or containers in the aircraft (e.g., cockpit, fuel tanks, and hydraulic reservoirs) can experience a sudden compression/decompression cycle that could result in structural failure or loss of integrity even though they were not located directly facing the blast.

Coherent electromagnetic flux (laser beam).   One radiation-propagated damage mechanism is a coherent electromagnetic flux, commonly known as a laser beam. When absorbed, this flux can result in several damage processes.

(1) Burn-through. Burn-through is a flux-induced damage process resulting from the interaction between a high-energy laser beam and the target over a sufficiently long period of time. The beam must be applied to a spot on the target until energy sufficient to melt or burn through the target is absorbed. This requires an extremely precise pointing and tracking mechanism, possibly with appropriate feedback to identify and track the "spot" location on the target.

The time required for the beam to burn through a target material depends on the intensity of the beam and how accurately the pointing and tracking mechanism can maintain the beam on the designated spot. A good analogy is the application of a cutting torch to a sheet of metal. If the torch is held steady on the surface, it cuts through much faster than if it is continually moved around by an unsteady hand.

(2) Thermal weakening. When the energy of the laser beam is insufficient to cause burn-through of the irradiated material, another damage process called thermal weakening can become important. In this damage process, the material is rapidly heated by the incident radiation. This heating causes the stiffness or elastic modulus of the material within the vicinity of the irradiated zone to degrade and also creates a transient thermal stress field within the local structure. If the laser beam is swept over a portion of a major load-carrying structure, such as a wing, the combination of the material stiffness degradation, the thermal stresses, and the stresses due to the flight loads could lead to a structural failure by buckling, by excessive plastic deformation, or by fracture.

(3) Combustion. Heat generated by the incident electromagnetic flux can result in the ignition of combustible material aboard the airborne target. Combustion of the fuel-air mixture in the ullage of fuel tanks can occur directly, or damage to the fuel tanks due to the incident flux could allow fuel to leak into areas where it could subsequently be ignited, creating a fire or explosion. In addition, the aircraft structure itself may be prone to radiation-induced ignition. The use of various lightweight metals to reduce aircraft weight can introduce a survivability problem in that many of these materials can be ignited and will sustain burning at extremely high temperatures. Magnesium and titanium are two such metals.

(4) Vaporization. If the incident electromagnetic flux from a laser is delivered in a short-duration, high-power pulse, a dynamic loading damage process results. When energy sufficient to vaporize the surface layer of the target is rapidly applied, the material is instantaneously converted into the gaseous state. Inertia prevents the gaseous metal from immediately expanding, and tremendous pressures can result. The resultant effect is similar to one that would be obtained if a thin layer of plastic explosive was spread on the aircraft surface and detonated.

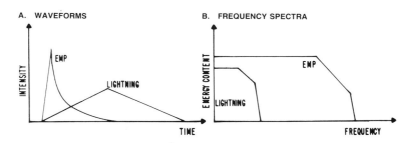

Fig. 3.17   Electric field of EMP compared with that of a lightning bolt.

Electromagnetic pulse (EMP).   Electromagnetic pulse is another radiation propagated damage mechanism and consists of an intense electronic signal of very short duration. It is not unlike a transmission from a radio station, except it is much stronger. Like any radio signal, it will be picked up by antennae of the appropriate dimensions. When the antenna of a radio picks up a signal, it is actually sensing the changes in the electric field at the antenna caused by the radiated signal. Signals in the EMP can vary in frequency from direct current all the way up to the ultrahigh-frequency (UHF) band. The aircraft itself acts as an antenna for a portion of this frequency spectrum. Pulse duration is on the order of hundreds of nanoseconds. Figure 3.17 compares the electric field of an EMP signal with that created by a lightning bolt. The rise time of the EMP signal is many times faster and may be of greater intensity. The damage due to EMP is concentrated in the onboard electronic equipment and can be permanent or temporary.

(1)   Permanent circuit damage (overloading).   The strong electric fields of the EMP produce current flows on the conducting surfaces of the aircraft that can penetrate into the aircraft's interior through cables, mechanical linkages, or apertures (e.g., access ports, inspection holes, or cracks). This can create large currents in various black boxes, burn out cables and connectors, fire explosive detonators, and destroy weapons circuitry. Arcing could occur that might ignite fuel-air mixtures in the ullages of fuel tanks, causing an explosion or fire. Certain types of circuits are more sensitive to current surges than others. Generally, the smaller the current carrying capability of a device, the more sensitive it is. For instance, large power tubes like the ones in old radios are relatively unaffected by EMP. However, integrated circuit chips contain minute photo-etched circuitry that would be highly sensitive to such a current surge.

(2)   Temporary circuit damage (disruptive).   EMP signals can create nonpermanent damage to digital equipment by altering the bit patterns in program memory. This would generally incapacitate any microprocessor

driven system, such as a digital fly-by-wire computer system, a stores management control panel, or an onboard navigational/weapons release computer.

Charged nuclear particles. The damage mechanism associated with this type of device is the accelerated nuclear material that can be directed toward a target. Particles, or more accurately "bunches" of particles, are radiated through the atmosphere after they have been accelerated to velocities near the speed of light. When these particles collide with a target, they can generate various damage processes.

(1) Atomic restructuring. At relatively low energy levels, the particle beam disturbs solid-state circuitry within the target. Nonlinear circuits are most vulnerable to this effect. Impacting particles can rearrange the doping levels of the various semiconductor materials. This can change characteristics, cause errors, and, in many cases, result in device failure or, in the case of missile targets, possible warhead detonation. The energy required for this level of damage, although considered low for the particle beam weapon, should be placed in perspective with respect to the biological effects it is capable of producing. For comparison purposes, such a weapon could kill the pilot of a manned vehicle long before it started to change the output of the onboard computer systems.

(2) Electric discharge. At slightly higher energy levels, the impacting particles strip electrons from the atomic shells on the surface of the target facing the weapon, leaving the surface positively charged. This charge imbalance within the target generates an internal potential, and a high current pulse can surge through the target to balance the static charge distribution. This current pulse can burn out circuits, cause arcing, disrupt logic states, and generate various other catastrophic results.

(3) Vaporization. The most dramatic of the damage processes associated with particle beam weapons is vaporization. This process, however, requires the highest energy levels. When the "atomic bullets" hit the target, the result is equivalent to the explosion of tons of TNT on the target surface. The actual damage process occurs as electrons in the target are torn from the nuclei of the structure to such an extent that the remaining charged ions repel each other, atomically decomposing or vaporizing the target.

3.4 THREAT OPERATIONS

Threat operations are those environmental factors and inherent capabilities that relate to the ability of the threat to perform its basic search, detection, tracking, and firing or launch functions. The sequence of threat operational events in almost any encounter between an aircraft and a threat is somewhat the same, regardless of the type of threat. A nonterminal element, such as a lookout, a man with a shoulder-launched missile, or a surveillance radar, searches the sky looking for aircraft. When one is detected, an identification of the aircraft is attempted to determine if it is a friend, a foe, or a neutral (IFFN). If the aircraft is thought to be hostile, it is tracked for a while, and as much information as possible on the aircraft's range, bearing, elevation or altitude, heading, and speed is gathered and processed. A decision may then be made to inform the platform element of the threat as to the location and track of the aircraft. In the case of a radar-guided SAM, a fire-control radar is slewed to the target. On an airborne interceptor, the seeker in an air-to-air missile will be uncaged. The target tracker will then attempt to acquire the target, and, once acquired, accurately track the aircraft. Estimates of the target's future position at the time of propagator intercept will be made, and the platform will be pointed in the appropriate direction. This is known as the fire-control solution. Eventually, the propagator will be launched or fired. Some of the important factors and elements in these operations are described below.

Environmental Factors

These factors include the mobility of the threat, its locational adaptability, and its weather capability.

Mobility.   Mobility refers to the ease with which a threat can be moved. Factors involved are the effort required for disassembling, loading, transporting, and setting up a new location so that effective firing or launching can be achieved. The measures of mobility are the operational time at one location and the downtime required to move from one operating site to another. Many gun systems and some missile systems are mounted on wheeled or tracked vehicles and can fire on the move or shortly after stopping.

Locational adaptability.   This refers to the ability of a threat to adapt to the sites at which its operation is desired in a combat environment. Factors that must be considered in site selection for the threats are the area required, the smoothness of terrain, access to a road or highway, the class of highway required for transporting the threat, etc.

Weather capability.   Weather capability refers to the ability of a threat to track and deliver the propagator to an aircraft during specified variations in visibility, cloud cover, or light conditions. Generic measures of weather with respect to tracking capability include:
    (1)   Clear day: the ability to maintain track under daylight conditions with no intervening clouds and with required visibility.
    (2)   Clear night: the ability to maintain track with no cloud or visibility constraints, but with reduced light level (i.e., half-moon, quarter-moon, etc.).

(3)   Hazy: a qualifier for day or night capability to indicate an increased amount of particulate matter in the air (i.e., smoke, dust, etc.), which will degrade the tracking effectiveness.

(4)   All weather: the ability to maintain track with extremely low light levels, complete cloud cover, or minimal visibility.

Search, Detection, and Tracking Capabilities

The goal of the nonterminal threat is the detection, identification, and tracking of aircraft (and possibly the propagator, too). The desired information on each aircraft consists of its azimuth, elevation, range, heading, and speed. The ability of the threat to obtain some or all of this information in sufficient time to launch or fire a propagator is dependent upon the equipment used, the target, and the scenario. Searching and tracking can be done with radar, the human eye (with or without the assistance of either direct-view optical or electro-optical devices), the human ear (aided or unaided), lasers, and forward looking infrared (FLIR) devices. Some of the important parameters are the initial reaction time, maximum slew rate, maximum target detection range, acquisition time or time to acquire the target, and the maximum tracking rate. The relative position of the tracker with respect to the target and to prominent features, such as the sun, the ground, and the sea, can strongly influence the ability of the nonterminal threat element to perform its functions.

Initial reaction time.   This is the time interval that elapses between the time a threat is made aware of a need to be fully operational and the time the threat is ready to begin its normal operational mode against the target aircraft. The functions that can be accomplished in parallel during this time interval consist of getting personnel in "combat ready" positions and transferring the equipment from a standby alert status to a fully operational status.

Maximum slew rate.   This is the maximum angular velocity in both azimuth and elevation at which the tracking carriage of the threat can be rotated in order to begin tracking and engaging an aircraft that was in a different sector of the sky than the carriage had been initially pointing. The parameters that determine the maximum slew rate include the mass or weight of the equipment to be rotated and the electrical, mechanical, or hydraulic power available to rotate the equipment.

Maximum target detection range.   The maximum target detection range is that range at which a target can barely be unambiguously discerned. It is often expressed numerically with respect to a target signature of a standard size. For example, the maximum detection range of a radar is usually given for a target with a 1-m^2 radar cross section.

Acquisition time.   This is the elapsed time from the time of alert to the time the tracker has acquired the target.

Maximum tracking rates.   These are the maximum rates in azimuth and in elevation that the tracking carriage can be rotated while measuring the aircraft's position vs time.

Firing and Launch Capabilities

Some of the important firing and launch capabilities for a typical terminal threat type are discussed in detail below.

Rate of fire and launch rate.   The rate of fire is the number of projectiles per unit time that a threat is capable of firing. This term is primarily used as a measure for small arms and AAA. Launch rate is a similar term that is used in connection with the number of missiles per unit time that can be launched by a SAM launcher or site.

Muzzle velocity.   Muzzle velocity is the velocity of a projectile with respect to the muzzle at the instant the projectile leaves the barrel. This velocity is a function of the projectile weight, firing charge of the projectile, barrel characteristics, etc. The weapon can be either small arms or AAA. The muzzle velocity of most small arms projectiles ranges from 2500 ft/s for the 7.62-mm projectiles to 3400 ft/s for 14.5-mm projectiles.

Salvo, shoot-look-shoot, and ripple fire.   Salvo refers to the number of missiles launched or projectiles fired at an aircraft in a relatively short period of time. For example, when two missiles are sequentially launched at a target, the salvo is two. Shoot-look-shoot is a firing doctrine in which one missile is launched, and a second missile is subsequently launched if the first missile fails to destroy the target. Ripple fire is the rapid firing of several propagators.

Firing and launch envelopes and the intercept envelope.   The firing or launch envelope is defined by the locus of points that represent the current position of an aircraft when a projectile or missile can be fired or launched with the expectation of achieving an intercept with the aircraft. The intercept envelope is like the launch and firing envelope, except that the locus of points now represents the location of the aircraft at the time of missile or projectile intercept. When considering ground-based and sea-based threats, the envelopes are generally depicted relative to the location of the threat platform. On the other hand, the envelopes are normally shown relative to the target aircraft for airborne threats. The launch envelope may also include the tracking time required before a launch can occur. A typical radar-guided SAM launch envelope is shown in Fig. 3.18.

Maximum range denotes the position of the aircraft when the launch occurs corresponding to the maximum distance the missile can reach and

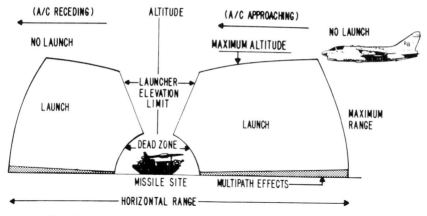

Fig. 3.18   Launch zones for a radar-guided surface-to-air missile.

still cause damage to the aircraft. The maximum launch range depends on the target speed or Mach number and is obviously shorter for receding aircraft than it is for approaching aircraft. The requirement for damage is often specified in terms of a specific missile miss distance, which is the closest point of approach of the missile to the target, or in terms of a minimum level of missile maneuverability available, or by the maximum time of missile flight based upon the self-destruct time set in the fuze. The maximum range at intercept is referred to as the maximum effective range. The dead zone is that volume around the launcher in which the missile warhead is unarmed as the missile passes through. The missile limit boundaries are a function of the aircraft direction, speed, and maneuvering and are due to rate limitations on the missile and its components. Multipath effects refer to that region where electromagnetic tracking beams bounce off the terrain or surface on their way to and from the aircraft. Tracking accuracy may be severely degraded in this region.

The maximum effective range for missiles can vary from several kilometers for the small missiles to many miles for the large ones. The maximum effective slant range for projectiles can be estimated from the rule of thumb that says that the range in kilometers is given by the projectile diameter in millimeters divided by 10. Thus, the maximum effective slant range of a 12.7-mm gun is approximately 1.3 km.

3.5   THREAT LETHALITY

The term "threat lethality" is used to refer to the collection of factors that relate to the fire control, the propagator trajectory, and the terminal effects parameters. Note that threat lethality is independent of the target aircraft. It only depends upon the inherent capabilities of the threat in directing or projecting the propagator in the direction of the aircraft and on the size of the damage mechanisms.

Fire-Control Factors

Fire-control factors consist of the types of fire control, the types of coverage, and the types of errors.

Types of fire control. The usual types of fire control are an open sight, an on-mount optical or mechanical lead computing sight, radar, and electro-optical. Small arms and light AAA typically use either the open or on-mount sight, whereas most heavy AAA and the guided missile systems use radar and/or a direct-view optical or electro-optical device.

Types of coverage. The types of coverage are aimed fire (at a specific target), sector intercept (fire directed to a sector of air space), barrage (general coverage of the air space), and any combination of these three.

Types of errors. There are three major fire-control errors: tracking error, aiming error, and lead angle prediction error.

(1) Tracking error. Tracking error is the error introduced into the firing or launch and guidance operations of a threat system by the inability of the tracking system to provide an exact record of the aircraft flight path. Tracking data are utilized by the enemy defenses for many purposes, such as alerting appropriate threat units, establishing threat tactics, establishing lead angle information for weapon firing, and propagator guidance. Therefore, the source and magnitude of tracking errors are very significant factors in threat effectiveness. The term tracking error is used to represent the net effect of all contributors or sources in specifying target position and rate data.

(2) Aiming error. Aiming error is the error introduced into the firing or launching operations of threats due to the inability to correctly position or aim the appropriate equipment in a desired direction. Aiming errors are used to represent those errors involved in pointing or positioning a device such as a weapon or weapon platform at the desired point predicted by the fire-control system. These errors may stem from a human interface, from a machine, or from a combination of both. As an example, pilot aiming error results from an interaction between the pilot and the response of the aircraft.

(3) Lead angle prediction error. Lead angle prediction is that fire-control computational process used to establish the desired weapon positioning or aiming information. All weapons that fire ballistic projectiles must have some means of solving the fire-control problem. From the measurement of current target position and velocity, the future target position must be estimated, weapon aim angles determined, and the weapon positioned and fired so that the projectile and the target will arrive at the same point in space (the intercept point) simultaneously. Most prediction methods use a

linear extrapolation of the target's trajectory (assuming a constant velocity vector) to estimate the future target position. Lead angle prediction error is the projectile miss distance resulting from errors in the prediction of the target flight path. Prediction errors may be the result of unexpected or evasive target maneuvers (jinking) during the flight time of the projectile or due to limitations in the process used to predict future target position. The prediction error for any firing situation is usually defined as the minimum distance from the predicted intercept point to the target's actual position at the time of intercept.

(4)   Jitter.   Jitter is the combination of aiming and tracking errors produced by rough motion of the weapon system or by atmospheric effects (turbulent jitter) that cause an HEL beam to move about on the target surface.

Trajectory Factors

Trajectory factors relate to or influence the missile, projectile, or radiation path from the platform to the aircraft. These factors can be divided into two categories: those associated with nonguided propagators and those associated with guided propagators.

Nonguided propagator factors.   The nonguided propagators are projectiles and radiation. There are several factors that affect the trajectory of these propagators.

(1)   Gravity drop.   Gravity drop is a measure of the displacement of the flight path of a ballistic projectile attributable to gravitational force. The gravity drop is proportional to the time of flight and has been approximated by $gt^2/2$, where g is the gravitational force and t is the time of flight.

(2)   Ballistic dispersion.   This is the scatter of impact points of projectiles about a mean point under fixed firing conditions and exclusive of aiming and installation factors. Ballistic dispersion refers to those variations in the impact point attributable only to gun and ammunition characteristics. Causes of ballistic dispersion are weight and surface variations between projectiles, variation in burning efficiencies, and variations in the aerodynamic forces on the projectile.

(3)   Ballistic coefficient.   This is a parameter or measure that is used to account for the attenuation of the velocity of a projectile or fragment in transit from the platform to the target. Ballistic coefficients are normally used in approximate formulations to determine average speed or time-of-flight for the projectile or fragment.

(4)   Thermal blooming.   Thermal blooming is a nonlinear dispersion of electromagnetic radiation due to atmospheric index-of-refraction changes

caused by molecular absorption of the propagating energy. When a beam of electromagnetic radiation passes through a gas, some of its radiant energy will be absorbed by the gas molecules. The resultant temperature rise will force the gas particles away from the beam until the particle density has been reduced to the proper level for that particular temperature and pressure. If the beam is nonuniform, i.e., more intense at the center than at its edges, the resultant atmospheric density will be less at the center than at the edges. Hence, the atmospheric index of refraction, which is proportional to density, will vary across the beam. Since light rays are bent away from areas of low index of refraction, a dispersion of the beam results. The magnitude of this dispersive effect depends on many factors, such as radiation wavelength, beam intensity, time of radiation in one direction, and atmospheric conditions.

(5)   Atmospheric attenuation.   This is the attenuation of electromagnetic radiation energy as it propagates through the atmosphere owing to absorption by gases and scattering by particles.

Guided propagators.   Guided propagators can be guided missiles or guided projectiles. However, since most antiaircraft guided propagators are guided missiles, this terminology will be used here. The guided missile system contains a guidance package that attempts to keep the missile on a course that will eventually lead to an intercept with the target. Several types of guidance are possible, and a given missile system may use more than one type. For most antiaircraft applications, the types include command, beam-rider, homing, and retransmission.

(1)   Command guidance.   Command guided missiles are missiles whose guidance instructions or commands come from sources outside the missile. Figure 3.19 illustrates one example of a command guidance system. In this type of guidance, a tracking system that is separated from the missile is used to track both the missile and the target. The tracking system may consist of two separate tracking units, one for the missile and one for the aircraft, or it may consist of one tracking unit that tracks both vehicles. The tracking can be accomplished using radar, optical, laser, or infrared systems. A radar beacon or infrared flare on the tail of the missile can be used to provide information to the tracking system on the location of the missile. The target and missile ranges, elevations, and bearings are fed to a computer. Using the position and position rate information, the computer determines the flight path the missile should take that will result in a collision with the aircraft. It compares this computed flight path with the predicted flight path of the missile based on current tracking information and determines the correction signals required to move the missile control surfaces to change the current flight path to the new one.

These signals are the command guidance and are sent to the missile receiver via either the missile tracking system, or a separate command link, such as a radio, or it can be sent along a wire between the launching

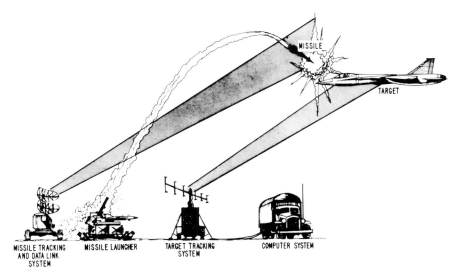

MISSILE TRACKING   MISSILE LAUNCHER   TARGET TRACKING   COMPUTER SYSTEM
AND DATA LINK   SYSTEM
SYSTEM

Fig. 3.19   Typical command guided missile system.

platform and the missile. Besides steering instructions, the command link
may be required to transfer other instructions to the missile, such as fuze
arming, receiver gain setting, and warhead detonation. The specific path
along which the missile is navigated is determined by the type of guidance
law used by the system. A particular type of command guidance and
navigation where the missile is commanded to always lie on the line of sight
between the aircraft tracking unit and the aircraft is known as command-
to-line of sight (CLOS) or three-point guidance. Command guidance all the
way to the target is used mostly with short-range missile systems because of
the relatively large tracking errors that occur at long range.

   (2)   Beam-rider guidance.   In the three-point beam-rider type of guidance, illustrated in Fig. 3.20a, the aircraft is tracked by an electromagnetic
beam transmitted by a tracking system offboard of the missile. The guidance
equipment onboard the missile includes a rearward-facing antenna that
senses the target tracking beam. Steering signals that are based on the
position of the missile with respect to the center (or the scanning axis) of the
target tracking beam are computed onboard and sent to the control surfaces.
These correction signals produce control surface movements intended to
keep the missile as nearly as possible in the center of the target tracking
beam (or scanning axis). The missile can thus be said to ride the beam; it
does not see the target. There is usually a wider, lower-power beam used to
capture the missile shortly after it is launched.
   The beam the missile rides can either track the aircraft directly, or a
computer can be used to predict the direction the missile beam should be

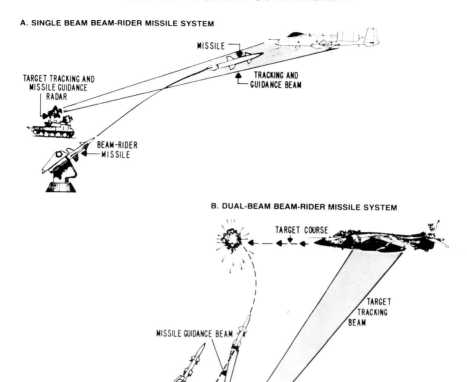

Fig. 3.20 Beam-rider missiles.

pointing to effect an eventual collision of the missile with the aircraft. In this situation, a separate tracker is required to track the target, as shown in Fig. 3.20b.

The beam-rider missile guidance system has both advantages and disadvantages. It permits the launching of a large number of missiles into the same control or target tracking beam, since all of the guidance equipment is carried in the missile. This, however, makes each missile relatively large and expensive. Furthermore, the tracking beam must be reasonably narrow to insure an intercept, and the chance of loss of the missile through target maneuvering and evasion is increased. The problem of large tracking error for long-range targets usually restricts beam-rider missiles to short range.

(3) Homing guidance. The expression homing guidance is used to describe a missile guidance system that can determine the position of the

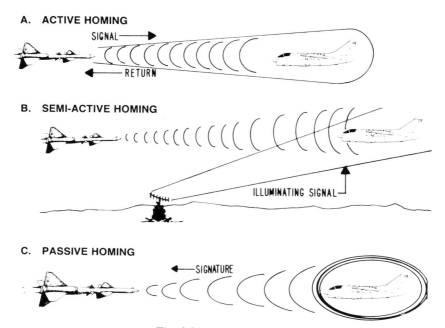

A. ACTIVE HOMING

SIGNAL——▶

◀——RETURN

B. SEMI-ACTIVE HOMING

ILLUMINATING SIGNAL—

C. PASSIVE HOMING

◀—SIGNATURE

Fig. 3.21   Homing missiles.

aircraft and can formulate its own commands to guide itself to the aircraft. With homing guidance, the tracking error is usually reduced as the missile approaches the aircraft. There are three major types of homing systems: active, semiactive, and passive. They are illustrated in Figs. 3.21a, 3.21b, and 3.21c, respectively.

If the aircraft is tracked by electronic radiation equipment in the missile, the system is referred to as active. An example is a system that uses a radar transmitter located on the missile to illuminate the aircraft, and then uses the radar reflections from the aircraft for guidance. A major advantage of active homing is the fact that the missile can be launched and forgotten by the operational unit. No further tracking is required. This is referred to as fire-and-forget, launch-and-leave, or shoot-and-scoot. Disadvantages of active homing are the additional weight and expense for each missile and the fact that the radiation from the missile can reveal its presence.

If the aircraft is illuminated by a tracking beam from some source not on the missile, and if the beam reflections from the aircraft in the direction of the missile are used by the missile for guidance, the system is referred to as a semiactive homing (SAH) system. The missile may also require direct illumination from the illuminator on to a rearward-facing receiver to use in the processing of the reflected signal from the target. With this type of guidance, the aircraft may know it is being tracked, but it does not know if a missile is on the way. An SAH missile may or may not require continual target illumination. This type of guidance has progressed from a require-ment for one continuous illuminator per target to a system with a single

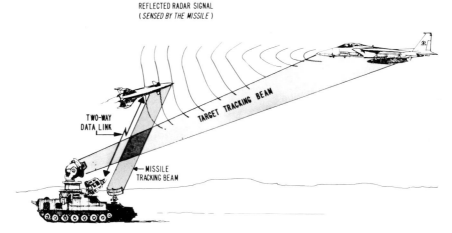

Fig. 3.22   Retransmission (TVM) guidance system.

illuminator that can track and illuminate several targets on a time-share basis. Thus, the missile receives the reflected illumination periodically. This is referred to as sample-data SAH.

Passive homing systems use electromagnetic emissions or natural reflections from the aircraft itself for guidance. One example is an infrared homing guidance system that homes in (closes) on the heat generated by the aircraft. Another is the antiradiation missile that homes in on radar navigation or fire-control signals or on jamming signals from electronic countermeasure equipment in the aircraft.

(4)   Retransmission guidance.   This type of guidance, also known as track-via-missile (TVM), is the latest technique to be used to direct missiles toward air targets. An illustration of TVM is given in Fig. 3.22. Typically, a radar tracking system tracks both the target and the missile, as in command guidance. However, in TVM the target tracking beam also serves as a target illuminator, and a receiver on the missile detects the reflected illumination, as in semiactive homing guidance. The information on the relative target angular position gathered by the missile is relayed to a control unit. Guidance equipment at the control unit processes the echoes received directly from the target and missile and the information on relative target position received from the missile and determines the appropriate guidance commands, which are then sent to the missile on a data link. The tracking system usually has the capability to track several targets at one time, and the control system can direct several simultaneous engagements between missiles and aircraft.

(5)   Phases of guidance.   Missile guidance is generally divided into three phases: boost or launch, midcourse, and terminal.

Table 3.1   Missile Guidance Methods, Surface-to-Air

COMMAND	BEAM RIDER	HOMING	
		SEMI-ACTIVE	PASSIVE
SPARTAN	SEASLUG	SEA SPARROW	CHAPARRAL
SPRINT	RBS 70	STANDARD, MR	REDEYE
CROTALE	TALOS (+ SAH)	STANDARD, ER	STINGER
RAPIER (CLOS)	TERRIER (+ SAH)	TARTAR	REDTOP
SEAWOLF (CLOS)		MASURCA	TAN-SAM (R)
SEACAT (CLOS)		BLOODHOUND	SA-7
BLOWPIPE (CLOS)		ASPIDE	SA-9
INDIGO		SEADART	
ROLAND (CLOS)		SA-6	
PATRIOT (+ SAH)		THUNDERBIRD	
SA-2 (SA-N-2)		HAWK	
SA-3 (SA-N-1)			
SA-4 (SAH)			
SA-8 (SA-N-4)			

SA-6 GAINFUL

The boost phase lasts from the time the missile leaves the launcher until the booster burns all of its fuel. The missile may or may not be guided during this phase.

The midcourse phase is usually the longest phase in both distance and time. During this phase, guidance may be required to bring the missile onto the desired course and to make certain it stays on that course.

The terminal phase is the last phase of guidance and must have high accuracy and fast reaction to ensure an intercept with the aircraft.

(6)   *Composite guidance systems.*   Generally, no one type of guidance is best suited for all three guidance phases. Consequently, many missile systems use more than one type of guidance, with each one operating during a certain phase of the missile trajectory. A system may use beam-rider guidance or semiactive homing from launch until midcourse, at which time the guidance switches to active or passive homing for more accurate tracking and guidance during the terminal phase. This combination also allows launching aircraft to break away from the engagement earlier than otherwise possible. These systems are referred to as hybrid or composite guidance systems. Several types of guidance may also be used simultaneously to avoid any countermeasures employed by the aircraft, such as the use of a decoy flare to draw an infrared homing system off of the radiation from the aircraft. If an active homing system is used in conjunction with a passive one, the missile may reject the flare and continue on toward the

Table 3.2   Missile Guidance Methods, Air-to-Air

SEMI-ACTIVE HOMING	PASSIVE HOMING
FALCON	SIDEWINDER
SPARROW	MAGIC
SUPER 530	SHAFRIR
SKYFLASH	SAAB 327
ASPIDE	AA-1 THRU AA-8
PHOENIX (+ ACTIVE)	SUPER R530
AA-1 THRU AA-7	REDTOP
AA-8 (Possibly)	FALCON
	SHRIKE (R)
	STANDARD ARM (R)
	HARM (R)

PHOENIX

aircraft. Tables 3.1 and 3.2 present the types of guidance possibly used by many of the current missile systems.

(7)   Trajectories.   Guidance systems can use any one of several methods or laws to navigate a missile along a trajectory or flight path to an intercept with an aircraft. Four common laws are pursuit, lead angle, three-point, and proportional navigation. The specific target flight path information required by the guidance package depends on which law is used. The most important types of information are the angle between the missile heading and the line of sight (LOS) from the missile to the target, the target range, and the rate of change of both the LOS angle and the range.

(a) Pursuit: In the pursuit trajectory, illustrated in Fig. 3.23a, the missile flies directly toward the target at all times. Thus, the line of sight between the missile and the aircraft is maintained essentially along the heading of the missile by the guidance system. Missiles flying a pursuit course usually end up in a tail chase situation, similar to a dog chasing a rabbit. There are two basic objections to the pursuit method. First, the maneuvers required of the missile become increasingly hard during the last, and critical, stages of flight. Second, the missile speed must be considerably greater than the aircraft speed. The sharpest curvature of the missile flight path usually occurs near the end of the flight. At this time, the missile must overtake the aircraft. If the aircraft attempts to evade, the last-minute angular acceleration requirements placed on the missile could exceed its aerodynamic capability, thereby causing a large miss distance. Near the end of the flight, the missile is usually coasting because the booster (and sustainer) motor thrusts last for only a short part of the flight. Consequently, more energy is required to make short-radius, high-speed turns at a time when the missile is

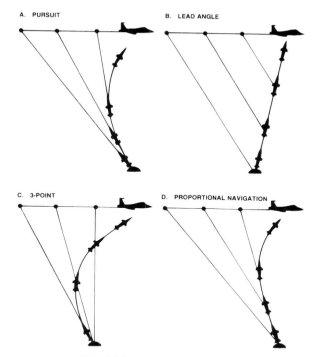

Fig. 3.23   Missile trajectories.

losing speed and has the least turning capability. The most favorable application of the pursuit course is against slow moving aircraft, or for missiles launched from a point directly to the rear of the aircraft, or head on toward an incoming aircraft.

(b) Lead angle: In the lead angle or constant bearing trajectory, shown in Fig. 3.23b, the guidance system flies the missile along a lead trajectory that results in an eventual intercept with the aircraft. For constant-speed, nonmaneuvering aircraft, the LOS between the missile and the aircraft remains at a constant angle, and the missile flies a straight-line trajectory. This is often referred to as a collision course. If the aircraft changes direction, the new lead angle required for a collision is determined, based on an assumed straight-line target flight path, and the missile is maneuvered to the new heading.

(c) Three-point: In three-point guidance, the missile is constantly being steered to lie on the line between the target tracker and the target, as shown in Fig. 3.23c; thus the name three-point guidance. This type of trajectory is typically used only in short-range missile systems employing CLOS or beam-rider guidance. An example of a CLOS system is one in which the target is tracked visually, using optics, and the missile is tracked by a sensor at the tracker that observes the off-axis position of a flare located on the tail of the missile. The amount of offset of the missile from the LOS from the tracker to the target and the range from the tracker to the missile are used by the guidance system to determine the appropriate steering commands to drive the missile back to the target tracking line. These commands are then relayed to the missile over a data link, such as a wire or radio.

(d) Proportional navigation: The most common method for changing the missile heading to cause a target intercept is proportional navigation, or pro nav. In order to do proportional navigation, the guidance system must be able to determine the time rate of change of the LOS between the missile and the target, as illustrated in Fig. 3.23d. This can be accomplished by equipment located on the missile or on the ground. When ground-based equipment is used, the location of both the missile and the target must be determined. In proportional navigation, the guidance system attempts to maintain an essentially constant LOS angle, and hence cause a collision, by making the rate of change of the missile heading directly proportional to the rate of change of the LOS.

Terminal Effects Parameters

The terminal effects parameters are quantitative descriptors of the inherent capability of the damage mechanisms to cause damage. They describe the intensity of the damage mechanisms. For example, the terminal effects parameters associated with a blast-generated fragment are the fragment weight and its velocity at impact. Other examples of some terminal effects parameters and their relationship with the damage mechanisms and damage processes are given in Fig. 3.4.

3.6 SPECIFIC THREAT SYSTEMS

In most instances, it is not difficult to determine the identity of the enemy. On Nov. 27, 1920, the Soviet Premier, Nikolai Lenin, stated one of the basic tenets of the Soviet Communist doctrine: "As long as Capitalism and Socialism remain side by side, we cannot live peacefully—the one or the other will be the victor in the end."

History to date has yielded no direct confrontation between the US and the Soviet Union. Experience, however, has shown that the Soviet Union is the major arms supplier for the many other Communist and third world countries where minor conflicts periodically erupt. Consequently, the Soviet systems are the ones usually confronted when an armed conflict occurs, and for that reason only the Soviet threat systems will be addressed here. The material presented in this section is available in the open literature and is of necessity *unclassified*, *unofficial*, and, hence, *incomplete*.

Land-Based Systems

Since the middle of the 1960's, the Soviets have developed and deployed a large number of mobile and semimobile surface-to-air missiles and anti-aircraft guns for air defense of their field units. This mix of guns and missiles provides a mobile umbrella that accompanies each echelon of the Soviet armies, including forward deployed battalions. These air-defense units are assigned to a major branch of the Soviet Ground Forces known as

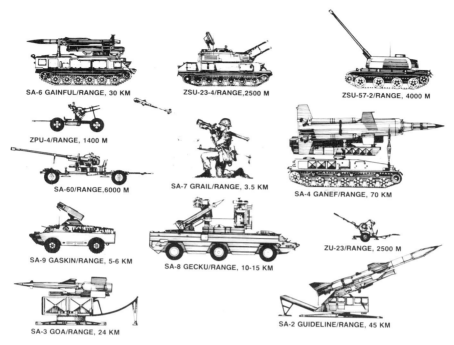

Fig. 3.24   Land-based threat.

the "troops of air defense of the Ground Forces" (voiska protivovozdushroi oborony Sudhoputniykh Voisk, abbreviated as PVO SV). The underlying philosophy of PVO SV is one of mobility and deployment in mass, with overlapping coverage. As new air-defense systems are introduced into the Soviet forces, the older systems are still retained in the active weapon inventory. Figure 3.24 shows many of the Soviet land-based systems in operation today; Fig. 3.25 illustrates the overlapping coverage of the systems.

Small arms and AAA.   Standard weapon calibers defined as small arms and available in Communist bloc countries are 7.62, 7.92, 12.7, and 14.5 mm. The types of small arms weapons using the 7.62- and 7.92-mm projectiles include hand-held pistols, shoulder-fired rifles, carbines, assault rifles, and submachine guns, and mounted light machine guns. These weapons are normally only effective against slow and low-flying aircraft within 600 m and are usually employed in the barrage fire mode. Mounted heavy antiaircraft machine guns use 12.7- and 14.5-mm projectiles. One such system is the ZPU-4. This antiaircraft weapon has four 14.5-mm heavy machine guns with a combined cyclic rate of fire of 2200 to 2400 rounds per minute. It traverses 360 deg and, with its optical fire control, has a tactical range of 1400 m. It is currently being replaced by more modern equipment.

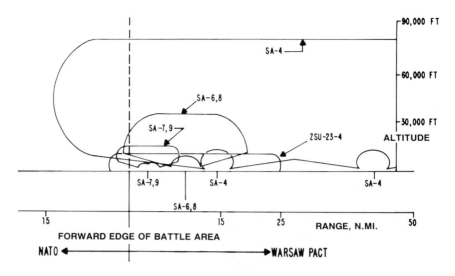

Fig. 3.25   Mobile SAM/AAA overlapping coverage; redundant, overlapping cover-age of mobile Soviet surface-to-air missiles and antiaircraft guns typifies Warsaw Pact Frontal forces. Range, altitude, tracking and acquisition radars also overlap (*Aviation Week*, Feb. 6, 1978).

Antiaircraft artillery have sizes that range from 23 mm up to and including 130 mm. Weapons through 57 mm are usually mobile. The larger systems are located in fixed installations. Weapons larger than 85 mm are deployed in limited numbers, with the frequency of deployment decreasing with size. A typical 23-mm system is the ZU-23. This weapon consists of two 23-mm cannons and fires a maximum of 2000 rounds per minute. The ZU-23 traverses 360 deg and, with its optical fire control, has a tactical range of 2500 m. It also is currently being replaced by more modern equipment.

One of the most important Soviet mobile air-defense weapons is the ZSU-23-4, sometimes referred to as the Shilka. This system is a self-con-tained package of mobile firepower with its own target acquisition and fire-control equipment. It has a crew of four (commander, driver, radar observer, and gunner) in a nuclear-biological-chemically (NBC) sealed chas-sis mounted on a modified PT-76 armored vehicle. It can fire on the move at speeds up to 25 km/h. It has four 23-mm cannons and a maximum practical rate of fire of 2000 rounds per minute. It traverses 360 deg and, with the Gun Dish radar, has a tactical range of 3000 m. Using optical sights, the tactical antiaircraft range is 2500 m. First seen in the early 1960's, this vehicle is used throughout the Warsaw Pact armies. It is found in the tank and motorized rifle regiments of tank and motorized rifle divisions and is integrated into the attack formations. The ability to move with the leading tank elements through underbrush and mud with sufficient armor to survive close enemy contact gives this system an advantage over the more fragile missile systems. Furthermore, pilots will find it difficult to distinguish this modern "flakpanzer" from the tanks it is accompanying.

In the 57-mm category of AAA, the S-60 and the ZSU-57-2 are the most common systems. The S-60 has one 57-mm cannon with a cyclic rate of fire of 105 to 120 rounds per minute. It traverses 360 deg and, when directed by the off-carriage Flap Wheel radar, has a tactical range of 6000 m. The tactical range with on-carriage optical sights is 4000 m. Normally, six S-60 guns with associated fire-control equipment constitute a battery. This system is usually found in antiaircraft regiments of maneuver divisions, but is being replaced by SAM systems.

The ZSU-57-2 first appeared in the late 1950's and equips all Warsaw Pact forces and at least 11 other nations. This system has two 57-mm cannons with a combined rate of fire of 210 to 240 rounds per minute. It traverses 360 deg and has a tactical range of 4000 m. The ZSU-57-2 is mounted on a modified T-54 tank chassis and carries a five-man crew. Fire control is optically directed. The ZSU-57-2 is presently being replaced by more modern equipment. When found in maneuver units, it is normally located with tank regiments.

Surface-to-air missile systems. The current Soviet land-based surface-to-air missile systems are the SA-1 through the SA-9. The SA-1, with the Guild (NATO designation) missile, and the SA-5, with the Gammon missile, are not elements of the PVO SV. They are for the defense of Soviet cities and are part of the Soviet Troops of National Air Defense, PVO Strany.

The PVO SV employs the SA-2, 3, 4, 6, 7, 8, and 9 for tactical air defense of armored assaults. The SA-2, with the Guideline missile, is a high- to medium-altitude air-defense system. Several versions have appeared. The missile is command guided and has a slant range of approximately 40 km. It has two stages, a solid fuel booster and a liquid fuel rocket sustainer, that boost its 130-kg HE warhead to a maximum altitude of about 27,000 m. The typical SA-2 site consists of six launchers arranged in a starlike configuration around the Fan Song radar guidance equipment. The SA-2 system is assigned at the front or Army level. It is a standard antiaircraft weapon in about 30 countries.

The SA-3 system uses the Goa missile and the Flat Face and Low Blow radars. This air-defense missile probably is command guided and may have some type of homing capability. The missile has an effective range of about 24 km. Powered by a two-stage solid fuel booster and solid fuel sustainer, the missile can carry its HE proximity-fuzed warhead to altitudes in excess of 13,000 m. This system is assigned at the front or Army level. It is being deployed in increasing numbers in Communist bloc countries.

The SA-4 system uses the Ganef missile and the Pat Hand and Long Track radars. This air-defense missile has a range of approximately 70 km and is command guided to a maximum altitude of about 27,000 m. It is powered by four solid fuel boosters with canted nozzles and a ramjet sustainer and carries an HE proximity-fuzed warhead. The SA-4 system may be assigned at the front or Army level.

The SA-6 system employs the Gainful missile. This air-defense missile has a slant range of 30 km. It is powered by an integral solid rocket/ramjet system and is initially command guided by the Straight Flush fire-control radar. Final intercept is by semiactive homing using continuous wave radar. The missile carries an 80-kg HE fragmentation warhead and can be employed against aircraft flying at altitudes from about 100 to 11,000 m. Mounted on a triple launcher on a modified PT-76 tank chassis called the TEL, a missile group consists of three triple launchers, one loading vehicle, and one Straight Flush radar, also PT-76 mounted. This system was used effectively during the 1973 Middle East War. It may be assigned at Army and division levels.

The SA-8, with the Gecko missile, is a short-range, low-altitude, all-weather air-defense system. The missile operates by command guidance with proportional navigation and is effective at altitudes from 50 to 6500 m. It is fully self-contained, with acquisition, tracking, and two missile guidance radars mounted on a six-wheeled, amphibious vehicle. Four missiles are carried in an integrated mount. The two guidance radars make it possible to launch two missiles at the same target with each missile responding to a different frequency. The system also contains an electro-optical tracker, probably television. With a slant range of approximately 10 to 15 km and a 50-kg HE warhead, the highly mobile SA-8 can provide close support to armored and mechanized forces.

The SA-7 and SA-9 are short-range, low-altitude weapons with missiles that use passive infrared homing guidance. They are used mainly for defense against low- and slow-flying aircraft. The SA-7 is a man-portable air-defense missile system 1.2 m long. The Grail missile, which is fired from a shoulder launcher, has an HE warhead. A solid fuel booster and sustainer propel the Grail missile to a maximum slant range of approximately 3.5 km. It can be fired from the ground or from a vehicle and may be used against aircraft flying at altitudes from approximately 50 to 3000 m. Nine SA-7 Grail launchers are found in each tank and motorized rifle battalion and are further assigned in groups of three to the company level.

The SA-9 uses the Gaskin missile. It is transported on a modified BRDM-2 amphibious armored vehicle that carries a probable crew of four. The SA-9 has a slant range of approximately 5 to 6 km. The missile has an HE warhead and probably is powered by a solid propellant. Four missile cannisters, each with one missile, are normally carried on the launcher turret. The SA-9 Gaskin is used in conjunction with the ZSU-23-4 at the regimental level.

Two antitank guided missiles, the Sagger and the Swatter, can be a threat to low-flying helicopters. Normally, they are mounted on the BMP personnel carrier or BRDM reconnaissance vehicle. The Swatter can be mounted on the Hind A and D helicopter models.

Sea-Based Systems

Too often in the past, the Soviet Navy has been written off as a purely defensive force, reminiscent of its 1950's and early 1960's capabilities. This conclusion is no longer valid, for in recent years the Soviet Navy has been

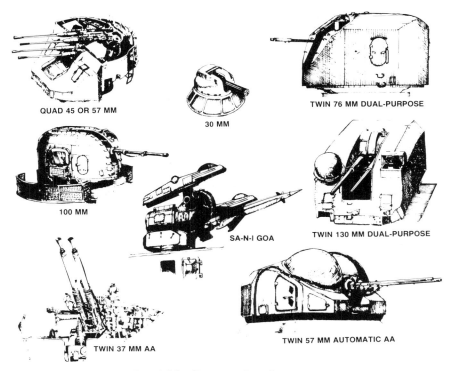

QUAD 45 OR 57 MM

30 MM

TWIN 76 MM DUAL-PURPOSE

100 MM

SA-N-I GOA

TWIN 130 MM DUAL-PURPOSE

TWIN 37 MM AA

TWIN 57 MM AUTOMATIC AA

Fig. 3.26   Some sea-based weapons.

transformed into a wide-ranging ocean power specifically tailored to challenge the US Navy's dominance as a tactical and strategic force on the high seas. *Jane's Fighting Ships*, a respected reference work on international Naval strengths, has noted that the "Soviet Navy has reached a strength uncalled for in the protection of its fast-increasing merchant marine." Jane's further comments that "an offensive type of long-range armed force" flies the flag of the "Soviet Navy over the oceans of the world."

The air-defense systems onboard operational Soviet surface ships consist of AAA ranging in size from 23 to 76 mm and of four surface-to-air missile systems, the SA-N-1 through SA-N-4. Figure 3.26 illustrates some of these weapons.

The SA-N-1 system uses the Goa missile and the Peel Group radar system. The missile is assumed to be identical to that used in the SA-3 system, with a roll-stabilized launcher. The Soviets consider this a dual-purpose antiship and antiaircraft weapon.

The SA-N-2 is the sea-based version of the SA-2 system. Apparently, it is installed on only one Soviet ship.

The SA-N-3 uses the Goblet missile and is deployed on Soviet helicopter carriers and several cruisers. Fire control is provided by the Head Light radar group.

The SA-N-4 is a short-range missile system. The missile is concealed in a bin-type launcher with a pop-up launching mode. Conjecture is that the missile is the Gecko missile used with the SA-8 system. The fire-control radar is the Pop Group.

The AAA and SAM systems appear on many different Soviet ships. The Kiev "aircraft carrier" carries two twin mounts with 76-mm barrels, eight "Gatling" guns, and two twin SA-N-3 and SA-N-4 launchers. The Kresta I guided missile cruiser is armed with two twin launchers for the SA-N-1 Goa missile and two twin 57-mm antiaircraft guns. On the Kresta II cruiser, the fore and aft SA-N-1 systems were each replaced with the SA-N-3 system. The Krivak guided missile destroyer carries two twin mounts of 76-mm AAA and two launchers for the SA-N-4 missiles. The Nanuchka guided missile patrol ship carries a launcher for the SA-N-4 and one twin mount 57-mm system. Radars such as Head Net and Top Sail provide surveillance coverage for the major combatants, while Hawk Screech and Muff Cob direct the fire of the AAA.

Aircraft

The Soviet Air Forces that pose a threat to US aircraft, known as Frontal Aviation or FA (Frontovaya aviatsiya), have not received the attention that the land- and sea-based systems have received. This is due in some part to the fact that there has been a major Soviet drive in the past decade to provide the all-altitude "organic" surface-based air-defense systems for the Ground Forces described above. Nevertheless, FA does maintain and continues to modernize a major force of manned interceptors armed with air-to-air missiles and/or guns. These include the MiG-17 (Fresco), MiG-19

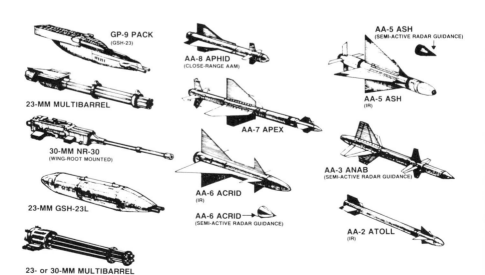

Fig. 3.27   Some airborne weapons.

(Farmer), MiG-21 (Fishbed), MiG-23 (Flogger), and MiG-25 (Foxbat). All of these aircraft except the Foxbat carry 23- or 30-mm guns. There are seven air-to-air missiles, AA-1 through AA-8, except AA-4, carried by these aircraft. Most of the systems have both passive (infrared) and semiactive (radar) homing versions. Both versions are usually carried by one aircraft. These missiles have maximum ranges from 3 to 20 n. mi. Figure 3.27 illustrates some of the airborne weapons.

There are other airborne threats to US aircraft, such as the Hind D attack helicopter and the defensive armament on the Soviet fixed-wing attack aircraft, bombers, and the antisubmarine warfare aircraft.

3.7   THE MISSION-THREAT ANALYSIS

In order to properly develop a survivability design for a specific aircraft that will enable it to effectively conduct its assigned missions, the specific threats to the aircraft must be determined, as well as the conditions that exist at the time of the encounter. This determination is referred to as the mission-threat analysis. It is a required program task specified in MIL-STD 2069. According to that document:

> The missions and threat systems considered in this mission-threat analysis shall be those specified in the aircraft detail specification, operational requirements, and implementing documentation. The contractor shall:
> - Define each operational mode required by the specified missions. Aircraft configuration factors (weights, C. G. locations, fuel status, armament loading, etc.) and proposed operational concepts and tactics shall be included in the maximum detail possible.
> - List the threats and the threat characteristics applicable to the defined operational modes.
> - Analyze the aircraft operational modes and the threats and determine the encounter conditions.
> The derived encounter conditions shall be used as a basis for the required survivability assessments and tradeoff studies.

In general, the mission-threat analysis consists of three phases of study. In the first phase, the missions and flight envelopes of the aircraft are defined. The output of this study would be the aircraft theaters of operation and types of missions, and the flight and operating conditions, including airspeeds, altitudes, configurations, and types of electromagnetic radiation, for each mission type. The second phase is the definition of the expected threat environment for each mission and theater. Here, potentially hostile weapon systems, including land, sea, and air units, are analyzed to determine their operating conditions and envelopes. The third phase combines the data gathered in the first two phases. The likelihood that the aircraft will be engaged by each threat system is estimated, and the conditions of both systems at the time of encounter are identified.

It is very important that all of the threats to an aircraft be correctly identified in the mission-threat analysis. Some situations are obvious. For example, aircraft conducting a close air support mission will most likely encounter the ZSU-23-4, SA-7, and SA-8 systems; whereas aircraft on an antisubmarine mission in the open ocean today are not as likely to encounter these three threats. New threats must also be forecasted. For example, a new long-range interceptor with long-range air-to-air missiles and a submarine-launched antiaircraft missile are possible future threats to ASW aircraft in the open ocean.

Selected Bibliography

Airwar-Vietnam, Bobbs-Merrill Co., Inc., Indianapolis/New York, 1978.

Fuhs, A. E., Class notes for Naval Postgraduate School Course AE 4505, "Laser Technology," 1977.

Gunston, B., *Rockets and Missiles*, A Salamander Book, London, 1979.

Held, M., "Air Target Warheads," *Guided Missiles, International Defense Review*, Special Series No. 10.

International Defense Review, Special Series "Air Defense Systems" and "Combat Aircraft."

Jane's All The World's Aircraft, Biennial Publications, Jane's Publishing Company, Ltd., London.

Jane's Weapons Systems, Biennial Publications, Jane's Publishing Company, Ltd., London.

Malone, D. K., "Air Defense of Soviet Ground Forces," *Air Force Magazine*, March 1978, pp. 70–83.

Principles of Guided Missiles and Nuclear Weapons, Naval Training Command, NAVTRA 10784-B, U.S. Government Printing Office, 1972.

Taylor, J. W. R., "Gallery of Soviet Aerospace Weapons," *Air Force Magazine*, Special Edition, March 1983, pp. 79–94.

Weapons Systems Fundamentals, Analysis of Weapons, Vol. 2, Naval Ordnance System Command, NAVORD OP 3000, 15 January 1971.

4. COMBAT DATA ANALYSIS

4.1 TYPES OF ANALYSES

Combat data analysis is the study of actual battle damage reports and loss statistics to determine the effectiveness of the enemy's weapon systems, the susceptibility and vulnerability of US aircraft, and the effectiveness of survivability enhancement techniques. There are many variables that affect each combat incident, and a reliable, accurate, and complete description of the circumstances surrounding the incident is very difficult to obtain in the hectic combat environment. Nevertheless, much data have been gathered, and many analyses have been made.

Since almost all of the data and analyses are classified, very little of this material can be presented here. However, some of the kinds of analyses that have been made are described below to give the reader a general idea of the wide use of combat data. The interested reader can obtain most of the available combat data from the Combat Data Information Center (CDIC), which is described in Sec. 4.2 of this chapter.

Loss Rates

A combat loss rate is the ratio of the number of aircraft lost in combat to the number of sorties flown, where a sortie is an operational flight by one aircraft. The rate, which is a measure of the probability that an aircraft will be killed on one sortie, is sometimes expressed as the number of aircraft lost in 1000 sorties, and sometimes it is expressed as a percentage. For example, a loss rate of 30, or 3%, implies that 30 aircraft were (or would be) lost after 1000 sorties were (or would be) flown.

The loss rate has a substantial impact upon the ability of an air force to sustain operations. If there are M aircraft available for combat at the beginning of a conflict, and if these M aircraft go on a raid, only MS aircraft will survive the raid, where $S = 1 - K$ and K is the loss rate. If these MS surviving aircraft then go on another raid, MS^2 aircraft will survive, according to Eq. (1.3). Thus, the surviving fraction of the M aircraft after two raids is S^2.

The surviving fraction of aircraft S^n is plotted in Fig. 4.1a as a function of the number of raids n for several values of the loss rate. For large numbers of raids, the reduction in the number of surviving aircraft is drastic, even for what appears to be very low loss rates, such as 5 per 1000. For example, if the loss rate is 5 (per 1000), only 60.6% of the original number of aircraft are left after 100 raids.

117

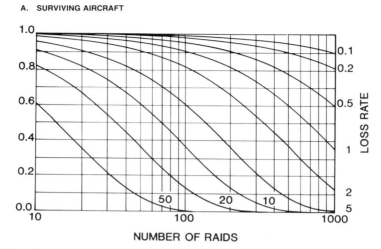

Fig. 4.1a   Surviving fraction of aircraft vs the number of raids for several loss rates.

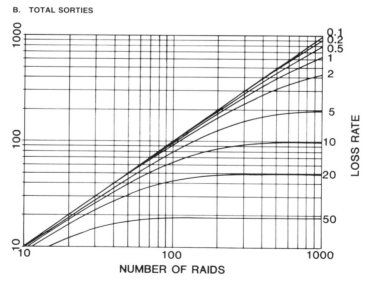

Fig. 4.1b   Total sorties flown vs the number of raids for several loss rates.

Another way to illustrate the operational consequence of the loss rate is to plot the total number of sorties flown by the surviving aircraft on the n raids. On the first raid, MS sorties are completed. After the second raid, MS plus MS^2 sorties have been made. Thus, after n raids, $M(S + S^2 + \ldots S^n)$, or $M(S^n - S)/(S - 1)$, sorties have been completed. Figure 4.1b presents the total number of sorties (for M equal to 1) as a function of the number of raids for several values of the loss rate. For the loss rate of 5, $77.8M$ sorties are flown in the 100 raids. Thus, only about 78% of the planned number of sorties are actually flown. Two examples of actual loss rates from past conflicts are given below.

World War II bomber attrition. Loss rates vary greatly, depending upon the conflict. In World War II, the overall attrition suffered by the Royal Air Force (RAF) Bomber Command on their night raids over Europe during 1942 and 1943 was nearly 40, with some raids losing over 10% of the attacking bombers. Heavily escorted day raids by the RAF during the latter half of 1942 suffered an overall loss rate of over 5%. This heavy loss rate on the escorted daylight raids caused the Bomber Command to conduct most of their subsequent operations at night.

B-24

The US 8th Air Force heavy bombers had a loss rate of over 8% of the attacking bombers on their daylight raids over Europe in 1943, excluding the losses over Schweinfurt in October, when over 25% of the attacking

HE-111

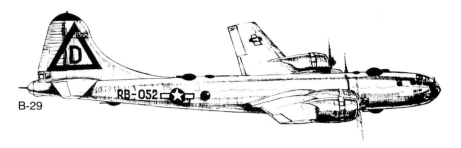

B-29

force was lost. The German bombers suffered similar loss rates on their raids against the United Kingdom, and US B-29 operations against Japan in 1944 resulted in a loss rate of about 4%. The reader should be aware that a loss rate of 5% results in a probability of an aircraft surviving 25 sorties (the typical tour of duty for aircrews in World War II) of $(1 - 0.05)^{25}$, or about 28%, according to Eq. (1.4) and Fig. 4.1a.

US Air Force fighter attrition in the Korean conflict. In the Korean conflict, the loss rates (in ascending order) of the Air Force F-86 Sabre, F-80 Shooting Star, F-84 Thunderjet, and P/F-51 Mustang were between 1 and 3, respectively. Nearly all of the F-80, F-84, and P/F-51 losses were to ground fire, whereas most of the F-86 losses were to enemy aircraft. When comparing the loss rates of these aircraft, the P/F-51 appears to be less survivable than the other aircraft. However, the missions of the aircraft and the intensity of the threat must be examined before that conclusion can be drawn. For example, the Mustang was heavily used in the dangerous low-level ground attack role because it was the only Air Force aircraft that

F-80

F-84

F-86

had the necessary range, flying qualities, and endurance that could carry sufficient ordnance to inflict damage. Care must be taken not to misinterpret combat data.

Threat System Effectiveness

Several analyses have been conducted to determine the effectiveness of specific threat systems. One was a study of the relationship between the probability an aircraft was either damaged or lost and the relative location of the detonation of a guided missile warhead. This information could be used to develop a probability of aircraft kill versus warhead detonation distance curve. The geographic location and the mission of the aircraft were also noted, as were the aircraft altitudes, speed, and any maneuver at the time of the incident. A general result was the average number of missiles launched per aircraft killed.

Aircraft Vulnerability

Examination of the damage to aircraft that return to base can provide a great deal of information on the vulnerability of the aircraft to the threats that caused the damage and on the direction and intensity of the threat fire. Some of the important items that have been noted are the type and number of hits on the aircraft during the incident, and the hit or entry hole locations versus the aircraft speed and altitude. A spatial plot of all of the hits taken by returned aircraft of a particular type can be very revealing. A typical example of a hit plot on the bottom of an aircraft is illustrated in Fig. 4.2. Each dot represents a hole caused by a damage mechanism. When the number of hits from any one direction is sufficient to nearly cover the aircraft in a random distribution, as in Fig. 4.2, locations on the aircraft

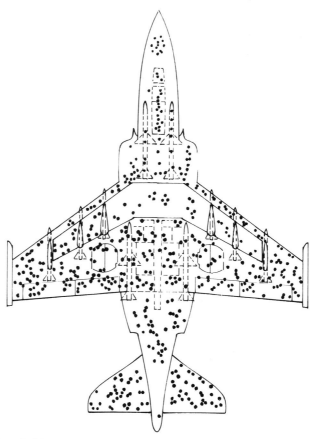

Fig. 4.2   Bottom hit plot; each dot represents one or more closely spaced entry holes.

where no hits are recorded are locations that either are shielded or are locations of components that, when hit, lead to an aircraft kill.

Certain critical components may very quickly be identified from these hit plots. For example, an area in Fig. 4.2 nearly devoid of hits is at the tail of the aircraft. Here, redundant hydraulic lines usually come together to provide two sources of power for the stabilator actuator. One hit here could damage both lines. If all hydraulic power is lost to the stabilator, the stabilator may go hard-over due to aerodynamic forces, causing the aircraft to become uncontrollable. This can happen so fast the crew may not be able to eject. Another area in Fig. 4.2 with few holes is that over the bottom of the wing. This particular area corresponds to the location of the wing fuel tanks. Most of the aircraft that were hit here may have been killed. However, another possible explanation for the lack of holes in this area could be the fact that the wing skin in this area is extremely thick, and the damage mechanism could not penetrate the skin; hence, the absence of holes.

4.2 COMBAT DATA INFORMATION CENTER (CDIC)

The Combat Data Information Center is the central repository and data dissemination center for combat, combat-related, operational, and test data that can be utilized in aircraft, ship, and ground vehicle survivability, vulnerability, maintenance, logistics, and military operations studies. The CDIC was established at Wright-Patterson Air Force Base, Ohio, in April 1970, when design work on a storage and retrieval system for the combat damage/loss data from Southeast Asia was initiated. The final design of the storage and retrieval system was implemented on a data base management system supported by a large-scale Control Data computer. The Center became fully operational in the fall of 1971. CDIC is operated (under contract) by the Air Force Wright Aeronautical Laboratories, Flight Dynamics Laboratory.

The Center contains among its holdings actual situation data, most of which are classified, on damages and losses in Southeast Asia and the Middle East. CDIC was established as an aid to those involved in the analysis of weapon systems including:

(1) The initial design or modification of military vehicles for enhancement of survivability and the reduction of vulnerability.

(2) The analysis of enemy munitions effectiveness.

(3) The development and substantiation of survivability computer simulation models.

(4) The identification of damage location or cause of loss on US systems.

Data on fixed- and rotary-wing aircraft, armored personnel carriers, riverine craft, ships, tanks, and trucks are included in the CDIC collection.

The CDIC came about as a result of a serious deficiency in the collection of accurate and valid combat damage/loss data on US materiel, personnel, and facilities in Southeast Asia. In September 1968, the Joint Technical

Coordinating Group for Munitions Effectiveness (JTCG/ME) advised the Joint Materiel Commanders of the deficiency. As a result, the JTCG/ME was directed to collect and disseminate such data, the outcome being the establishment of the Battle Damage Assessment and Reporting Program (BDARP). This tri-Service effort consisted of two parts: (1) the collection of combat damage/loss data, for which the battle damage assessment and reporting teams (BDART) were formed; and (2) the storage, collation, retrieval, and dissemination of the data through the CDIC.

The BDART were special groups designated to collect as much combat data as was available. The Army assigned 47 men who worked in small teams covering selected combat units. The Air Force employed 8 to 12 civilians and a military leader who worked individually covering selected air bases. The Navy had a three-man team working together covering one type of vehicle. Some of the items noted for each incident included the vehicle model and serial number, service, incident type, and date. The scenario information included the mission type, incident location, target type, speed, altitude, and country. The threat and encounter conditions were identified, where possible, and items such as casualties, systems damaged, and repair time were described. A narrative was obtained during interviews with the crew. The BDART collected data in Southeast Asia from July 1969 through May 1971 and then again from October 1972 through January 1973. During this period, over 2450 combat damage/loss incidents were documented by these tri-Service teams.

Originally, CDIC handled only the data generated during the 1969–1973 time period by the BDART. However, it soon became apparent that there was a demonstrated need for supplemental and related data on combat incidents occurring throughout the entire period of hostilities in Southeast Asia. Using other sources of data, the combat incident files were expanded both in time frame and depth. Today, these files contain over 30,500 documented cases of damage/loss to US military equipment and personnel. These unique data, in both computerized and original source form, provide researchers with the largest and most complete combat data bases in existence in the world.

As the CDIC began processing requests for data, it became evident that the Center had to supply more than combat damage/loss information. Basic reference material on the enemy threat and vehicle systems was needed, along with other reference material, to fully support the user's needs. In response to this, the CDIC began collecting reports and studies for a reference library, combat-related and operational data, and the results of tests conducted in various vehicle survivability and vulnerability programs. In addition, the Center has obtained combat and operational data from the conflicts in the Middle East.

The Center's data are grouped into three main areas:
(1)   Combat
    (a)   Southeast Asia (fixed- and rotary-wing aircraft; ground vehicles)
    (b)   Middle East (ground vehicles)

(2)   Test
      (a)   ballistic (components, materials, and subsystems)
      (b)   laser (components and materials)
(3)   Library
      (a)   vehicle survivability
      (b)   laser
      (c)   technical orders and manuals

Each of the combat data bases contains information describing combat damage/destruction of individual pieces of military equipment. Each incident is uniquely identified by Service, vehicle designator (e.g., F-4E, M48A1), serial number, and date of occurrence. All source data for a particular incident, including available photographs, are consolidated into a single package. Selected items of information are extracted from the collated multiple data sources and input to a computerized storage and retrieval system. Figure 4.3 shows the type of data that is available for computer retrieval from these data bases. Figures 4.4 and 4.5 show the number of incidents in the fixed- and rotary-wing aircraft data bases by Service and model.

The ballistic and laser data bases contain data from individual test shots. Each data base was developed independently. Appropriate test parameters were selected and input to a computerized storage and retrieval system. This facilitates the handling of the large amount of data contained in these files.

At the present time, the ballistic test data bases at the CDIC contain information on fuel systems, engines, and structures. The fuel system data base contains over 2100 test-firing records on aircraft fuel system components impacted by both projectiles and fragments. The engine data base contains almost 150 test records, including fuel ingestion tests, controlled damage tests, firings against static engine components, and projectile and fragment impacts on running engines. The structures data base contains over 2600 static firing tests using fragments and various explosive devices against aircraft wings and fuselage sections.

The laser data base was developed to provide a central repository for laser test data relating to the terminal effects of laser radiation as a potential weapon, the response characteristics of aerospace materials and components to laser radiation, and the investigation of countermeasures to the laser threat. In this data base, selected information from individual experiments (test shots) has been input to a computerized storage and retrieval system. At the present time, this data base contains information on almost 4000 shots against an assorted array of materials, components, simulated components, and hardware material, as well as generic testing.

The reference library at the Center actually contains three separate libraries: vehicle survivability, laser, and technical orders and manuals. The vehicle survivability library contains over 3400 documents relating to the survivability of US materiel and personnel. Documents in this library include survivability analyses (susceptibility, vulnerability, lethality, etc.); survivability methodologies; survivability enhancement and vulnerability reduction techniques; test reports; Middle East data/analyses; Southeast

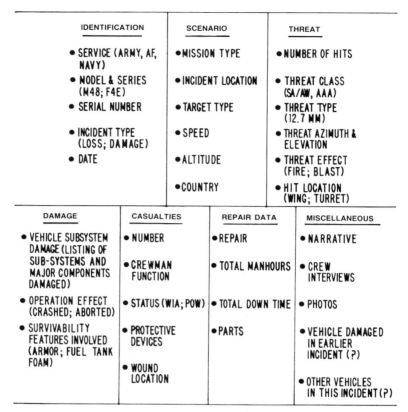

IDENTIFICATION	SCENARIO	THREAT
• SERVICE (ARMY, AF, NAVY)	•MISSION TYPE	•NUMBER OF HITS
• MODEL & SERIES (M48; F4E)	• INCIDENT LOCATION	• THREAT CLASS (SA/AW, AAA)
• SERIAL NUMBER	• TARGET TYPE	• THREAT TYPE (12.7 MM)
• INCIDENT TYPE (LOSS; DAMAGE)	• SPEED	• THREAT AZIMUTH & ELEVATION
• DATE	•ALTITUDE	• THREAT EFFECT (FIRE; BLAST)
	•COUNTRY	• HIT LOCATION (WING; TURRET)

DAMAGE	CASUALTIES	REPAIR DATA	MISCELLANEOUS
• VEHICLE SUBSYSTEM DAMAGE (LISTING OF SUB-SYSTEMS AND MAJOR COMPONENTS DAMAGED)	• NUMBER	•REPAIR	• NARRATIVE
	• CREWMAN FUNCTION	• TOTAL MANHOURS	• CREW INTERVIEWS
• OPERATION EFFECT (CRASHED; ABORTED)	• STATUS (WIA; POW)	•TOTAL DOWN TIME	• PHOTOS
• SURVIVABILITY FEATURES INVOLVED (ARMOR; FUEL TANK FOAM)	• PROTECTIVE DEVICES	•PARTS	•VEHICLE DAMAGED IN EARLIER INCIDENT (?)
	• WOUND LOCATION		• OTHER VEHICLES IN THIS INCIDENT(?)

Fig. 4.3 Typical information in the combat data base. Note: All categories of data may not be available in each incident depending on the amount of information available in source material.

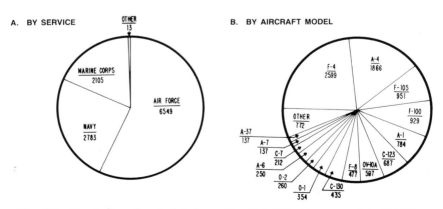

Fig. 4.4 Fixed-wing aircraft data base: 11,447 total incidents as of April 1982.

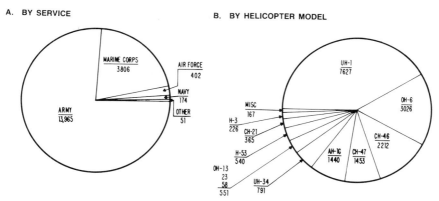

Fig. 4.5   Rotary-wing aircraft data base: 18,398 total incidents as of April 1982.

Asia operations data/analyses; intelligence reports/analyses; combat data analyses; symposia proceedings, etc.

The laser reference library contains over 200 documents. The test reports in this library are used as the source for the individual experiments input to the computerized data base previously discussed. In addition to the test reports, this library contains laser symposia proceedings, laser weapon reports, vulnerability reports, and a wide range of analyses involving the laser weapon or its effects.

Bibliographic information [title, author(s), originating and sponsoring activities, report number(s), release restrictions, security classification, and date of report] as well as the abstract and keywords for the documents in the vehicle survivability and laser libraries have been input to a full text computerized storage and retrieval system. This greatly facilitates the rapid identification of reports contained in the libraries relating to a specific area.

The third library at the Center contains technical orders (flight manuals and illustrated parts breakdown) and technical manuals for most of the aircraft and vehicles used in Southeast Asia and the Middle East, as well as those currently in the inventory.

In addition to these major data bases, the CDIC also possesses a multitude of specialized data bases comprised of exploitation data on foreign equipment (T-65, HITVAL, GRAPH ANGLE, MEXPO, COM-PASS GHOST, and HAVE EDUCATION), Army equipment development and evaluation programs (ACTIV, ENSURE, MASSTER, STANO, and VLAPA), Southeast Asia operations data (COACT, OPREA, SITRA, STRKHIST, VNDBA, COLED-V, AVDAC, and VCOD), plus many more.

Any Government agency may use the services of the CDIC. Contractors may also avail themselves of the services if a sponsoring Government agency certifies that the information is required for a current project and that the need-to-know exists.

The CDIC has supported all of the organizations within the Department of Defense involved in vehicle survivability, munitions effectiveness and related areas, as well as their contractors. The Center has responded to hundreds of user requests of varying complexity. Some types of analyses that have been supported, and examples of others which can be supported, include:

(1)   Crew survivability analysis.

(2)   Operations analysis including loss studies by aircraft type, by type of threat, by cause of loss, and by mission.

(3)   Cost analysis of alternative survivability techniques.

(4)   Threat analysis including correlation of loss ratios with ECM activity.

(5)   Effectiveness of personnel armor.

(6)   Effectiveness of vehicle armor.

(7)   Effectiveness of vehicle survivability enhancement features.

(8)   Engineering analysis of vehicle component damage.

(9)   Combat effectiveness of design features.

(10) Maintenance burden from combat damage.

(11) Logistics studies.

(12) Weapons effectiveness studies.

(13) Historical studies of military operations.

The CDIC staff consists of information system specialists and engineers with supporting data researchers and clerical personnel. The staff is prepared to acquaint users with the CDIC data resources, to work with users in formulating requests for optimal manual or machine searches for specific data from the various collections, to explain the significance and limitations of the data, and, in certain instances, to perform screening and preliminary analysis of data for specific tasks. The staff will prepare and submit the actual computer search and retrieval runs if such are needed. If the data required are not available at the CDIC, the staff is often able to refer requesters to other centers or agencies that may possess the data.

For the most efficient service, it is recommended that requesters first call the CDIC request adviser to discuss the nature of the data required and how it is to be used. This will permit the staff to determine whether or not the Center possesses the information and if there are any release limitations that must be satisfied before service can be provided. If large amounts of data or extensive searches are involved, a personal visit to the CDIC may be required to review the data and discuss the request in more detail. All visitors coming to the Center should forward security clearance information well in advance of the date of the proposed visit.

In summary, the CDIC has grown from a storehouse for data generated by the BDART to the central repository and data dissemination center for combat and combat-related operational and test data that can be utilized in aircraft, ship, and ground vehicle survivability, vulnerability, maintenance, logistics, and military operations studies. It is the intent of the sponsors of the CDIC, now the Joint Technical Coordinating Group on Aircraft Survivability as well as the JTCG/ME, to continue an effort of enlargement and improvement of the CDIC data bases and services and the development of new data bases in response to the needs of the research and development community.

For more information on the CDIC, its operation, and the data bases, the mailing address and telephone numbers for the Center are Air Force Wright

Aeronautical Laboratories, Combat Data Information Center, AFWAL/
FIES/CDIC, Wright-Patterson AFB, OH 45433. Telephone, (commercial)
(513) 255-4840, 255-3956; (autovon) 785-4840, 785-3956.*

4.3 DESCRIPTION OF SOME TYPICAL COMBAT INCIDENTS

In order to give the reader a general understanding of the kinds of
damage that can be expected from the various threat propagators and
damage mechanisms, several descriptions are presented here that are representative of battle damage received during the US involvement in Southeast
Asia.

Nonlethal Damage

The following descriptions are from fixed- and rotary-wing aircraft that
were able to return to base; the damage was not sufficient to cause a loss of
the aircraft.

Small arms fire. Some typical examples of nonlethal damage from
small arms fire are:
(1) Hole in port aft fuselage. Elevator control cable damaged.
(2) Hole in rear cockpit canopy.
(3) Hit in ammunition case in right-hand (RH) wing, caused one 20-mm
round to go off.
(4) Hole in rudder.
(5) Hit in center section of wing. Fuel lost.
(6) Oil cooler air scoop hit.
(7) Port horizontal stabilizer hit, and small section of rear spar web
shattered.
(8) Port drop tank ruptured.
(9) One-inch hole through starboard aileron.
(10) One-quarter-inch hole in left-wing fuel cell. No fire.
(11) Hydraulic lines severed.
(12) Bullet hit in bottom of port wing. Internal fire resulted. Extinguished
in flight.
(13) Hole through RH wing inlet duct and into engine.
(14) Radome hit. All electrical power lost.
(15) Aircraft sustained numerous small holes (approximately $\frac{3}{8}$ in.)
scattered along the left-hand (LH) side of aft fuselage section, with some
projectiles going through both sides of vertical stabilizer. Three holes in LH
horizontal stabilizer. Small holes in both RH and LH leading-edge flaps;
three holes in LH wing.
(16) Projectile entered wing leading edge, followed by an explosion that
ruptured utility hydraulic lines; subsequent fire.
(17) Copilot hit in leg.

---

*In 1985, the CDIC was incorporated into the newly established Survivability/Vulnerability
Information Analysis Center (SURVIAC). This Center is described in Appendix C.

(18) Aircraft was hovering when it received heavy ground fire. One crewman was hit. Aircraft took one hit in a fuel cell, one in a fuel filter, two hits in rotor blades, and 16 hits total.

High-explosive AAA projectiles.   The damage from the HE projectiles is usually much more severe than that from the penetrators. Some typical examples are:

(1)   Major damage to RH wing. Projectile entered bottom of RH wing just aft of leading-edge flap near fuselage. Hole in bottom of wing, and 16-in. hole in top. Six holes in fuselage ranging in size from $\frac{1}{2}$ in. to 2 in. One fragment entered engine intake and was injested by engine. Engines and RH wing will have to be changed.

(2)   Projectile struck LH wing and exploded, causing 4-in. holes and fuselage damage. Port engine secured, and aircraft returned on one engine.

(3)   Shell exploded in port-wing wheel well and caused fire.

(4)   Twelve-inch section removed from LH elevator.

(5)   Lost 12–18 in. of wing panel.

(6)   RH wing suffered internal explosion with a 2-in. bulge from front to rear spar with multiple popped rivets top and underside wing. Fire indicated for 10 s.

(7)   Hole approximately 40×27 in. on LH engine duct; 1- and 3-in. holes on RH side of fuselage. Holes through RH engine duct. Wires cut, hydraulic and fuel lines broken, and further undetermined damage.

(8)   Top of fuselage creased, and parts of frame torn out forward of tail. Damaged longerons.

Missiles.   Two sample incidents where the aircraft returned are:

(1)   Approximately 150 holes in fuselage, port inner and outer wing, empennage, and control surfaces. Port outer wing stiffener ruptured, 5-in. hole in outer wing rib, and 8-in. hole in port forward fuselage keel.

(2)   Port engine damaged and secured. Aircraft returned on one engine.

Lethal Damage

Some typical descriptions of the events leading to an aircraft loss are given here for several incidents to illustrate the various kinds of lethal damage:

(1)   Aircraft received a hit in the belly. Controls vibrated violently. There was a fire in the left engine.

(2)   Aircraft explodes in midair.

(3)   Aircraft was hit by several rounds of AAA fire. Large hole and flames were observed in right wing. Aircraft started porpoising and control was lost.

(4)   Pilot felt a thump, fire warning and overheat lights came on, and controls became mushy. Hydraulic pressure decreased and engine stopped.

(5)   AAA hit caused excessive fuel loss and engine flameout.

(6)   Aircraft hit by ground fire, lost airspeed and utility hydraulic system. Electrical fire, smoke, and heat were observed in cockpit.

(7)   Aircraft was hit in rear of right engine which then burst into flames. Four minutes later, the left engine was on fire and control was lost.

(8)   Pilot was fatally hit. Navigator assumed control of aircraft and departed target area.

(9)   Aircraft was hit in right horizontal stabilizer. Pilot lost control.

(10) Aircraft was hit in right wing by medium-caliber AAA. Immediate hydraulic system failure and fire in wing near forward edge of flap. Fire burned forward for 15 min until it reached the main wing spar. Aircraft became impossible to control and crew ejected.

(11) Aircraft hit in starboard wing. Fuel streamed from hit. PC-1 failed and PC-2 was unstable initially, then stabilized when emergency power package (EPP) was extended into airstream. Starboard aileron jammed full up, and full left aileron required for level flight. Fire in wing (hydraulic fluid and burning metal) all the way back to base. As aircraft slowed to land, fuel vapor ignited and flames spread to aft of aircraft. Aircraft touched down, missed short field gear, broke midfield gear, pilot ejected, and aircraft left runway.

(12) Aircraft hit on bomb run. Pilot completed bomb run and egressed target area while climbing to altitude. Wingman reported damage in starboard aft section of aircraft. After 25 min, engine seized and aircraft went out of control.

(13) Aircraft hit by AAA in area aft of cockpit. Fire in aft fuselage, probably fuel, possibly hydraulics, smoke in cockpit. Lost electrical power to instruments and communications; lost normal oxygen; engine continued to operate. Crew ejected 3 min after hit due to fire.

(14) Direct hit by SAM under starboard wing. Wing blown off.

(15) Crew felt thump underneath cockpit, followed by immediate utility hydraulic failure, followed by sloppy controls and throttles stuck at full military power. Egressed target area using rudders. Aircraft on fire. Weapons officer ejected; pilot could not due to loss of canopy emergency jettison air bottle.

(16) Aircraft on strike mission. AAA hit in nose and starboard engine area, followed by fire warning in starboard engine and smoke in cockpit. Starboard engine secured. Ordnance could not be jettisoned, and aircraft could not maintain flight on port engine. Crew ejected.

(17) Aircraft was in hover. Pilot felt loss of power. Aircraft settled into the trees, rolled left, inverted, and caught fire and burned.

(18) Aircraft hit above landing zone. Parts of rotor blades were seen to leave the aircraft. Aircraft nosed up, inverted, crashed, and burned.

(19) Aircraft hit in cockpit by small-caliber bullet. Pilot suffered wound in shoulder and began to lose consciousness. Crew ejected.

4.4   IDENTIFICATION OF CRITICAL COMPONENTS AND SYSTEMS

Loss-Cause Relationships

Determining the critical components or systems on an aircraft is one of the most important aspects of combat data analysis. Consequently, the

Aircraft Type:
Squadron:
Call Name:
Carrier:

DATE:

PILOT/STATUS:

MOST DETAILED SOURCE OF DATA:

SUMMARY OF EVENTS:
   Aircraft was alpha strike lead. Multiple SAM firing, medium 85-mm AAA barrage
fire. While in process of evading SAMs, pilot observed one go overhead and one
underneath followed immediately by explosion under tail of aircraft from either
SAM or AAA. Master caution light. PC-1 failure almost immediately. Pilot egressed
to feet wet. PC-2 surge followed by failure. PC-3 fluctuation with "mushy"
controls. Successful ejection and pickup by destroyer.

CONFLICTING DATA, IF ANY, AND SOURCE:
   None.

RECONSTRUCTION:
   SAM or AAA hit close to tail. Loss of PC-1 system probably due to holes in lines
or pump damage. No fire. PC-2 system surge followed by failure. Subsequent loss
of control as third PC system failed.

EVALUATION OF PRIMARY AND CONTRIBUTORY CAUSES OF LOSS:
   Multiple PC failure followed by loss of control. Apparently failure of PC system
was caused by holes in all system lines and/or pump damage.

OTHER COMMENTS/UNCERTAINTIES:
   None.

Fig. 4.6   CNA loss-cause evaluation form.

Center for Naval Analysis (CNA) has established several reasons-for-crash
or loss-cause categories to assist in this determination. These are: (1) fire
intensity; (2) pilot incapacitation; (3) pilot error; (4) explosion; (5) loss of
control; (6) engine failure or loss of thrust; (7) loss of stable flight (structural); and (8) unknown. Many of the Navy aircraft losses in the recent
Vietnam conflict have been studied and the ultimate cause for loss attributed to one of these reasons. An example of one form of examination for
the ultimate loss-cause is the CNA loss-cause evaluation form shown in Fig.
4.6

   A detailed study of the chain of events that led to each loss can often help
in the identification of the critical components of the aircraft. Consequently,
loss-cause failure sequences have been prepared by CNA from loss review
panel evaluations for several carrier tactical aircraft operating in Southeast
Asia from 1965 through January 1973. Examination of the failure sequences

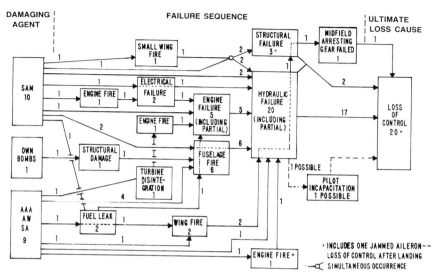

Fig. 4.7   Loss-of-control losses (gross).

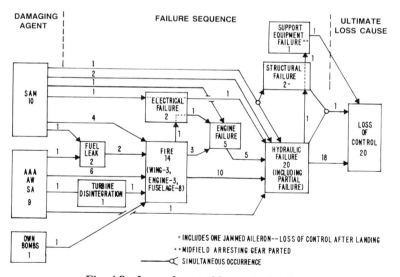

Fig. 4.8   Loss-of-control losses (refined).

shows that each loss can be thought of as a chain of events connecting an initial damage with an ultimate loss-cause.

The chain of events for all incidents for each ultimate loss-cause has been combined into networks of failure paths leading to that particular ultimate loss-cause. These networks are called loss-cause networks. Figures 4.7 and 4.8 show the loss-cause networks for 20 aircraft of one type whose loss was ultimately attributed to loss of control. Figure 4.7 contains the gross network, showing essentially all failures listed in the loss-cause failure sequence. Eliminating from Fig. 4.7 the component or system failures that did not contribute directly to the loss and combining similar specific failures into common broad failure types give the refined network shown in Fig. 4.8. Each node in both the gross network and the refined network represents a component or system failure. The paths between nodes depict the progression of failures to the ultimate loss-cause. The number of occurrences of each node is presented within the node, and the number of times a path was encountered is indicated along that path.

Conclusions on aircraft vulnerability drawn from the attributed ultimate cause-of-loss must always be seasoned with intuition. For example, an examination of the loss-cause networks for the 20 aircraft shown in Figs. 4.7 and 4.8 reveals that all 20 aircraft suffered hydraulic failure just prior to the loss. Consequently, one might conclude that failure of the hydraulic subsystem was the primary cause of the 20 losses. On the other hand, further examination of these two figures reveals that 14 of the 20 aircraft were on fire. Had they not been on fire, the hydraulic subsystem might not have failed; or perhaps many of the 20 aircraft would have eventually been lost due to fire intensity, even if the hydraulic subsystem had not failed. Thus, perhaps fire was the real primary reason for the loss of 14 out of these 20 aircraft, not the loss of hydraulic power.

Combat Results

Examination of the combat data for World War II has revealed that damage to the engines, the cooling and lubrication subsystems, the fuel system, and the flight control system would most likely lead to an aircraft loss (in that order) and that the majority of aircraft lost were on fire.

With the change over to gas turbine engines after World War II, the aicraft in Korea and Southeast Asia were lost mainly due to hits on the fuel system, which now occupies a much larger volume within the aircraft, on the engine, on the flight controls and hydraulics, and on the crew. Again, fire played a major role.

A study of the Southeast Asia combat data for the most frequent causes of helicopter adverse reactions concluded that helicopter crashes were due mainly to hits on the engine, the flight controls, the crew, and the fuel system. Forced landings were caused most often by hits on the fuel system, the lubrication subsystem, the engine, the flight controls, and the main rotor. Mission aborts occurred due to hits on the crew, the fuel system, the main rotor, and the hydraulic subsystem.

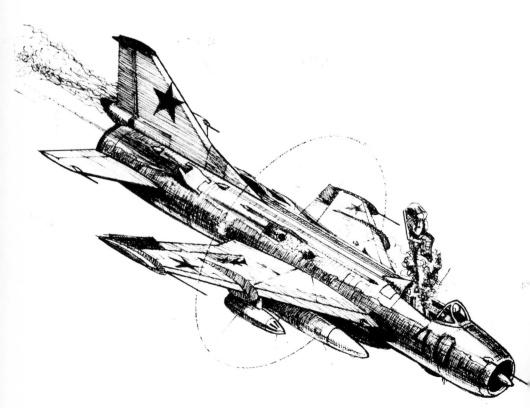

5. VULNERABILITY

5.1 WHAT IS VULNERABILITY?

Aircraft vulnerability refers to the inability of the aircraft to withstand one or more hits by the damage mechanisms, to its vincibility, to its liability to serious damage or destruction when hit by enemy fire. Aircraft that are more vulnerable are softer, whereas those that are less vulnerable are harder or tougher. The more vulnerable an aircraft is, the more likely it will be killed when hit.

Each of the individual components in the aircraft has a level, or degree, or amount of vulnerability; and each component's vulnerability contributes in some measure to the overall vulnerability of the aircraft. Some components contribute more than others. The critical components on an aircraft are those components which, if either damaged or destroyed, would lead to an aircraft kill. The systematic description, delineation, and quantification of the vulnerability of the individual components and of the total aircraft vulnerability is known as a vulnerability assessment. A vulnerability assessment is a required survivability program task and should be conducted early in the life of any aircraft development.

Once the vulnerability of each of the components, subsystems, and systems has been determined, steps should be taken to reduce the vulnerability of the aircraft to its lowest possible value within the design constraints of cost, performance, weight, maintainability, and the other important aspects of aircraft effectiveness. This process is known as vulnerability reduction. In essence, vulnerability reduction consists of reducing the likelihood that one or more of the critical components will be killed if the aircraft is hit.

5.2 IDENTIFICATION OF THE CRITICAL COMPONENTS AND THEIR DAMAGE-CAUSED FAILURE MODES

The first step in either a vulnerability assessment or a vulnerability reduction study is the identification of those components whose damage or loss could lead to an aircraft kill. The components so identified are referred to as the critical components, and the identification process is called the critical component analysis. A component may be a critical component because it provides an essential function, such as thrust (engine), or lift (rotor blade), or control (stabilator); or it may be a critical component because its mode of failure leads to the failure of a critical component that does provide an essential function. For example, a fuel tank in a wing can

135

be perforated by a fragment, causing a slow fuel leak and eventual fuel depletion from that tank, with no substantial effect on the continued operation of the aircraft. In this situation, the wing fuel tank is not a critical component. On the other hand, the fragment impact and penetration of the tank could cause ignition of the fuel vapor in the ullage, with a subsequent fire or explosion and loss of first the wing and then the aircraft. In this event, the wing tank is definitely a critical component.

A general procedure has been developed for determining the critical components, their possible damage or failure modes, and the effects of the component damage or failure upon the continued operation of the aircraft. This procedure consists of (1) a selection of the aircraft kill levels or categories to be considered, (2) an assembly of the technical and functional description of the aircraft, and (3) the determination of the critical components of the aircraft and their damage-caused failure modes for the selected kill levels.

Aircraft Kill Levels

The vulnerability discussed above refers to a generic aircraft kill. However, there are several categories of aircraft kill that measure the degree to which the aircraft suffers performance degradation. The categories normally used in vulnerability assessments are the attrition kill, the mission abort kill, and the forced landing kill. There are other categories that are used in special circumstances.

Attrition kill.   Attrition kill is a measure of the degree of aircraft damage that renders it incapable of being repaired, or not economical to repair, so that it is lost from the inventory. Because the elapsed time between the onset of damage and the eventual loss of the aircraft is an important parameter of vulnerability (the longer the damaged aircraft can continue to fly, the better the chance of recovering the crew), four different attrition kill levels have been defined:

(1) KK kill: Damage that will cause an aircraft to disintegrate immediately upon being hit. This is sometimes referred to as a catastrophic kill.

(2) K kill: Damage that causes an aircraft to fall out of manned control within 30 s after being hit.

(3) A kill: Damage that causes an aircraft to fall out of manned control within 5 min after being hit.

(4) B kill: Damage that causes an aircraft to fall out of manned control within 30 min after being hit.

Mission abort kill.   A mission abort kill is the measure of the degree of aircraft damage that prevents the aircraft from completing its designated mission, but is not sufficient to cause a loss of the aircraft to the inventory.

Forced landing kill.   A forced landing kill is a helicopter kill category in which damage to the helicopter causes the pilot to land (powered or unpowered) because he/she receives some indication of damage such as a red light, low fuel level warning, difficulty in operating controls, or loss of power. The extent of damage may be such that very little repair is required to fly the helicopter back to base; however, if the pilot were to continue to fly, the aircraft would be destroyed. The forced landing kill category includes a forced landing at any time after damage occurs, but before the expenditure of the aircraft fuel load.

Aircraft Description

At the beginning of any vulnerability study, as much of the aircraft's technical and functional description as possible must be gathered on each of the major systems of the aircraft. The technical description of each system should include information on the location, size, material, construction, and operation of all subsystems and components. The functional description should define the functions provided by each component, including re-dundancies. Perspective drawings, schematics, scaled three-view drawings, detailed inboard profiles, and numerous cross-section drawings are required for a thorough assessment. For existing aircraft, the manufacturer and the operator and maintenance manuals are sources of some of this information. They usually provide complete descriptions of the components and systems of the aircraft, how they function, and how they relate to the overall operation of the aircraft. For aircraft in development, it is very important to obtain and use as much of the preliminary design information as possible. The importance of reliable vulnerability studies in all stages of aircraft development cannot be overemphasized.

Critical Component Analysis

A critical component is any component which, if either damaged or destroyed, would yield a defined or definable aircraft kill level. For example, the engine in a single engine aircraft would be a critical component for an A kill if its loss when hit would lead to an aircraft loss within 5 min after the hit, whereas the horizontal stabilator would be a critical component for a K kill if the aircraft becomes uncontrollable within 30 s of the hit without the use of the stabilator. Note that all critical components for a KK kill and a K kill are also critical components for an A kill.

When two or more of the aircraft components are redundant, such as two engines, the loss of any one of the redundant components, such as the left engine, will not result in the total loss of an essential function, such as thrust; hence that component, the left engine, is not a critical component according to the definition of a critical component given above.* However,

---

*This statement assumes that the damage process and loss of one redundant component will not cascade into a loss of any of the other redundant components. For example, if one engine starts to burn, the assumption is made that the fire will not spread to the other engine and destroy it. If, in fact, that were to happen, there is no actual redundancy, and both engines are nonredundant critical components.

since more than one hit can be expected in a typical threat encounter, all redundant components could eventually be killed, leading to an aircraft kill. Thus, the fact that a component is redundant does not eliminate it as a critical component. It just means that a distinction between the two kinds of critical components, nonredundant and redundant, needs to be made. Nonredundant and redundant critical components have been referred to in the past as singly vulnerable components and multiply vulnerable components, respectively. This terminology is somewhat confusing and will not be used here. Because the critical components are dependent upon the assumed kill level, components can be nonredundant for one kill level or category and redundant for another level or category. For example, in a twin-engined helicopter, if the loss of either engine causes a mission abort, the engines are said to be nonredundant for the mission abort category. On the other hand, if the loss of both engines is required to cause a crash or forced landing, the engines are said to be redundant for these two kill categories.

The first step in a critical component analysis is to identify the flight and mission essential functions that the aircraft must perform in order to continue to fly and to accomplish its mission. The second step is the identification of the major systems and subsystems that perform these essential functions. The third step is to conduct a failure mode and effects analysis (FMEA) to identify the relationship between each possible type of individual component or subsystem failure mode and the performance of the essential functions. The fourth step consists of relating component or subsystem failure modes to combat-caused damage. This is known as the damage mode and effects analysis (DMEA). (The combination of the third and fourth steps is referred to as the failure mode, effects, and criticality analysis, or FMECA.) The fault tree analysis (FTA) is sometimes used to provide additional insight in the identification of the critical components. Finally, a visual presentation of the list of critical components, known as the kill tree, and/or a logical expression, known as the kill expression, are developed. The kill tree and the kill expression identify the redundant and nonredundant critical components for the selected kill level.

Flight and mission essential functions.   Flight essential functions are those system and subsystem functions required to enable an aircraft to sustain controlled flight. Mission essential functions are those system and subsystem functions required to enable an aircraft to perform its designated mission. The analysis for the essential (or critical) functions should consider each phase of the mission. For example, a typical mission for an attack aircraft would include such phases as takeoff, climb, cruise out, descend, locate the target, deliver the ordnance, exit the target area, climb, cruise back, descend, and land. During each of these phases, the flight and mission essential functions should be identified and the priority for possible protection established. For example, the operation of the electronic weapons computer during takeoff is not a flight essential function, but it is a mission essential function during ordnance delivery. Furthermore, the flight essential functions, such as lift, thrust, and control, should be qualified by requiring a

ITEM	ESSENTIAL FUNCTIONS	MISSION PHASES							
		ALERT	TAKEOFF	CRUISE TO LAAGER AREA	CRUISE TO HOLDING POSITION	CRUISE TO ASSAULT POSITION	ENGAGE TARGETS	RETURN CRUISE	LAND
	FLIGHT:								
1	Provide lift and thrust								
2	Provide controlled flight								
	MISSION:								
3	Communications • secured voice • unsecured voice • ICS								
4	Start systems								
5	Monitor systems								
6	Provide air data intelligence								
7	Maintain terrain clearance								
8	Employ IFF/ECM								
9	Navigate								
10	Locate/identify targets								
11	Employ weapons								

Fig. 5.1   Some essential functions and mission phases for an attack helicopter.

particular level of operation. For example, loss of one engine on a two-engined helicopter may not cause a total loss of lift and thrust, but will lead to a partial reduction of performance capabilities. However, this partial loss of performance may not be tolerable under certain flight conditions or in a particularly hostile environment when the helicopter would become an easy target. Thus, the continued operation of both engines may be required to prevent an attrition kill. Special functions, such as those required for vertical flight of a vertical takeoff and landing aircraft or for arrested landing aboard an aircraft carrier, must also be identified. A chart identifying some of the mission phases and some of the flight and mission essential functions is given in Fig. 5.1 for an attack helicopter. (The laager area is like a staging or bivouac area that is located between the logistics support center and the FEBA.)

System essential functions relationships.   The ability of the aircraft to fly and to conduct its mission depends upon the continued operation of those systems and subsystems that perform the essential functions. If the aircraft is damaged in combat, the operation of certain subsystem compo-

ITEM	ESSENTIAL FUNCTIONS	RELATED SYSTEMS									
		ELECTRICAL POWER	HYDRAULIC POWER	FLIGHT CONTROL SYSTEM	PROPULSION SYSTEM	CREW SYSTEM	FUEL SYSTEM	POWER TRAIN/ROTOR BLADE SYSTEM	AVIONICS	ARMAMENT	STRUCTURE
	FLIGHT:										
1	Provide lift and thrust										
11	Employ weapons										

Fig. 5.2   Essential system-function relationships; systems compared with the same functions as shown in Fig. 5.1.

nents may be impaired or stopped, and some essential functions may be lost. The severity and rapidity of the loss of the essential functions are directly related to the kill levels.

A general examination of each system and subsystem on the aircraft must be conducted to determine its specific contribution to the essential functions identified in the previous step. Figure 5.2 presents a sample tabulation of those systems and subsystems that contribute to the essential functions shown in Fig. 5.1; and Fig. 5.3 illustrates a more detailed tabulation of the relationship between the functions performed by one specific subsystem and the essential functions.

Failure mode and effects analysis (FMEA).   The failure mode and effects analysis is a procedure that: (1) identifies and documents all possible failure modes of a component or subsystem and (2) determines the effects of each failure mode upon the capability of the system or subsystem to perform its essential functions. The FMEA process and requirements are defined in MIL-STD-785 and MIL-STD-1629A; and the FMEA is usually conducted by personnel in the reliability, maintainability, or safety disciplines.

The types of component failure modes generally considered in the FMEA include premature operation, failure to operate, failure to cease operation, failure during operation, and degraded or out-of-tolerance operation. Other unique failure modes for specific components are also considered. An example of a summary format for the FMEA is given in Fig. 5.4 for two flight control rod failure modes. Note in Fig. 5.4 that the rod is a critical component for an attrition kill when it jams, but not when it is severed.

The FMEA is applicable to both single component failures and the failures of multiple components. The consideration of multiple component

Subsystem function ID letter	SUBSYSTEMS FUNCTIONS	ESSENTIAL FUNCTIONS										
		Provide lift and thrust	Provide controlled flight	Communications	Start systems	Monitor systems	Provide air data intelligence	Maintain terrain clearance	Employ IFF/ECM	Navigate	Locate/identify targets	Employ weapons
a	Generate electrical power											
b	Provide automatic control and protection of power generation											
c	Distribute electrical power											
d	Provide automatic protection of power distribution											
e	Provide power conversion (dc and low-voltage ac)											
f	Provide battery power											
g	Control subsystem loads											
h	Process and transmit subsystem data and power control signals											
i	Provide automatic electrical load management											
j	Provide controls and displays											
k	Provide illumination											

Fig. 5.3   Subsystem functions-essential functions relationships.

failures is extremely important when the failure is due to combat damage because of the likelihood that more than one component is damaged when the aircraft is hit.

The examination of the effects of a component failure should also include the consideration of any transients that might occur when the failure occurs. For example, consider a single engine, fly-by-wire, statically unstable aircraft, with no mechanical flight controls backup. Suppose the engine-driven generator that supplies the electrical power to the flight control computer was to immediately cease operation. Suppose further that the computer relies on an emergency ram-air turbine (RAT) for backup electrical power. The RAT is designed to be deployed into the airstream when the electrical power failure is sensed. However, this takes time. While the RAT is being deployed, the computer could be without sufficient power. This might cause problems with the fly-by-wire control system, such as the loss of the SAS or the issuance of hard-over commands to the control surfaces, that could cause the aircraft to become uncontrollable, leading to an aircraft loss. Thus, the assumption of redundancy in the electrical power system is, in fact, erroneous.

SUBSYSTEM		FAILURE MODE	EFFECT ON SUBSYSTEM	EFFECT OF DEGRADED SUBSYSTEM ON AIRCRAFT	AIRCRAFT KILL CATEGORY
COMPONENT	LOCATION				
ROD 3127	LEFT WING	SEVER	AILERON GOES TO HARDOVER (UP) POSITION	HARDOVER EFFECT CAN BE BALANCED WITH OTHER CONTROL SURFACES	AIRCRAFT CAN FLY AND LAND USING OTHER CONTROL SURFACES
		JAM	PILOT'S CONTROL STICK IS LOCKED	NO CONTROL OF FLIGHT	ATTRITION

Fig. 5.4   Example of FMEA summary format.

Damage mode and effects analysis (DMEA).   In the FMEA, the cause of the component failure is not stipulated; the failure may or may not be related to combat damage. When specific component failures due to combat damage, such as mechanical damage to components caused by projectile or fragment penetration or damage caused by a fire or explosion, are identified and examined, the analysis is referred to as a damage mode and effects analysis. In the DMEA, the potential component or subsystem failures identified in the FMEA, as well as other possible damage-caused failures, are associated with the damage mechanisms and the damage processes and are evaluated to determine their relationship to the selected kill level. The quantification of the component kill criteria is also part of the DMEA, but this procedure is described in the vulnerability assessment presentation. The possibility of any secondary hazard that may be caused by the primary damage processes is also identified in the DMEA. Examples of secondary hazards are ingestion of fuel by an engine and the seepage of toxic fumes from a fire into the cockpit. The DMEA is referred to as the criticality analysis of the FMECA.

The output of the DMEA can take many forms. The DMEA matrix is a form similar to the FMEA summary format shown in Fig. 5.4, in which the components and their damage-caused failure modes are related to the kill level or category. Component redundancy relationships and the appropriate component kill criteria should be indicated in the matrix. An example of a DMEA matrix is given in Fig. 5.5. A disablement diagram can add to the understanding of the DMEA output by graphically showing the locations of the components and stating the effects of component kills. A sample disablement diagram is presented in Fig. 5.6.

There are many different kinds of damage-caused failure (or kill) modes that can occur within each of the systems of an aircraft. Some of the most

AIRCRAFT_____
SYSTEM FLIGHT CONTROLS (MECHANICAL)
FMEA REF_____

COMPONENT NAME	COMPONENT NUMBER	DISABLE-MENT DIAG. NO.	DAMAGE MODE	"KILL" CATEGORY NON REDUNDANT			REDUNDANT			REMARKS	$P_{k/h}$ FUNC. NO.
				ATTRITION	MISSION ABORT	VERTICAL	ATTRITION	MISSION ABORT	VERTICAL		
STICK			BREAK OR DISABLE								
ASSEMBLY										DEGRADED	
(GRIP)	3001				X					FLIGHT CONTROL	32
		1									
			LOSS OF ELECTRICAL							LOSS OF CAS PITCH AND	
CAS SENSOR	3002		CONNECTIONS		X		X			ROLL CONTROL	32
		2	(LOSS OF CAS)							CONTROL THROUGH DEL.	
			LOSS OF ELECTRICAL							REVERSION TO MECH. (IF DEL	
			AND MECHANICAL	X	X					IS LOST). (DEL = DIRECT	
			LINKAGES							ELECTRICAL LINK)	
RUDDER PEDALS	3006		BREAK OR DISABLE								
ARMS	3007		ONE ARM								32
SUPPORT	3008	3									32
FEEL SPRING SUPPORT	3301		BREAK OR DISABLE								32
SPRING	3302		SUPPORT, FEEL							NO ELECTRICAL	32
TRANSDUCER	3303		SPRING ASSY, OR	X	X					INPUTS TO	24
			TRANSDUCER							RUDDERS	

Fig. 5.5   DMEA matrix.

important ones are listed in Table 5.1 and are briefly described below. The order of the systems is indicative of their relative contribution to the total aircraft vulnerability.

(1)   Fuel system kill modes.   The following is a listing and brief description of the potential damage-caused fuel system failure modes.

(a)   Fuel supply depletion: This kill mode is caused either by damage to fuel storage components that results in excessive leakage leading to a significant reduction in the amount of fuel available for aircraft operation, or by damage to fuel pumping and transfer systems that prevents fuel from reaching the engine(s).

(b)   In-tank fire and explosion: This can be caused by the ignition of the fuel-air mixture in the ullage by incendiary particles or by a hot tank wall. The in-tank fire or explosion can cause substantial damage to the tankage and adjacent structure and components, and the fire may quickly spread to other parts of the aircraft.

(c)   Void space fire and explosion: This can be caused by fuel leakage into void spaces or dry bays (adjacent to punctured fuel tanks and lines) that is subsequently ignited by incendiary particles, by hot metal surfaces, or by the hot gases from punctured bleed air lines or engine cases. Fire or explosion in the enclosed spaces can eventually cause significant damage to

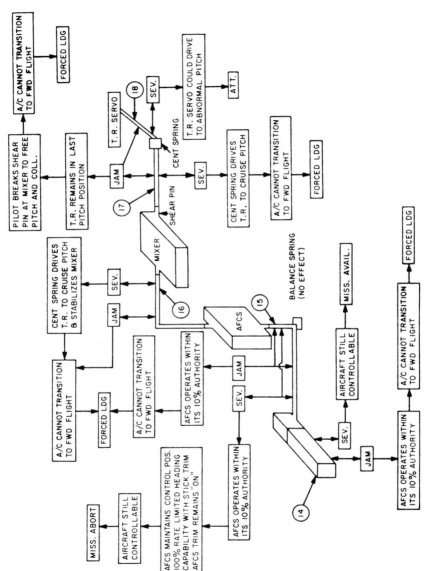

Fig. 5.6 Sample disablement diagram.

Table 5.1 A List of System Damage-Caused Failure (Kill) Modes

Fuel	Propulsion	Flight Control
Fuel supply depletion	Fuel ingestion	Disruption of control signal path
In-tank fire/explosion	Foreign object ingestion	Loss of control power
Void space fire/explosion	Inlet flow distortion	Loss of aircraft motion data
Sustained exterior fire	Lubrication starvation	Damage to control surfaces and hinges
Hydraulic ram	Compressor case perforation or distortion	Hydraulic fluid fire
	Combustor case perforation	
Power Train and Rotor Blade/Propellor	Turbine section failure	**Structural**
Loss of lubrication	Exhaust duct failure	Structure removal
Mechanical/structural damage	Engine control and accessories failure	Pressure overload
		Thermal weakening
Electrical Power	**Crew**	Penetration
Severing or grounding	Injury, incapacitation, or death	
Mechanical failure		**Avionics**
Overheating	**Armament**	Penetrator/fragment damage
	Fire/explosion	Fire/explosion/overheat
		Radiation damage

nearby subsystem components and structure that would result in their failure. The generation of smoke and toxic fumes may also occur and migrate to crew stations, causing a possible mission abort, forced landing, or aircraft abandonment.

(d) Sustained exterior fuel fire: This kill mode is caused by damage to fuel tank walls that results in fuel spillage outside of the aircraft, which is subsequently ignited, producing a sustained fire. Sometimes the exterior fire is snuffed out by the airflow over the surface; however, the condition of the damaged surface, the altitude, and the flight speed may prevent this from occurring.

(e) Hydraulic ram: Damage to container walls or components within the container caused by the intense pressure waves generated in the contained liquid by penetrators or fragments passing through the liquid is referred to as hydraulic ram damage. The fluid pressure can cause large cracks and gaping holes in the container walls, leading to excessive leakage either externally or internally into dry bays, engine inlets, etc.

(2) Propulsion system kill modes. The following kill modes of the propulsion system have been observed.

(a) Fuel ingestion: Fuel ingestion is caused by fuel entering the engine air inlet following rupture of walls that are common to both a fuel tank and the inlet. Fuel ingestion effects normally include compressor surge, severe stall, unstable burning in the inlet and the tail pipe, and/or engine flameout.

(b) Foreign object ingestion: Foreign objects consist of projectiles, fragments, and pieces of damaged aircraft components that enter the engine inlet and subsequently damage the fan and compressor blades. This could cause an engine failure or the throwing of blades through the engine case, leading to additional component damage.

(c) Inlet flow distortion: Distortion of airflow to the engine can be so severe as a result of combat damage to the inlet that uncontrollable engine surging or engine failure occurs.

(d) Lubrication starvation: Penetrator, fragment, or fire damage to the lubrication circulation and cooling subsystem can result in loss of lubrication and subsequent deterioration of bearing surfaces, followed by engine inoperability. Loss of lubrication failure is most often related to the bearings, where loss of heat removal eventually results in bearing seizure.

(e) Compressor case perforation or distortion: This kill mode is caused by penetrator or fragment penetration through the case, by distortion of the case, or by damaged compressor blades exiting through the case.

(f) Combustor case perforation: Penetrator or fragment penetration and holing of the combustor case, with subsequent hot gas emission or torching through the hole, can cause secondary damage effects, such as severe heating of adjacent fuel tanks or control rods, and can also cause a combustion pressure drop that may result in a significant loss of engine power.

(g) Turbine section failure: Turbine failure can be caused by penetrator or fragment damage to the turbine wheels, blades, and case. This results in a loss of engine power or secondary perforation and possible fire damage.

(h) Exhaust duct failure: Penetration by penetrators and fragments into the exhaust duct may result in damage to nozzle control lines and actuator mechanisms and possible fuel spillage and secondary fire if an augmentor is operating at the time of hit.

(i) Engine controls and accessories failure: A kill of the controls and accessories can be caused by penetrator, fragment, or fire damage. The result can be loss of control of the engine or loss of one of the important accessories.

(3) Flight control system kill modes. Some possible flight control kill modes are given below.

(a) Disruption of control signal path: Severance or jamming of the mechanical or electrical path that transmits the control signals from the pilot to the control surfaces or the actuators can partially or totally incapacitate the control system.

(b) Loss of control power: Control power can be lost as a result of damage to hydraulic power components that causes a loss of hydraulic pressure. Types of power system damage are thermal degradation due to fire, perforation of hydraulic reservoirs, cylinders, or lines, leading to a loss of hydraulic fluid, and deformation of hydraulic components, actuators, or lines that cause a hydraulic lock or jammed condition.

(c) Loss of aircraft motion data: Damage to the aircraft motion sensors or to the sensor data signal paths to the flight control computer can prevent the autopilot and the stability augmentation system from properly controlling the motion of the aircraft. The result can vary from a partial loss of control, leading to a mission abort, to the loss of an out-of-control aircraft. These components are relatively soft and are easily damaged or severed by penetrators, fragments, and fire.

(d) Damage to control surfaces and hinges: Penetrators, fragments, blast, and fire damage can result in the physical removal of a portion or all of a flight control surface or in the jamming of the hinges, rods, and other linkages between the servoactuators and the control surfaces.

(e) Hydraulic fluid fires: Fires can result from the ignition of pressurized or gravity-leaked hydraulic fluid; and smoke or toxic fumes from the fire can affect the aircrew.

(4) Power train and rotor blade / propeller system kill modes. Some of the possible damage-caused failures within the power train and rotor blade system of helicopters and propeller-driven fixed-wing aircraft are described below.

(a) Loss of lubrication: This kill mode can occur due to projectile or fragment perforation of oil- or grease-containing components, with subsequent loss of lubrication oil or grease. Lubrication starvation is especially critical in oil-cooled helicopter transmissions, where the oil systems are not self-contained and usually consist of externally mounted components, such as sumps, filters, coolers, and interconnecting lines and hoses. Loss of lubrication prevents the removal of heat and lubrication of rubbing surfaces, which eventually results in component seizure. In helicopter transmissions and gearboxes, failures are often catastrophic, causing case rupture and fire after input pinion failures and rotor blade seizure after planetary assembly failures.

(b)   Mechanical/structural damage: Mechanical or structural failure of power train components can be caused by fragment and penetrator impact or penetration, or by fire. Bearings, gears, and shafts are prone to damage and failure when hit, shafts can be severed, and bearings and gears can jam. Chips and debris from damaged components or structures can jam the oil pump, causing loss of lubrication. Rotor blades and propellers when hit can result in rotor unbalance, blade instability, blade out-of-track, and loss of lift. Rotor unbalance is perhaps the most critical consequence of ballistic damage and occurs when a portion of the blade is removed. This loss of mass in one blade can cause large, alternating hub forces and intense cockpit and control vibrations, leading to structural failure or loss of control. Blade instability is caused by a reduction of blade stiffness due to damage and can result in severe flutter or divergent pitch oscillation that can be catastrophic. Blade out-of-track is usually a less severe result of the reduction of blade stiffness, but it could result in blade contact with the fuselage. Although some loss of lift normally accompanies any ballistic damage, the consequences are usually not as catastrophic as those associated with the other types of blade reactions.

(5)   Crew system kill modes.   The inability of the pilot and his or her replacement to operate the aircraft because of injury, incapacitation, or death will usually lead to an aircraft kill in a very short period of time.

(6)   Structural system kill modes.   The structural system is usually the toughest system on the aircraft. However, structural damage can be sufficient to cause an aircraft kill.

(a)   Structure removal: Physical severance or complete loss of large portions of the load-carrying aircraft structure caused by multiple penetrators and fragments, blast, fire, or radiation effects can result in either an immediate or a delayed aircraft loss.

(b)   Pressure overload: Immediate failure or subsequent failure under maneuver loads can be caused by external blast effects that result in overstressing the load-carrying structure.

(c)   Thermal weakening: Structural failure can occur to portions of the load-carrying structure as a result of internal void space fires, externally sustained fires, or radiation over a portion of the aircraft surface.

(d)   Penetration: A single penetration of one load-carrying member will usually not cause structural failure; several members must be penetrated or cut before failure can occur. Since the likelihood of structural failure from penetration by a few fragments or armor-piercing projectiles is extremely small, this type of failure would most likely result from continuous rod warhead effects.

(7)   Electrical power system kill modes.   The failure of electrical system components is due to the severing or grounding of electrical circuits, the destruction or unbalancing of rotating components, such as generators and alternators, and the penetration or overheating of batteries.

(8)   Armament system kill modes.   Two major reactions can occur when gun ammunition, bombs, rockets, and missiles are hit by a damage mechanism. One is a sustained fire in the magazine that could cause cook-off or detonation of the stored ammunition, and the other is a severe explosion of either the armament warhead or the propellant.

(9)   Avionics system kill modes.   Avionics components are usually very soft and are easily damaged by penetrators and fragments, blast, radiation, and thermal hazards, such as fire or hot gas torching. Their failure mode is usually failure to operate, although a degraded operation can occur.

Fault tree analysis (FTA).   The FMEA is a bottom-up approach for determining the critical components; the failure of a component is assumed and the consequences identified. Another procedure for identifying the critical components is the fault tree analysis. This is a top-down approach that starts with an undesired event (a fault) and then determines what event or combination of events can cause the undesired event. It is one of the principal methods of system safety analysis, and can include both hardware failures and human effects. The FTA and its logic symbology are illustrated by the generic fault tree diagram shown in Fig. 5.7. The undesired event U can only occur when both event A and event B occur. (This is the logical AND gate.) Event A can occur when either event C occurs or D occurs or both occur. (This is the inclusive OR gate.) Event B can occur when event E occurs or when event F occurs, but not when both occur. (This is the exclusive OR gate.)

Figures 5.8a–c illustrate a portion of the fault tree diagram for a twin-engined aircraft with a single source of fuel supply to both engines. The undesirable event shown in Fig. 5.8a is an aircraft attrition kill. An attrition kill occurs if the aircraft can neither fly nor land. The aircraft cannot fly if it loses lift, or thrust, or control. (The notation on the bottom

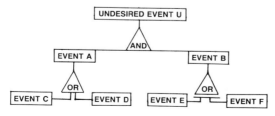

Fig. 5.7   Generic fault tree diagram.

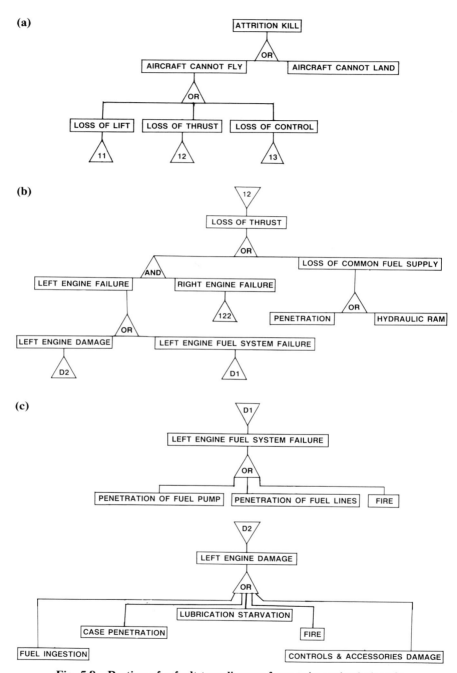

Fig. 5.8   Portion of a fault tree diagram for a twin-engined aircraft.

of the figure refers to other locations on the fault tree diagram.) Examining the continuation of the diagram in Fig. 5.8b for the loss of thrust event reveals that total thrust is lost when both engines fail or when the common fuel supply to both engines fails. The feed tank that supplies fuel to both engines can fail due to leakage from damage caused by penetration and hydraulic ram. The left engine can fail due to loss of the left engine fuel supply or to engine damage.

Continuing the diagram in Fig. 5.8c, the left engine fuel supply system can fail due to penetration of many of the fuel transfer components from the feed tank to the engine combustor; or these components can fail due to fire caused by leaking fuel, leaking hydraulic fluid, or a holed combustor. The left engine can fail due to damage caused by fuel ingestion; penetration of the engine compressor, combustor, or turbine; loss of lubrication; fire caused by leaking fuel; or damage to the engine controls or accessories. An examination of the components, their functions, and the damage processes that are involved in each of these damage-caused failures will reveal which of the components are critical and any redundancy that is available. For example, if the left engine accessory gearbox is cracked or holed due to ballistic impact or penetration, the gearbox could lose the lubrication oil. Eventually, it may self-destruct, leading to a loss of power to several essential engine functions, which in turn will cause a loss of the thrust from the left engine. Thus, the gearbox is a nonredundant critical component for the left engine.

Critical components, kill trees, and kill expressions. Examination of the assembled material and results of the steps described above leads to the identification of the set of critical components in a particular aircraft design, for a specific operational mode and selected kill level. In general, each critical component either makes a singular contribution to an essential function or each component is one of two or more redundant components, each of which can make the necessary contribution. However, critical components that are members of sets of redundant components may appear as nonredundant components if one of their kill modes causes the loss of an essential function. This feature has particular application to the fuel system components that may be redundant for fuel storage and transfer, but because of the possibility of fire or explosion they are treated as nonredundant critical components. The distinction between the nonredundant critical components and the redundant critical components is extremely important.

(1) Typical critical components. For a two-engined helicopter with a single pilot, the following nonredundant components are potential critical components for an attrition kill:

(a) Flight control system components (rods, rod ends, bellcranks, pitch links, swashplate, hydraulic actuators, collective lever, and control pedals).

(b)   Rotor blade and power train components (blades, drive shafts, rotor heads, main transmission, and gearboxes).

(c)   Fuel system components (fuel cells, the sump, lines, and valves).

(d)   Pilot.

(e)   Tail boom.

The potential redundant critical components for an attrition kill can include:

(a)   Propulsion system components (engines and engine mounts).

(b)   Hydraulic subsystem components.

(c)   Structural elements.

Some potential redundant and nonredundant critical components for an A level attrition kill of a single engine, single pilot, fixed-wing aircraft are:

(a)   Pilot.

(b)   Flight controls in the cockpit and the pitch axis flight control components.

(c)   Hydraulic reservoirs, lines, components, and actuators.

(d)   All fuel tanks, components, lines, and shut-off valves.

(e)   Engine fan, compressor, turbine, and combustor sections, drive shaft and bearings, engine mounts, the engine accessory drive, and the lubrication and fuel supply components.

(f)   Major structure, such as the wing box spars, the fuselage longerons, and the horizontal and vertical stabilizer spars and attachments.

(g)   External ordnance and the ammunition storage drum.

(h)   Liquid oxygen (LOX) bottle and components.

(i)   Liquid-cooled avionics with a flammable coolant.

(2) The kill tree.   A visual illustration of the critical components and component redundancy is provided by the kill tree, such as the one shown in Fig. 5.9 for a two engine, two pilot helicopter. A complete cut through the tree trunk is required to kill the aircraft. For example, according to Fig. 5.9, a loss of the pilot and either the copilot or the copilot's controls will kill the aircraft, as will a loss of the drive train.

Note that the left and right fuel tanks appear twice in the kill tree. This is because of the possibility of both an aircraft kill due to fuel supply depletion and a kill due to a fire or explosion. The two tanks provide a redundancy for the fuel depletion kill mode because either tank can provide fuel to both engines through the common (nonredundant) fuel feed subsystem. However, the fuel tanks are nonredundant critical components when the fire/explosion kill mode is considered because of the possibility that a fire or explosion in either tank will lead to the loss of the aircraft.

(3) The kill expression.   The relationship between component loss and aircraft kill can also be expressed using the logical AND and OR statements. For example, the kill tree given in Fig. 5.9 can be expressed in the logical form: [(PILOT .OR. PILOT CONTROLS) .AND. (COPILOT .OR.

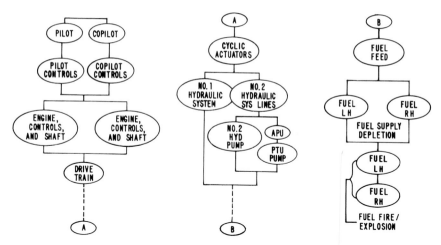

Fig. 5.9   Example kill tree for a two-engine, two-pilot helicopter.

COPILOT CONTROLS)] .OR. (ENGINE 1 .AND. ENGINE 2) .OR. (DRIVE TRAIN) .OR., etc. This logical statement is called the kill expression.

5.3   VULNERABILITY ASSESSMENT

What Is a Vulnerability Assessment?

A vulnerability assessment is the process of determining numerical values for the measures of vulnerability. This is accomplished using vulnerability assessment techniques. The assessment may be carried out entirely "by hand," or one or more computer programs may be used. Assessments are usually conducted to help the designer evaluate the vulnerability of his/her design, or to help the military in evaluating competing designs, or to help the field commander make operational decisions regarding the use of his/her aircraft.

The assessment is carried out at one of three general levels of detail. These levels consist of estimates, evaluations, and analyses. Estimates typically use simple equations for the aircraft vulnerability measures that are functions of a few major parameters of the aircraft, the damage mechanisms, and the terminal effects parameters. When these equations are fitted to historical data on several aircraft or to the results from several engineering studies, they are referred to as regression equations. Evaluations are more detailed assessments that may include such items as the individual component locations, sizes, and vulnerability measures. (For convenience, the use of the word "component" hereafter will imply a critical component.)

Analyses are very detailed studies that use specific technical and functional information about the components and their vulnerability. Analyses are usually conducted on a digital computer using complex geometric models.

The computational methodology used in the assessment should have the capability to account for the six vulnerability reduction concepts presented in Chap. 1 in order to properly reflect the payoffs associated with the application of vulnerability reduction techniques. These six concepts are component redundancy, component location, passive damage suppression, active damage suppression, component shielding, and component elimination. (These six concepts will be examined in detail in the vulnerability reduction presentation given in Sec. 5.4 of this chapter.) The degree to which these concepts are accounted for in the computation of the vulnerability measures will depend to some extent upon the level of the assessment.

Vulnerability Measures

Because of the diverse nature of the hostile environment in which aircraft operate, the measures of the vulnerability of an aircraft vary with the type of threat encountered. For example, if a hit on the aircraft must occur in order for a threat to be effective, such as a small arms projectile and a contact-fuzed HE warhead, one measure of vulnerability is the conditional probability that the aircraft is killed given a random hit on the aircraft $P_{K/H}$. Another measure of vulnerability to impacting damage mechanisms is the aircraft's vulnerable area A_V. This is a theoretical, nonunique area presented to the threat that, if hit by a damage mechanism, would result in an aircraft kill. On the other hand, when damage is caused by the effects of a nearby HE warhead detonation, the vulnerability may be expressed in the form of a probability of kill given a detonation ($P_{K/D}$) envelope. This envelope represents a kill probability contour about the aircraft on which a specified detonation will result in a certain probability of aircraft kill. If only the blast from the exploding warhead is considered, the envelope represents the aircraft's vulnerability to external blast. A measure that is becoming more important relates to aircraft vulnerability to a laser threat. Laser vulnerability can be measured by the probability of kill, given a specific power laser lock-on for a specified period of time $P_{L/O}$.

General Requirements

Certain required elements of a vulnerability assessment are common to all studies, regardless of the type of threat considered. The elements are: (1) a selection of the aircraft kill levels or categories to be assessed, (2) an assembly of the technical and functional descriptions of the aircraft, (3) a determination of the critical components of the aircraft, (4) a selection of the specific threats the system will encounter, (5) an analysis to identify the type and amount of damage required to kill each critical component, and

(6) the computation of the appropriate vulnerability measures for the components and the aircraft based upon the threat selected. The first three steps of the assessment have been described in the preceding section. A presentation of the last three steps is given below.

Threat selection.   Because of the many and diverse terminal effects of the various damage mechanisms, each vulnerability assessment is usually made considering either a specific threat or a specific damage mechanism. The threats and damage mechanisms that are typically considered are: (1) a nonexplosive penetrating projectile or fragment, (2) the fragments and blast from internally detonating warheads, (3) external blast, (4) the fragments, penetrators, and missile debris from externally detonating warheads, and (5) the laser. Vulnerability to lasers is a relatively recent addition.

Critical component kill criteria.   Once the set of critical components for a given aircraft has been identified, the damage or kill criteria for each of the failure modes of these components must be determined for the selected threats. A kill criterion is the specific descriptive characteristic or quantification of a component failure. Very few kill criteria are precisely known, nor can they easily be determined. Battle damage reports are an important source of component damage effects information. The results of tests conducted on all types of aircraft components and subsystems provide another increasingly important and expanding source of data.

The major result of this task is the specification of numerical values for the kill criteria for each failure mode for each critical component for each threat to be considered. Three specific kill criteria are currently in use for the impacting damage mechanisms. They are the probability of component kill given a hit (the $P_{k/h}$ function), the area removal criterion, and the energy density criterion. A fourth criterion applies to the blast damage mechanism.

(1)   The $P_{k/h}$ function.   The $P_{k/h}$ function defines the probability of a component kill when impacted by a fragment or penetrator. This criterion can be presented graphically as a function of the mass and velocity of the damage mechanism, or it can be expressed in an analytical form. Figure 5.10a is a sample of $P_{k/h}$ data for a flight control rod. The $P_{k/h}$ criterion is normally used for components that can be killed by a single hit, such as servoactuators, crew members, control rods, and electronic equipment. These components are sometimes referred to as single fragment vulnerable components. It can also be used for some of the larger components, such as engines and fuel tanks. In this instance, the volume of the large component is usually divided into several smaller volumes, and a different numerical value of $P_{k/h}$ is assigned to each volume. For example, a fuel tank could be

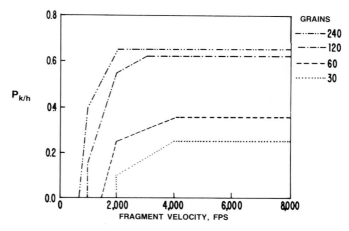

Fig. 5.10a   Typical $P_{k/h}$ data for a flight control rod.

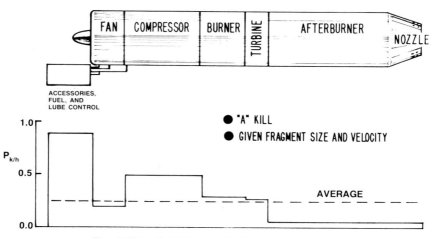

Fig. 5.10b   Subdivision of a large component.

divided into the ullage, fuel, and external void spaces, and a turbojet engine could be subdivided into the major sections illustrated in Fig. 5.10b.

The determination of the $P_{k/h}$ for each component or part of a component is a very difficult undertaking. It requires a combination of critical component analysis data and sound engineering judgment. Although limited gunfire testing provides some insight into the effects of projectile and fragment damage potential, there is no universal methodology for arriving at a numerical value for $P_{k/h}$. Each critical component must be examined carefully to assess the effects on the component of the striking velocity, the striking obliquity, and the mass and shape of the penetrator or fragment. The presence of incendiary particles or flashes must also be accounted for. The larger components, such as the fuel tanks and engines, are especially difficult to evaluate due to the multitude of local environments, the constantly changing operating conditions, and the many different kill modes. Numbers for $P_{k/h}$ are eventually assigned based upon a combination of empirical information, engineering judgment, and experience.

The location of the component inside the aircraft will have an influence on its ultimate numerical value for the probability of kill given a hit, but not on its $P_{k/h}$ function. Components located behind thick structure or dense equipment will receive a level of protection due to the slowdown of the damage mechanism as it attempts to penetrate the shielding components. The numerical value of the $P_{k/h}$ for the lowered velocity of impact will generally be less than the $P_{k/h}$ value for the impact of a penetrator or fragment that was not slowed down. For example, a 30-grain fragment that impacts the control rod of Fig. 5.10a at 5000 ft/s will have a probability of killing the rod of 0.25, but the $P_{k/h}$ will drop to 0.2 if the fragment is slowed down to 3000 ft/s by intervening components. Other considerations, such as spall and fragment breakup caused by the intervening components, also may become important.

(2) Area removal. The area removal criterion defines a specific amount of area that must be removed from a component in order to kill that component. This criterion is applicable to large penetrators, such as rods, and to the closely spaced hits from many fragments. The total component damage from a collection of closely spaced hits can be greater than the sum of the individual damages from the same number of widely spaced hits. There often is a synergism of damage due to the cracking and petaling between the individual holes, and large areas of component structure can be removed or destroyed. This criterion is used mainly for structural components.

(3) Energy density. In this criterion, a component kill is expressed in terms of a required minimum component surface area that must be exposed to a threshold level of the kinetic energy density of the impacting damage mechanisms. This criterion is applicable to multiple, closely spaced fragment hits and is used for the structural components, as well as for other large components, such as the fuel tanks and engines. For some compo-

nents, there may be a minimum mass of the damage mechanism below which the criterion is not applied.

(4) Blast. The damage criterion for blast is generally the critical values of pressure and impulse on an aircraft surface necessary to cause the specific component damage level associated with the assumed kill level. For example, a dynamic overpressure of 2 lb/in.^{2} over the upper surface of a horizontal tail for 1 ms may be sufficient to cause crushing of the skin, leading to a loss of stiffness and an inability to support the flight loads. Although this criterion is usually applied to the structural components and control surfaces, the effects of the blast can extend into the interior of the aircraft and can damage electrical wiring, hydraulic lines, fuel tank walls, and other internal components located close to the aircraft skin.

Computation of the vulnerability measures.   The procedures used to compute the vulnerability of an aircraft and its components to nonexplosive penetrators or fragments, to an internally detonating HE warhead, and to an externally detonating HE warhead are described below.

Vulnerability to Nonexplosive Penetrators or Fragments

The vulnerability of an aircraft to a single impacting penetrator or fragment is usually expressed as a total vulnerable area A_V, or as a probability of aircraft kill given a random hit on the aircraft $P_{K/H}$. The vulnerable area concept is applicable to both the aircraft and to its critical components. The vulnerable area of the typical ith component is denoted by A_{v_i}; and the component kill criterion used is the probability of kill given a hit P_{k/h_i}. (To assist the reader in keeping track of the notation used in this presentation, the variable and subscript definitions are summarized in Table 5.2. Note that a distinction is made between component and aircraft designated variables by using lower and upper case subscripts, respectively. The upper case subscript version of the variables will also be used to refer to the generic term.)

Table 5.2   Vulnerability Assessment Variable Definitions

	ith Component	Aircraft
Probability of killing the ____ given a hit on the ____	P_{k/h_i}	$P_{K/H}$
Probability of killing the ith component given a hit on the aircraft	P_{k/H_i}	
Probability of survival of the _____ given a hit on the aircraft	P_{s/H_i}	$P_{S/H}$
Vulnerable area of the _____	A_{v_i}	A_V
Presented area of the _____	A_{p_i}	A_P

The vulnerable area of the ith component is defined as the product of the presented area of the component in the plane normal to the approach direction of the damage mechanism (the shotline) A_{p_i} and the probability of kill of the component given a hit on the component P_{k/h_i}. Thus,

$$A_{v_i} = A_{p_i} P_{k/h_i} \qquad (5.1)$$

Since both A_{p_i} and P_{k/h_i} are generally functions of the threat direction or aspect, the vulnerable area will also vary with aspect. In the discussion that follows, it is important to recall that the probability of killing an aircraft or a component P_K, plus the probability of survival of that aircraft or component P_S, is unity. Hence, given a hit on the aircraft

$$P_{S/H} = 1 - P_{K/H} \qquad (5.2)$$

where $P_{S/H}$ is the probability the aircraft or component survives the hit.

The kill probability of the ith component given a random hit on the aircraft P_{k/H_i} is the product of the probability the component is hit (given the hit on the aircraft) P_{h/H_i} and the probability the component is killed given a hit on the component P_{k/h_i}. Thus,

$$P_{k/H_i} = P_{h/H_i} P_{k/h_i} \qquad (5.3a)$$

and

$$P_{s/H_i} = 1 - P_{k/H_i} \qquad (5.3b)$$

Solving for P_{k/h_i} in Eq. (5.1) gives

$$P_{k/h_i} = A_{v_i}/A_{p_i} \qquad (5.4)$$

When the hit on the aircraft is randomly located, P_{h/H_i} is given by

$$P_{h/H_i} = A_{p_i}/A_P \qquad (5.5)$$

where A_P is the presented area of the total aircraft in the plane normal to the threat approach direction. Thus, for any random hit on the aircraft, the probability the ith component is killed is given by

$$P_{k/H_i} = A_{v_i}/A_P \qquad (5.6)$$

according to Eqs. (5.3a), (5.4), and (5.5).

The numerical value for P_{k/H_i} depends upon the presented area of the critical component A_{p_i} and of the aircraft A_P, and upon the component kill criterion P_{k/h_i}. The presented area of the critical components and of the aircraft can be obtained from the available technical description of the aircraft. The procedure for determining the numerical value for P_{k/h_i} is described in the presentation on the critical component kill criteria given above.

Note that in this assessment a component is assumed to be either operating and performing all of its functions or killed. No degradation of component capabilities is considered due to an aircraft hit, and no compounding of component damage is recognized. Although these assumptions are usually made in a vulnerability assessment, they are not necessary. Furthermore, theoretically, only the component hit can be killed. Although the kill of adjacent components, perhaps by fire, is not directly considered here, a procedure for indirectly accounting for kills of adjacent components will be described later.

Now that the concepts of vulnerable area and probability of kill given a hit have been explained, the scenario must be considered. In any given combat engagement, the aircraft will either not be hit, or will be hit only once, or will be hit more than once. The no hit situation is, of course, not of interest here. The location on the presented area of the aircraft of the single hit and of the multiple hits is assumed in the vulnerability assessment to be a random distribution, with each damage mechanism having the same approach or attack direction. In other words, the assumptions are usually made that there is no capability by the enemy to direct hits to any one particular component, subsystem, or part of the aircraft, and that the damage mechanisms travel along parallel shotlines. The single hit case lays the ground work for the multiple hit case. In both cases, the influence of nonredundancy and redundancy of components on the vulnerable area must be examined. Overlap of components is an important consideration as well.

Single hit vulnerability.   The aircraft models developed in this section are assumed to receive only one hit, and both a nonredundant aircraft model and a redundant aircraft model are considered. The nonredundant aircraft model is composed of only one of each of the critical components. Thus, the loss of any one critical component will cause the loss of the aircraft. In the redundant aircraft model, some of the critical component functions are duplicated by the same or different components. The effects of the overlapping of both nonredundant and redundant critical components are also examined.

(1)   An aircraft composed of nonredundant components with no overlap. This aircraft consists of N critical components whose functions are not duplicated by any other component. The components are arranged in such a manner that no one component overlaps any other component when viewed from a given aspect. Any hit on the aircraft takes place along a shotline that passes completely through the aircraft. Thus, no more than one component can be hit on any one shotline. As an example of such a model, consider the aircraft shown in Fig. 5.11. This aircraft consists of three critical components, a pilot, one fuel tank, and one engine, and none of the critical components overlap from this aspect.

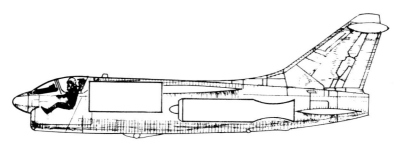

Fig. 5.11   Nonredundant aircraft model with no component overlap.

The probability of killing this aircraft, given a random hit on the presented area shown in Fig. 5.11, can be derived using the kill expression and Eqs. (5.1) and (5.6). Recall from the kill expression presentation above that the logical AND and OR statements are used to define an aircraft kill in terms of component kills. For an aircraft composed of N nonredundant critical components, the kill expression uses only the logical OR statement and is given in the form

$$\text{Kill} = (\text{Nrc1}) \,.\text{OR}.\, (\text{Nrc2}) \,.\text{OR}.\, \dots \,.\text{OR}.\, (\text{Nrc}N) \qquad (5.7)$$

where Nrc1 refers to a kill of nonredundant component 1. In other words, the aircraft kill is defined by the kill of nonredundant component 1, or nonredundant component 2, or..., or nonredundant component N. Because a kill of any one of the critical components causes an aircraft kill, the aircraft will survive only when all of the nonredundant critical components survive. Thus, according to Eq. (1.3),

$$P_{S/H} = P_{s/H_1} P_{s/H_2} \cdots P_{s/H_N} = \prod_{i=1}^{N} P_{s/H_i} \qquad (5.8)$$

where $\prod$ denotes the product of the P_{s/H_i}. Applying Eq. (5.3b), $P_{S/H}$ becomes

$$P_{S/H} = \left(1 - P_{k/H_1}\right)\left(1 - P_{k/H_2}\right) \cdots \left(1 - P_{k/H_N}\right) = \prod_{i=1}^{N} \left(1 - P_{k/H_i}\right) \quad (5.9)$$

For example, if $N = 3$, Eq. (5.9) becomes

$$P_{S/H} = 1 - \left(P_{k/H_1} + P_{k/H_2} + P_{k/H_3}\right) + P_{k/H_1}P_{k/H_2} + P_{k/H_1}P_{k/H_3}$$

$$+ P_{k/H_2}P_{k/H_3} - P_{k/H_1}P_{k/H_2}P_{k/H_3} \qquad (5.10)$$

Because of the assumptions that only the component hit can be killed and because none of the components overlap in this model, the kills of the components are said to be mutually exclusive; that is, only one component can be killed by the one hit. Hence, the products of the $P_{k/H}$ given in Eq. (5.10) are not applicable. Therefore, Eq. (5.9) simplifies to

$$P_{S/H} = 1 - \left(P_{k/H_1} + P_{k/H_2} + \cdots + P_{k/H_N} \right) \qquad (5.11)$$

and thus the probability of killing the aircraft given a hit on the aircraft is just the sum of the individual probabilities of killing each of the critical components given a random hit on the aircraft. Thus, for an aircraft kill given a hit,

$$P_{K/H} = P_{k/H_1} + P_{k/H_2} + \cdots + P_{k/H_N} = \sum_{i=1}^{N} P_{k/H_i} \qquad (5.12)$$

Substituting Eq. (5.6) for P_{k/H_i} into Eq. (5.12) gives

$$P_{K/H} = \sum_{i=1}^{N} \frac{A_{v_i}}{A_P} = \frac{1}{A_P} \sum_{i=1}^{N} A_{v_i} \qquad (5.13)$$

Applying the vulnerable area concept for $P_{k/h}$ expressed by Eq. (5.4) to Eq. (5.13) for $P_{K/H}$ leads to

$$P_{K/H} = A_V / A_P \qquad (5.14)$$

where the aircraft vulnerable area A_V is given by

$$A_V = \sum_{i=1}^{N} A_{v_i} \qquad (5.15)$$

For the example aircraft, the kill expression is (PILOT) .OR. (FUEL TANK) .OR. (ENGINE). Thus, according to Eqs. (5.12) and (5.15),

$$P_{K/H} = P_{k/H_p} + P_{k/H_f} + P_{k/H_e} \qquad (5.16)$$

and

$$A_V = A_{v_p} + A_{v_f} + A_{v_e} \qquad (5.17)$$

where the subscripts p, f, and e denote the pilot, the fuel tank, and the engine, respectively. The individual component vulnerable areas are given by

$$A_{v_p} = A_{p_p} P_{k/h_p}, \quad A_{v_f} = A_{p_f} P_{k/h_f}, \quad A_{v_e} = A_{p_e} P_{k/h_e} \qquad (5.18)$$

according to Eq. (5.1).

Table 5.3 Assumed Values for a Nonredundant Aircraft Model

Critical Component	A_{p_i}, ft^2	× P_{k/h_i}	= A_{v_i}, ft^2	P_{k/H_i}
Pilot	4	1.0	4	0.0133
Fuel	60	0.3	18	0.0600
Engine	50	0.6	30	0.1000
	$A_P = 300$ ft^2		$A_V = 52$ ft^2	$P_{K/H} = 0.1733$

As a numerical illustration, consider the assumed values for the component and aircraft presented areas and the component kill criteria given in Table 5.3. The computed values for A_{v_i} and P_{k/H_i}, A_V, and $P_{K/H}$ are indicated in the table.

The kill of one critical component due to damage caused by a hit on another critical component and the consideration of multiple kill modes of one critical component can be indirectly accounted for in this model by increasing the numerical value of the kill criterion for the component hit. For example, suppose the probability that the fuel tank of an aircraft is destroyed by a fire when the fuel tank is hit, leading to a loss of the aircraft, is taken as 0.3. Suppose further that the probability that the fuel tank is penetrated and that hydraulic ram damage causes fuel to be dumped into the air inlet and ingested by the engine, also leading to a loss of the aircraft, is taken as 0.1. (Note that the two failure modes are not mutually exclusive, that is, both can occur when the fuel tank is hit.) The aircraft will survive a hit in the fuel tank only if there is neither a fire nor any fuel ingestion. The probability that neither of these failure modes will occur when the fuel tank hit is given by the product of the probability that there is no fire, $(1 - 0.3)$, and the probability that there is no fuel ingestion kill of the engine, $(1 - 0.1)$, or 0.63. Therefore, the probability that there will be a fire kill and/or a fuel ingestion kill, given a hit on the fuel tank, is given by $(1 - 0.63)$, or 0.37. (Note that the modified P_{k/h_i} is not the sum of the two individual kill probabilities because there can be both a fire kill and a fuel ingestion kill on the one hit.) Thus, accounting for the additional failure mode of fuel, ingestion by the engine increases the fuel tank $P_{k/h}$ from 0.3 to 0.37. This same procedure can be used to compute the P_{k/h_i} due to multiple failure modes of one critical component.

(2) Nonredundant components with overlap. The model will now be extended by allowing two or more critical components to overlap in an arbitrary manner. Figure 5.12 illustrates an overlap for the example aircraft. The dimension of the overlap area or region is determined by the overlap geometry. There can be any number of critical components along a shotline within the overlap region. For the aircraft to survive a hit along a shotline within a region of C overlapping nonredundant critical components, each critical component along the shotline must survive. Therefore, the probability the aircraft survives a hit on the overlap region P_{s/h_0} is given by an

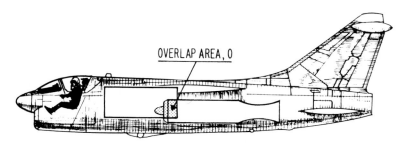

OVERLAP AREA, O

Fig. 5.12   Component overlap.

equation of the same form as Eq. (5.8) or (5.9),

$$P_{s/h_0} = P_{s/h_1} P_{s/h_2} P_{s/h_3} \cdots P_{s/h_C} = \prod_{i=1}^{C} \left(1 - P_{k/h_i} \right) \qquad (5.19)$$

Because two or more of the critical components in the overlap region can be killed by the one hit, the kills of more than one component are not mutually exclusive, and Eq. (5.11) is not valid in the overlap region; Eq. (5.19) must be used for hits in the overlap region.

If the overlap area A_{p_0} is now considered as a separate component, the probability of kill of the component given a hit on the component can be defined as

$$P_{k/h_0} = 1 - P_{s/h_0} \qquad (5.20)$$

where P_{s/h_0} is the probability of survival calculated in Eq. (5.19). Hence, the vulnerable area of the overlapping area A_{v_0} is given by

$$A_{v_0} = A_{p_0} P_{k/h_0} \qquad (5.21)$$

As an example of the computation of the vulnerable area in the overlap region, assume that the overlap area in Fig. 5.12 is 10 ft^2, the fuel tank $P_{k/h}$ is taken as 0.3, as before, and the $P_{k/h}$ for the overlapped engine is conservatively taken as 0.6; the fuel is assumed to slow the damage mechanism down, but not enough to change the engine $P_{k/h}$. Because the $P_{k/h}$ values are the same as in the nonoverlapping example, any reduction in the vulnerable area of the aircraft is due only to the component overlap. Thus, in the overlap region

$$P_{k/h_0} = 1 - P_{s/h_0} = 1 - (1 - 0.3)(1 - 0.6) = 0.72$$

and

$$A_{v_0} = A_{p_0} P_{k/h_0} = 10 \times 0.72 = 7.2 \text{ ft}^2$$

according to Eqs. (5.19–5.21).

Table 5.4   Vulnerable Area with Overlap

Critical Component	A_{p_i}, ft^2	$\times$	P_{k/h_i}	=	A_{v_i}, ft^2
Pilot	4		1.0		4.0
Fuel	60 − 10		0.3		15.0
Engine	50 − 10		0.6		24.0
Overlap area	10		0.72		7.2
	$A_P = 300$ ft^2				$A_V = 50.2$ ft^2

The vulnerable area of the overlap area contributes to the aircraft vulnerable area in the same manner as the vulnerable areas computed in the nonredundant, no overlap case. However, overlapping also requires that the overlap area be subtracted from the total presented area of each overlapping component contributing to the overlap. The component area outside of the overlap is treated in the usual way. Table 5.4 lists the parameters for computing the vulnerable area of the example aircraft with overlapping components. Note that locating two of the critical components such that one overlaps the other reduces the aircraft vulnerable area from 52 ft^2 to 50.2 ft^2. Thus, this is one example of how location of the critical components can reduce the aircraft vulnerable area.

The net effect of component overlap can be a desirable reduction in aircraft vulnerable area (as demonstrated above), provided the damage inflicted by the hit in the overlap area does not cause other problems. For example, consider the shotline through the fuel tank that overlaps the engine, as shown in Fig. 5.12. Fuel could leak from the punctured tank onto hot engine parts, causing a fire. Thus, the probability the engine is killed by the hit could be higher than 0.6 because of the overlapping fuel tank. An example of the computation of the vulnerable area for the aircraft shown in Fig. 5.12, with the possibility of an engine fire, is given in Table 5.5. The overlapping area is assumed to be 10 ft^2; the fuel tank $P_{k/h}$ is taken as 0.3, as before; and the $P_{k/h}$ for the overlapped engine area is taken as 0.9, because an engine fire is assumed to nearly always occur due to a hit on the overlapping fuel tank. Thus,

$$P_{k/h_0} = 1 - (1 - 0.3)(1 - 0.9) = 0.93$$

and the aircraft vulnerability increases to 52.3 ft^2.

Comparing the aircraft's vulnerable area given in Tables 5.3, 5.4, and 5.5 reveals that overlapping the engine with the fuel tank reduces the vulnerable area from 52 ft^2 to 50.2 ft^2, provided no fire can occur. However, if a fire is likely to occur, the vulnerable area is increased to 52.3 ft^2. Thus, overlapping nonredundant critical components can reduce vulnerability provided that no undesirable secondary kill modes occur.

Another facet of the overlap situation is the change in the vulnerable area of the overlap area that occurs when one of the components along a shotline

Table 5.5   Vulnerable Area with Overlap and an Engine Fire

Critical Component	A_{p_i}, ft^2	×	P_{k/h_i}	=	A_{v_i}, ft^2
Pilot	4		1.0		4.0
Fuel	60 − 10		0.3		15.0
Engine	50 − 10		0.6		24.0
Overlap area	10		0.93		9.3
	$A_P = 300$ ft^2				$A_V = 52.3$ ft^2

has its vulnerability reduced by one of the many techniques presented in Sec. 5.4 of this chapter. For example, suppose the overlapping fuel tank has its $P_{k/h}$ reduced from 0.3 to 0.0. The vulnerable area of the overlap area without a fire will be reduced from 7.2 ft^2 to 6.0 ft^2 as a result of this change. This amount of reduction appears to conflict with the fact that 10 ft^2 of fuel tank with a $P_{k/h}$ of 0.3, and hence a vulnerable area of 3 ft^2, has been made invulnerable. The actual reduction in vulnerable area of the overlap area is 1.2 ft^2, not 3 ft^2, as might be expected. The reason for this apparent contradiction is, of course, the fact that the fuel tank is only one of two overlapping components.

In general, when the vulnerability of one component is reduced, the vulnerability of another component along the shotline will become more important. In order to distinguish between the 3 ft^2 of vulnerability reduction of the fuel tank and the net reduction of 1.2 ft^2 in the vulnerable area of the overlap region, the vulnerable area of each component along the shotline is referred to as the true vulnerable area, and the component's contribution to the overlap vulnerable area is referred to as the incremental vulnerable area. Both the true and the incremental vulnerable areas are computed considering the velocity decay and mass degradation due to successive component penetrations. Thus, using the data given in Table 5.4, the true vulnerable areas are 3 ft^2 and 6 ft^2 for the overlapping fuel tank and engine areas, whereas the incremental vulnerable areas of these two overlapping components are 1.2 ft^2 and 4.2 ft^2, respectively.

(3)   An aircraft composed of some redundant components with no overlap. The nonredundant aircraft model described above will now be expanded by adding a second, separated engine, as shown in Fig. 5.13. The second engine is assumed to have the same presented area as the first engine, 50 ft^2, but its $P_{k/h}$ is taken as 0.7 because of the presence of an additional accessory drive. (The larger vulnerable area of the second engine will help to distinguish it from engine 1 in the following presentation.) The presented area of the aircraft is assumed to remain at 300 ft^2 for the purpose of comparison. Table 5.6 presents the values for the vulnerability parameters for this example aircraft. The kill expression for the redundant aircraft model becomes (PILOT) .OR. (FUEL TANK) .OR. [(ENGINE 1) .AND. (ENGINE 2)].

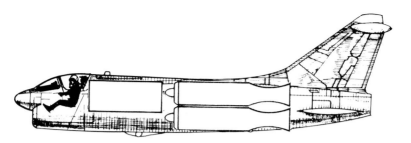

Fig. 5.13   Redundant aircraft model with no overlap.

Table 5.6   Example of a Redundant Aircraft Model

Critical Component	A_{p_i}, ft^2	×	P_{k/h_i}	=	A_{v_i}, ft^2	P_{k/H_i}
Pilot	4		1.0		4	0.0133
Fuel	60		0.3		18	0.0600
Engine 1	50		0.6		30	0.1000
Engine 2	50		0.7		35	0.1167
	$A_P = 300$ ft^2				$A_V = 22$ ft^2	$P_{K/H} = 0.0733$

The corresponding equation for the probability of aircraft survival given a random hit on the aircraft is

$$P_{S/H} = P_{s/H_p} P_{s/H_f} \left(1 - P_{k/H_{e1}} P_{k/H_{e2}} \right) \qquad (5.22a)$$

which can also be given in the form

$$P_{S/H} = \left(1 - P_{k/H_p} \right)\left(1 - P_{k/H_f} \right)\left(1 - P_{k/H_{e1}} P_{k/H_{e2}} \right) \qquad (5.22b)$$

Equation (5.22b) says that the aircraft is killed ($P_{S/H} = 0$) if the pilot is killed ($P_{k/H_p} = 1$), or the fuel tank is killed ($P_{k/H_f} = 1$), or both engines are killed ($P_{k/H_{e1}} P_{k/H_{e2}} = 1$). Carrying out the multiplications gives

$$P_{S/H} = 1 - \left(P_{k/H_p} + P_{k/H_f} \right) + P_{k/H_p} P_{k/H_f} - P_{k/H_{e1}} P_{k/H_{e2}}$$

$$+ \left(P_{k/H_p} + P_{k/H_f} - P_{k/H_p} P_{k/H_f} \right) P_{k/H_{e1}} P_{k/H_{e2}} \qquad (5.22c)$$

If the assumption is made that the single hit cannot kill both engines (recall the assumption that only the component hit is killed), then all of the component kills are mutually exclusive, and all of the products of the component kill probabilities are zero. Hence, the aircraft is killed only if the pilot or the fuel tank is killed, and $P_{K/H}$ and A_V are given by

$$P_{K/H} = P_{k/H_p} + P_{k/H_f} \quad \text{and} \quad A_V = A_{v_p} + A_{v_f} \qquad (5.22d)$$

In general, only those components whose loss or damage can cause a kill of the aircraft on a single hit will contribute their vulnerable area to the total. If the single hit kills only one of the redundant components, the aircraft is not killed, and, hence, nothing is contributed to the vulnerable area. Thus, the total vulnerable area of an aircraft for this case is just the sum of vulnerable areas for each of the nonredundant critical components. For the aircraft defined in Table 5.6, the single hit vulnerable area reduces from 52 ft² to 22 ft² due to the addition of the second engine. Thus, redundancy can significantly reduce the vulnerable area of the aircraft.

On the other hand, if the damage to the struck redundant component creates secondary damage mechanisms or damage processes that propagate to another redundant component and kill that component, causing a loss of the aircraft, the redundant components will contribute to the aircraft vulnerable area. For example, suppose the probability that a hit on one of the engines will cause that engine to throw blades into, or torch, or burn the other engine is 0.1. Because this can happen regardless of the engine hit, the component presented area becomes 50 + 50, or 100 ft², and the vulnerable area contributed by both engines is 10 ft². Thus, this kill mode increases the aircraft vulnerability to 32 ft².

(4) Redundant components with overlap. If redundant components are now allowed to overlap one another, as shown by the aircraft in Fig. 5.14, the computation of the vulnerable area given by Eq. (5.22d) must be modified because a single hit in the overlap region can kill both engines.

For this case, the cross-hatched area shown in Fig. 5.14 is defined as the overlap area. A single hit penetrating this area will have a probability of killing both redundant components, and hence the aircraft. Thus, it will be necessary to add the vulnerable area of the overlap region to that of the nonredundant critical components. In essence, the overlap region becomes another critical component, as in the nonredundant model with overlap.

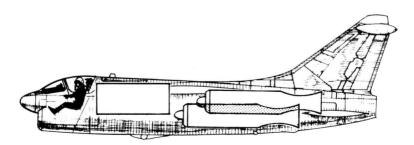

Fig. 5.14   Redundant aircraft model with overlap.

The vulnerable area is computed in the same manner as described previously; however, the details are slightly different. The expression for P_{s/h_0} given by Eq. (5.19) must be modified. According to Eq. (5.19), the probability that the aircraft survives a hit on an overlap area with no redundant components is given by

$$P_{s/h_0} = P_{s_1} P_{s_2} P_{s_3} \cdots P_{s_C} \tag{5.19'}$$

However, if there are two redundant components among the components along the shotline, such as components 2 and 3, the probability that both are killed, which is assumed to cause an aircraft kill, is equal to the product of their individual probabilities of kill, $P_{k/h_2} P_{k/h_3}$. The probability that both components are not killed, which is required for aircraft survival, is the complement of $P_{k/h_2} P_{k/h_3}$, or $(1 - P_{k/h_2} P_{k/h_3})$. Thus, $P_{s_2} P_{s_3}$ in Eq. (5.19') must be replaced with $(1 - P_{k/h_2} P_{k/h_3})$, just as in Eq. (5.22b). This procedure can be extended to the situation where there are three or more redundant overlapping components or multiple sets of overlapping redundant components.

The "elsewhere" or nonoverlapping areas of each of the redundant components are not used in the vulnerable area computations for the same reason as that used in the no overlap case. A single shotline through any one of the redundant components outside of the overlap region causes only a kill of that component, not of the aircraft, and hence no contribution is made to the aircraft vulnerable area.

If the $P_{k/h}$ values for the engines in the overlap region shown in Fig. 5.14 are taken as 0.6 for the first engine hit and 0.2 for the overlapped engine (the overlapping engine slows the damage mechanism down), the probability the aircraft will survive a hit on the overlap region is given by $(1 - 0.6 \times 0.2)$, or 0.88. Thus, the probability of an aircraft kill given a hit in the overlap region is 0.12. If the overlap area is assumed to be 10 ft^2, the vulnerable area increases to 23.2 ft^2 due to the overlapping engines.

Multiple hit vulnerability.   The analysis will now progress to the more reasonable expectation that in any combat engagement, an aircraft, if hit, will receive more than one hit. The distribution of these hits over the aircraft is assumed to be random, and all hits are assumed to travel along parallel shotlines from the same direction. (This latter assumption is not required, but is taken for ease of explanation.)

The probability the ith component still survives after n random hits on the aircraft, denoted by $\overline{P}_{s/H_i}^{(n)}$, is equal to the product of the component survival probabilities for each of the n hits on the aircraft. (The superbar notation on P indicates the joint probability, and the superscript n in parentheses indicates the number of hits.) Thus,

$$\overline{P}_{s/H_i}^{(n)} = P_{s/H_i}^{(1)} P_{s/H_i}^{(2)} \cdots P_{s/H_i}^{(n)} = \prod_{j=1}^{n} P_{s/H_i}^{(j)} \tag{5.23}$$

where $P_{s/H_i}^{(j)}$ is the probability the ith component survives the jth hit on the aircraft. The probability of survival of the ith component due to the jth hit on the aircraft is equal to 1 minus the probability of kill of the ith component due to the jth hit on the aircraft. Thus,

$$P_{S/H_i}^{(j)} = 1 - P_{k/H_i}^{(j)} \qquad (5.24)$$

Recall that P_{k/H_i} is assumed to be a constant value for all j. Thus, Eq. (5.23) can be given in the form

$$\overline{P}_{S/H_i}^{(n)} = \prod_{j=1}^{n} \left(1 - P_{k/H_i}^{(j)}\right) = \left(1 - P_{k/H_i}\right)^{n} \qquad (5.25)$$

The probability of survival of the aircraft after n hits can be derived in a similar manner to give

$$\overline{P}_{S/H}^{(n)} = \prod_{j=1}^{n} \left(1 - P_{K/H}^{(j)}\right) \qquad (5.26a)$$

where $P_{K/H}^{(j)}$ is the probability of kill of the aircraft due to the jth hit on the aircraft. (The $P_{K/H}^{(j)}$ may or may not be a constant for all j.) The probability the aircraft is killed after n hits, $\overline{P}_{K/H}^{(n)}$, is the complement of $\overline{P}_{S/H}^{(n)}$, or

$$\overline{P}_{K/H}^{(n)} = 1 - \overline{P}_{S/H}^{(n)} = 1 - \prod_{j=1}^{n} \left(1 - P_{K/H}^{(j)}\right) \qquad (5.26b)$$

In any multiple hit assessment, it is necessary to keep in mind the distinction between the effect of multiple hits on the vulnerable area of a nonredundant aircraft model as opposed to hits on a redundant aircraft model. Multiple hits on a nonredundant aircraft model do not change the total vulnerable area and the $P_{K/H}$ because of the assumption that components are either fully functional or killed. If a shot hits the aircraft, but not a critical component, the vulnerable area and the $P_{K/H}$ remain the same. Only when a hit actually strikes the vulnerable area of a nonredundant critical component is the aircraft killed.

The redundant aircraft model has to be viewed differently. If the redundant aircraft takes the first hit in the vulnerable area of a redundant component, the aircraft is not killed, but the aircraft vulnerable area and the $P_{K/H}$ will increase for the second hit because one of the redundant components has been killed. For instance, if one of two engines is killed on the first hit, the aircraft vulnerable area is now increased by the vulnerable area of the remaining engine, because a kill of the remaining engine on a subsequent hit causes an aircraft kill.

Three methods are presented below to show the effects of multiple hits: the kill tree diagram, the state transition matrix method, or Markov chain, and a simplified approach. The first method is more of an instructional tool, whereas the transition matrix method can be used in complex problems beyond the practical capability of the kill tree diagram. The simplified approach is the easiest to use.

(1)   The kill tree diagram. The sequence of events explained above regarding the effects of multiple hits can be illustrated diagrammatically using what is known as a kill tree diagram. The probability of kill of each component given a random hit on the aircraft is first computed using Eq. (5.6), then the kill tree diagram is created. To simplify the explanation, consider the nonredundant aircraft model with no overlap illustrated in Fig. 5.11 and defined in Table 5.3.

(a)   The kill tree diagram, nonredundant model: Figure 5.15 presents the kill tree diagram that defines the (mutually exclusive) kill probabilities of each nonredundant critical component (pilot, fuel tank, and engine), and hence the aircraft, and the probability that no critical components are killed after the first hit on the aircraft. In Fig. 5.15, $P = P_{k/H_p}$, $F = P_{k/H_f}$, $E = P_{k/H_e}$; and N represents the probability that no critical components are killed and is given by $N = 1 - (P + F + E)$. Note that $P + F + E + N$ is unity; all possibilities have been accounted for on this first hit. The probability the aircraft is killed on this first hit is given by $P + F + E$.

Figure 5.16 represents the kill tree diagram after the second hit. PP represents the situation where the first hit killed the pilot, and the second hit also killed the pilot. It is important to note, however, that once a probability of kill is defined for each critical component on the first hit, that component is considered killed at that probability value for all subsequent hits. (The pilot cannot be killed twice.) The four branches from that kill probability for the second hit add nothing new (no additional probability of pilot kill) to the sequence. This fact can be verified by examining the sum of the kill

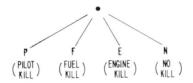

Fig. 5.15   Kill tree diagram: first hit, nonredundant model.

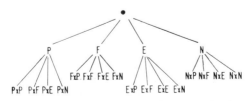

Fig. 5.16   Kill tree diagram: second hit, nonredundant model.

probabilities, $PP + PF + PE + PN$, which is the same as $P(P + F + E + N)$. This is equal to the probability calculated for P on the first hit because $P + F + E + N$ is unity. The only addition to the kill probability of the aircraft due to the second hit comes from critical components not killed on the first hit. Thus, only the N, or no kill, branch is of interest on the second hit.

In order to illustrate the development of a kill tree diagram, assume the numerical values for the component kill probabilities given in Table 5.3. Figure 5.17 illustrates the kill tree for the first hit. The probability the aircraft is killed after the first hit is the sum of the kill probabilities for each of the critical components. Thus,

$$\overline{P}^{(1)}_{K/H} = 0.0133 + 0.0600 + 0.1000 = 0.1733$$

and hence,

$$\overline{P}^{(1)}_{S/H} = 1 - 0.1733 = 0.8267$$

Figure 5.18 extends this example to the second hit. The probability the aircraft is killed after the second hit is the sum of the P_{k/H_i} for all critical components on the first hit plus the sum of the additional kill probabilities for each of the critical components for the second hit. Thus,

$$\overline{P}^{(2)}_{K/H} = \overline{P}^{(1)}_{K/H} + 0.8267 \times (0.0133 + 0.0600 + 0.1000)$$

or

$$\overline{P}^{(2)}_{K/H} = 0.1733 + 0.1433 = 0.3166$$

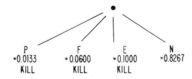

Fig. 5.17   Kill tree diagram: computed values, first hit.

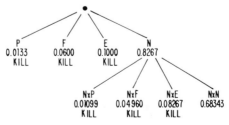

Fig. 5.18   Kill tree diagram: computed values, second hit.

and hence,

$$\overline{P}_{S/H}^{(2)} = 1 - \overline{P}_{K/H}^{(2)} = 1 - 0.3166 = 0.6834$$

The kill tree diagram procedure may be continued indefinitely to determine $P_{S/H}$ for any number of hits. However, the probability the nonredundant aircraft model survives a sequence of hits can also be computed using Eq. (5.26a). For the nonredundant aircraft model, $P_{K/H}$ is constant, as explained above. Thus, the probability the aircraft survives two hits is given by

$$\overline{P}_{S/H}^{(2)} = \left(1 - P_{K/H}^{(1)}\right)\left(1 - P_{K/H}^{(2)}\right) = \left(1 - P_{K/H}\right)^2$$

$$= (1 - 0.1733)^2$$

$$= 0.6834$$

Note that this value is the same as that obtained from the kill tree diagram, as it should be.

Equation (5.26a) can be used for any number of hits and is much easier to use than the kill tree diagram. The essence of this equation is that all of the nonredundant critical components can be combined into one composite critical component whose vulnerable area is 52 ft^2 and $P_{K/H}$ is 0.1733 in the numerical example.

(b) The kill tree diagram, redundant model: Consider now the redundant aircraft model shown in Fig. 5.13 and defined in Table 5.6. An evaluation for $\overline{P}_{K/H}^{(n)}$ and $\overline{P}_{S/H}^{(n)}$ can be performed in a manner similar to the previous discussion. Although the engines are redundant critical components, each must be shown as a separate branch in the kill tree diagram, because a kill of an engine is a possible outcome of an aircraft hit; and any engine kill will have an effect on the aircraft's vulnerability. Figure 5.19 illustrates the kill tree diagram for the first hit. Note that N now represents the probability that no nonredundant or redundant component is killed.

The logical kill expression for this redundant aircraft model is (PILOT) .OR. (FUEL TANK) .OR. [(ENGINE 1) .AND. (ENGINE 2)]. Because the first hit cannot kill both engines, the probability that the aircraft is killed after the first hit is just the sum of the kill probabilities for each of the

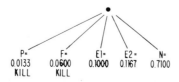

Fig. 5.19   Kill tree diagram: redundant model, first hit.

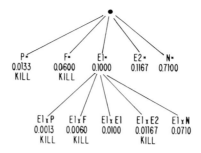

Fig. 5.20   Kill tree diagram: redundant model, second hit, partial.

nonredundant critical components (pilot and fuel). Thus,

$$\overline{P}_{K/H}^{(1)} = 0.0133 + 0.0600 = 0.0733$$

Figure 5.20 illustrates the event probabilities on the second hit after a kill of engine 1 on the first hit. The sequence represented by killing engine 1 on the first hit and then killing the pilot (0.00133), or fuel (0.0060), or engine 2 (0.01167) on the second hit results in additional aircraft kills. Thus, the cumulative probability of an aircraft kill is due to kills of the nonredundant critical components as well as kills defined by component redundancy restrictions. The five branches from a kill of engine 2 and from the N branch will also contribute additional kills. Thus, after two hits,

$$\overline{P}_{K/H}^{(2)} = 0.0733 + 0.1000(0.0133 + 0.0600 + 0.1167)$$

$$+ 0.1167(0.0133 + 0.0600 + 0.1000)$$

$$+ 0.7100(0.0133 + 0.0600) = 0.1646$$

and hence,

$$\overline{P}_{S/H}^{(2)} = 1 - 0.1646 = 0.8354$$

Note the significant increase in survivability (0.8354 vs 0.6834) after the second hit due to the addition of the second engine. This procedure can be continued indefinitely, as in the nonredundant case, but it is obvious that the computations quickly become overwhelming in complexity. The state transition matrix method described below is better suited to handle the problem.

(2)   The state transition matrix method (Markov chain).   Briefly, the state transition matrix method assumes that a sequence of independent events (random hits on the aircraft) can be modeled as a Markov process. In a Markov process, the aircraft is defined to have two or more states or conditions in which it can reside, and the probability of an aircraft kill due

to the $j + 1$ hit is the probability that the $j + 1$ hit on the aircraft will cause the aircraft to transition from a nonkill state, after j hits, to a kill state. The sequential process of evaluating the probability the aircraft exists in each of the several possible states after hits $1, 2, 3 \ldots J$ is based upon the probability the aircraft existed in each of the possible states after hits $0, 1, 2 \ldots J - 1$, respectively, and is referred to as a Markov chain. The results from the process after J events are independent of the order of the events. Rather than dwell on the mathematical theory, however, an example using the previously defined redundant aircraft model will serve much better to illustrate the methodology.

An aircraft consisting of a pilot, a fuel tank, and two engines can exist in five distinct states:

(a)   One or more of the nonredundant critical components (the pilot and the fuel tank) have been killed, resulting in an aircraft kill, denoted by Knrc.

(b)   Only engine 1 has been killed, denoted by krc1.

(c)   Only engine 2 has been killed, denoted by krc2.

(d)   Both engine 1 and engine 2 have been killed, resulting in an aircraft kill, denoted by Krc.

(e)   None of the nonredundant critical components and neither of the engines are killed, denoted by nk.

States Knrc and Krc are called absorbing states because the aircraft cannot transition from these two kill states to any of the other three nonkill states.

A transition matrix of probabilities, $[T]$, can now be constructed to specify how the aircraft will transition from one state to another due to a hit on the aircraft. Table 5.7 illustrates the computation of the $[T]$ matrix for the example redundant aircraft model defined in Table 5.6. Each element of the matrix represents the probability of transitioning from the state defined by the column location to the new state defined by the row location. The matrix is read as follows. The probability of the aircraft transitioning from the knrc state to the Knrc state is unity $(300/300)$ because Knrc is an absorbing state. The probability of transitioning from the krc1 state (kill of engine 1) to the Knrc state (kill of a nonredundant component) is the sum

Table 5.7   Computation of the State Transition Matrix, $[T]$

	Probability of Transitioning from this State[a]					To this State
	Knrc	krc1	krc2	Krc	nk	
$\frac{1}{300}$	300	(4 + 18)	(4 + 18)	0	(4 + 18)	Knrc
	0	(30 + 213)	0	0	30	krc1
	0	0	(35 + 213)	0	35	krc2
	0	35	30	300	0	Krc
	0	0	0	0	213	nk

[a] Note that the sum of each column is unity.

of the conditional probabilities of kill of the two nonredundant components, that is, $P + F$, or $(4 + 18)/300$. The probability of transitioning from krc1 to krc1 (remaining in krc1) is the sum of engine 1's probability of kill given a hit on the aircraft, E1, and that of the remaining "elsewhere" area of the aircraft, or $(30 + 213)/300$. Transitioning from krc1 to krc2 is zero because a kill of the second engine after the first engine is killed defines the state Krc. Thus, the state transitions from krc1 to Krc according to the conditional probability of kill of the second engine, E2, and so on.

Let the probability that the aircraft exists in each of the five possible states after the jth hit be expressed by a vector $\{S\}^{(j)}$, where

$$\{S\}^{(j)} = \begin{Bmatrix} \text{Knrc} \\ \text{krc1} \\ \text{krc2} \\ \text{Krc} \\ \text{nk} \end{Bmatrix}^{(j)} \tag{5.27}$$

Note that the sum of the elements in $\{S\}^{(j)}$ is always unity; the aircraft must exist in one of these five states. The probability the aircraft is in each one of the five states after the $(j + 1)$th hit is given by

$$\{S\}^{(j+1)} = [T]\{S\}^{(j)} \tag{5.28}$$

That is, the aircraft transitions from $\{S\}^{(j)}$ to $\{S\}^{(j+1)}$ according to $[T]$.

An aircraft kill is defined by those states that specify either a kill of any of the nonredundant components or a kill of enough members of the sets of redundant components, such as both engines. In this example, Knrc and Krc specify the kill states. Hence, the probability the aircraft is killed after n hits is given by

$$\overline{P}_{K/H}^{(n)} = \text{Knrc}^{(n)} + \text{Krc}^{(n)} \tag{5.29}$$

where $\text{Knrc}^{(n)}$ and $\text{Krc}^{(n)}$ are the probabilities the aircraft is in those two states after n hits.

Using the numbers generated in the previous numerical example, consider the first hit. Prior to the first hit, the aircraft is entirely in the nk state. Thus, according to Eq. (5.28),

$$\{S\}^{(1)} = [T]\{S\}^{(0)} = [T]\begin{Bmatrix} 0 \\ 0 \\ 0 \\ 0 \\ 1 \end{Bmatrix} \leftarrow \text{nk}$$

Carrying out the matrix multiplication gives

$$\{S\}^{(1)} = \begin{Bmatrix} 0.0733 \\ 0.1000 \\ 0.1167 \\ 0 \\ 0.7100 \end{Bmatrix} \begin{matrix} \leftarrow \text{Knrc} \\ \\ \\ \leftarrow \text{Krc} \\ \end{matrix}$$

Thus,

$$\overline{P}_{K/H}^{(1)} = 0.0733$$

as before. Similarly, for the second hit,

$$\{S\}^{(2)} = [T]\{S\}^{(1)} = [T] \begin{Bmatrix} 0.0733 \\ 0.1000 \\ 0.1167 \\ 0 \\ 0.7100 \end{Bmatrix}$$

Carrying out the matrix multiplication gives

$$\{S\}^{(2)} = \begin{Bmatrix} 0.1413 \\ 0.1520 \\ 0.1793 \\ 0.0233 \\ 0.5041 \end{Bmatrix} \begin{matrix} \leftarrow \text{Knrc} \\ \\ \\ \leftarrow \text{Krc} \\ \end{matrix}$$

Note that the sum of the elements of $\{S\}$ is unity, as it should be. This $\{S\}^{(2)}$ vector results reveal that after the second hit there is a 14.13% probability that either the pilot or the fuel tank or both have been killed, a 15.20% probability that engine 1 has been killed, a 17.93% probability that engine 2 has been killed, a 2.33% probability that both engines have been killed, and a 50.41% probability that none of the critical components have been killed. Thus, after the second hit,

$$\overline{P}_{K/H}^{(2)} = 0.1413 + 0.0233 = 0.1646$$

This value is the same as that obtained from the kill tree diagram after the second hit, as it should be. This process can easily be continued for as many hits as desired. Figure 5.21 shows the $\overline{P}_{K/H}^{(n)}$ as a function of n for both the redundant aircraft model and the nonredundant aircraft model given in Table 5.3. The difference between the two curves is the reduction in vulnerability due to redundancy. Note that as the number of hits becomes large, the effect of the engine redundancy on the aircraft's survivability is

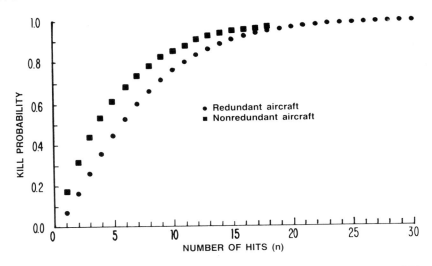

Fig. 5.21   Probability of kill for the redundant aircraft model vs the number of hits.

diminished. This is due to the increased likelihood that the large number of hits has killed both engines.

In the above presentation, the transition matrix was assumed to be the same for all hits. This assumption is not necessary. If multiple damage mechanisms hit the aircraft from several different aspects, a transition matrix can be constructed for each aspect of interest. The computation of the state vector for the $j+1$ hit, given by Eq. (5.28), would use the transition matrix for the approach direction of that particular hit. Another possible modification is the consideration of an increase in P_{k/H_i} due to multiple hits. Again, $[T]$ could be changed from one hit to the next.

(3)   A simplified approach for the $\overline{P}_{K/H}^{(n)}$.   If the probability of survival of each of the critical components after one hit on the aircraft (P_{k/H_i}) is known, an approximation for the probability that the aircraft has been killed by n hits can be obtained by neglecting the mutually exclusive feature of the individual component kills on any one hit. Thus, for the example redundant component aircraft model, Eq. (5.22b) can be used. For the n hit situation, Eq. (5.22b) becomes

$$\overline{P}_{S/H}^{(n)} = \left(1 - \overline{P}_{k/H_p}^{(n)}\right)\left(1 - \overline{P}_{k/H_f}^{(n)}\right)\left(1 - \overline{P}_{k/H_{e1}}^{(n)}\overline{P}_{k/H_{e2}}^{(n)}\right) \qquad (5.30)$$

where

$$\overline{P}_{k/H_p}^{(n)} = 1 - \left(1 - P_{k/H_p}\right)^n, \qquad \overline{P}_{k/H_f}^{(n)} = 1 - \left(1 - P_{k/H_f}\right)^n$$

$$\overline{P}_{k/H_{e1}}^{(n)}\overline{P}_{k/H_{e2}}^{(n)} = \left[1 - \left(1 - P_{k/H_{e1}}\right)^n\right]\left[1 - \left(1 - P_{k/H_{e2}}\right)^n\right]$$

Table 5.8   Comparison of Aircraft Kill Probabilities

Hits, n	1	2	3	4	5	10	20
$\overline{P}_{K/H}^{(n)}$, correct	0.0733	0.1646	0.2615	0.3566	0.4456	0.7619	0.9640
$\overline{P}_{K/H}^{(n)}$, approximate	0.0833	0.1757	0.2693	0.3595	0.4436	0.7470	0.9567

according to Eq. (5.25). Table 5.8 presents the $\overline{P}_{K/H}^{(n)}$ for both the transition matrix method and the simplified approach for several values of n. Note that the approximate $\overline{P}_{K/H}^{(n)}$ is both lower than and higher than the correct answer and that the approximate kill probability is reasonably close to the correct value, for this example.

(4)   Multiple hit vulnerable area.   The cumulative probability of kill given n hits derived above is not necessarily the best measure for assessing or comparing aircraft designs due to its dependence on the physical size of the aircraft. If two aircraft have identical vulnerable areas, but different presented areas, the one with the largest presented area will appear to be less vulnerable because its cumulative probability of kill given n hits will be less than that of the aircraft with the smaller presented area. On the other hand, being larger, it may suffer more hits; that is, it may be more susceptible.

The measure that is the most meaningful for vulnerability assessment and comparison of designs is vulnerable area. For nonredundant aircraft, the probability of kill given a hit and the vulnerable area are constant for each and every hit. Each subsequent hit has just as much chance of killing the aircraft as the previous hit (assuming component degradation is neglected). However, this is not true for aircraft with redundant critical components. For these aircraft, the probability of kill given a hit and the corresponding vulnerable area change with each hit because of the increasing possibility of the loss of one or more of the redundant components. In order to compute the multiple hit vulnerable area, an event-based probability of kill given a hit must be computed for each hit. In general, the probability of aircraft survival after taking n hits is given by Eq. (5.26a)

$$\overline{P}_{S/H}^{(n)} = \left(1 - P_{K/H}^{(1)}\right)\left(1 - P_{K/H}^{(2)}\right) \cdots \left(1 - P_{K/H}^{(n)}\right) \qquad (5.26a')$$

which also can be expressed in the form

$$\overline{P}_{S/H}^{(n)} = \overline{P}_{S/H}^{(n-1)}\left(1 - P_{K/H}^{(n)}\right) \qquad (5.31)$$

The value desired in Eq. (5.31) is $P_{K/H}^{(n)}$, the event-based probability that the aircraft is killed on the nth hit on the aircraft given that it has survived the first $n - 1$ hits. Rearranging terms in Eq. (5.31) gives

$$1 - P_{K/H}^{(n)} = \overline{P}_{S/H}^{(n)}/\overline{P}_{S/H}^{(n-1)} \qquad (5.32a)$$

Equation (5.32a) can also be given in the form

$$1 - P_{K/H}^{(n)} = \frac{1 - \overline{P}_{K/H}^{(n)}}{1 - \overline{P}_{K/H}^{(n-1)}} \tag{5.32b}$$

and hence,

$$P_{K/H}^{(n)} = \frac{\overline{P}_{K/H}^{(n)} - \overline{P}_{K/H}^{(n-1)}}{1 - \overline{P}_{K/H}^{(n-1)}} \tag{5.33}$$

The vulnerable area for the nth hit, $A_V^{(n)}$, is computed using the $P_{K/H}^{(n)}$ given by Eq. (5.33) and the basic vulnerable area equation, Eq. (5.1). Thus,

$$A_V^{(n)} = A_P P_{K/H}^{(n)} \tag{5.34}$$

Figure 5.22 shows the $A_V^{(n)}$ for the redundant model $\overline{P}_{K/H}^{(n)}$ given in Fig. 5.21. Note that the $A_V^{(1)}$ is just the sum of the vulnerable areas of the nonredundant components. Note also the asymptotic behavior of the redundant model. The constant vulnerable area of the nonredundant aircraft given in Table 5.3 is also plotted in Fig. 5.22 for the purpose of comparison. Note that the vulnerable area of the redundant aircraft is less than that of the nonredundant aircraft (with the 30 ft^2 vulnerable area engine) for the first 15 hits. On subsequent hits, the vulnerable area is slightly larger due to the fact that there is a strong likelihood that one or the other of the two engines has been killed, and the benefits of redundancy have been eliminated.

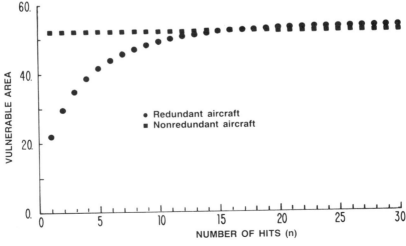

Fig. 5.22   **Multiple hit vulnerable area vs the number of hits.**

Required capabilities. One of the important requirements of any vulnerability assessment is the capability to account for the six vulnerability reduction concepts of component redundancy, component location, passive damage suppression, active damage suppression, component shielding, and component elimination. The methodology for assessing aircraft vulnerability to penetrators and fragments presented here has that capability. Component redundancy is accounted for in the kill expression, and its effects are measured by the $\bar{P}_{K/H}^{(n)}$ or the multiple hit vulnerable area. Component location is accounted for with respect to component overlap, the destruction of adjacent components due to damage to the struck component, the component presented area, and the effect of component location behind intervening structure and noncritical components on the component P_{k/h_i} value. Passive and active damage suppression can be accounted for by reducing the P_{k/h_i}. Component shielding is also accounted for by reducing the P_{k/h_i} to reflect the reduced velocity of the impacting damage mechanisms. Component elimination is accounted for by removing the component from the kill expression.

Presentation of results. The presentation of the vulnerable area results varies with the level of detail of the assessment. For a minimum level, the six major aspects shown in Fig. 5.23 are usually considered for each kill level. The 26 views depicted in Fig. 5.24 are usually considered when a more detailed or a computerized analysis is performed.

One important set of results that should be presented is the single hit vulnerable area of the aircraft. A typical aircraft single hit vulnerable area summary table is shown in Fig. 5.25. Multiple hit vulnerable area curves similar to the one shown in Fig. 5.22 should also be presented for at least six aspects.

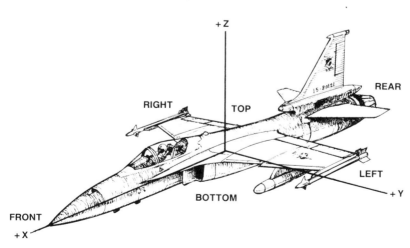

Fig. 5.23   The six aircraft aspects considered in a minimum assessment.

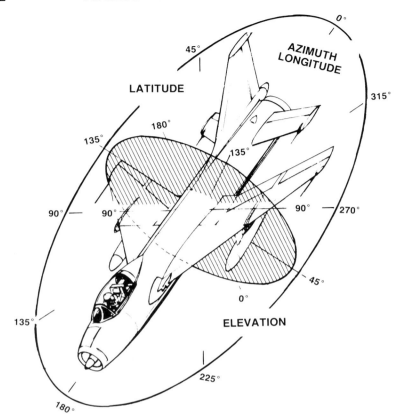

Fig. 5.24   The 26 aircraft aspects for a detailed analysis.

Assessment date_____	Aircraft _____
Performing organization_____	Threat _____
Kill category_____	

Projectile V_S, ft/sec (m/sec)	Total A_V, ft^2 (m^2)					
	Left side	Right side	Top	Bottom	Front	Rear
500 (152.4)						
1,000 (304.8)						
1,500 (457.2)						
2,000 (609.6)						
2,500 (762.0)						
3,000 (914.4)						
3,500 (1066.8)						

Fig. 5.25   Typical total aircraft single hit vulnerability summary table.

Fig. 5.26   Sample component vulnerable area summary form.

In addition to the total aircraft A_V presentation, the vulnerable area of each critical component should also be listed, and both the true and the incremental vulnerable areas should be presented for overlapping components. Redundant components should be identified, and the number of redundant components that must be killed to cause an aircraft kill should be noted. The single hit vulnerable area associated with overlapping redundant components should also be identified. Figure 5.26 shows a sample component vulnerable area summary form.

Vulnerability to Internally Detonating HE Warheads

Most guided missiles and antiaircraft projectiles 23 mm and larger have an HE core with a contact fuze that detonates the warhead either immediately or shortly after impacting the aircraft. This results in a detonation on or inside the aircraft, with the accompanying blast and fragment spray in many directions. The assumption of parallel trajectories or shotlines through the aircraft used in the preceding nonexplosive penetrator vulnerability assessment is not valid in this situation. Instead, the fragment shotlines emanate radially from the location of the warhead burst point. The probability of kill of any critical components that lie on any of the radial fragment shotlines needs to be evaluated and the aircraft vulnerable area and probability of aircraft kill given a hit computed.

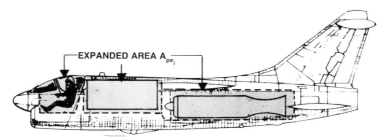

Fig. 5.27a   Expanded area approach.

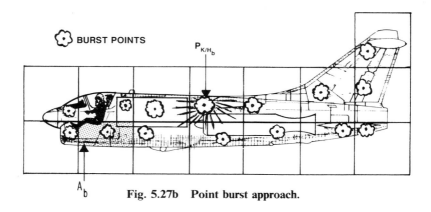

Fig. 5.27b   Point burst approach.

There are several approaches to this problem. One simple approach is to expand the presented area of each of the critical components beyond the actual physical size of the component, and then treat a hit by the HE round in the expanded area in the same manner as that used for the nonexplosive penetrator. For example, the presented area of the pilot could be the entire cockpit, because any hit and detonation within the cockpit could kill the pilot. Figure 5.27a illustrates this approach. If the expanded areas of two or more components intersect or overlap, the procedure for accounting for overlapping components described above must be used.

In another procedure, the warhead detonation is assumed to take place at individual locations within a grid superimposed on the presented area of the aircraft, as illustrated in Fig. 5.27b. Each cell contains one randomly located burst point. The probability of killing the aircraft is then evaluated for each burst point. This kill probability will be dependent upon the relative location of the adjacent critical components and on any shielding of these components provided by intervening structure and noncritical components. Critical components, or parts of critical components, outside of the cell in which the burst occurs must also be considered when they can be hit and killed by the damage mechanisms. Note that several redundant critical components can possibly be killed by the single HE burst. The burst point kill probability is determined using the kill expression for the aircraft. However, because more than one critical component can be killed given a single burst, the individual component kills are not exclusive; a single burst could kill both the fuel system and the pilot. Thus, the approach used in the overlapping component model to compute P_{k/h_0} must also be used here. The probability of an aircraft kill given a random hit from the attack aspect under consideration is obtained by multiplying the probability of aircraft kill given a hit computed for each burst point, P_{K/H_b}, by the probability of a random shot hitting the burst point area, P_{H_b}. The latter probability is given by

$$P_{H_b} = A_b / A_P, \qquad b = 1, 2 \ldots B$$

where B is the number of burst points or cells considered, and A_b is the local grid cell area around each burst point. (Note that even though critical components outside of the cell are included in P_{K/H_b}, just the area of the cell itself is used in the computation.) The $P_{K/H}$ for the aircraft given a random hit is given by

$$P_{K/H} = \sum_{b=1}^{B} P_{H_b} P_{K/H_b} = \frac{1}{A_P} \sum_{b=1}^{B} A_b P_{K/H_b} = \frac{1}{A_P} \sum_{b=1}^{B} A_{v_b}$$

where A_{v_b} is the vulnerable area of the bth cell.

The aircraft vulnerable area is computed using

$$A_V = \sum_{b=1}^{B} A_b P_{K/H_b} = \sum_{b=1}^{B} A_{v_b}$$

which is the sum of the vulnerable area of the individual cells.

The vulnerable area for internally detonating HE warheads is usually much larger than the vulnerable area for nonexplosive projectiles and fragments, but it can never exceed the aircraft presented area.

Vulnerability to Externally Detonating HE Warheads

The threats that employ externally detonating warheads are the large caliber AAA and most of the surface-to-air and air-to-air missiles. A typical encounter is shown in Fig. 5.28. Shortly after the detonation, the blast front precedes the fragments. Eventually, the fragments pass through the front of the blast because the decay of the fragment velocity is less than the blast front velocity decay. The primary damage mechanism of these threats is usually the high-velocity fragments or penetrators generated by the detonation. However, incendiary particles and the blast can also be important damage mechanisms. The vulnerability of aircraft to the externally detonating warhead is usually analyzed in two separate steps. One step is a determination of the aircraft's vulnerability to the blast, and the second

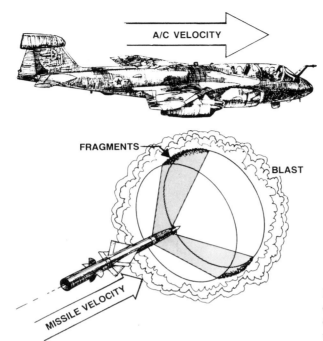

Fig. 5.28 Typical aircraft encounter with an externally detonating HE warhead.

examines the aircraft's vulnerability to the fragments and penetrators. Both analyses must consider the encounter conditions that exist between the aircraft and the missile at the time of warhead detonation. These include the missile and aircraft positions, velocity vectors, and the respective attitudes.

Blast.   Aircraft vulnerability to external blast is usually expressed as an envelope about the aircraft where the detonation of a specified charge weight of spherical uncased pentolite high explosive will result in a specified level of damage or kill to the aircraft. Detonation outside of such an envelope will result in little or no damage to the aircraft or in a lesser kill level. The damage mechanism is the blast resulting from the detonation of the high explosive in the vicinity of the aircraft. A spectrum of charge weights is often specified for which the aircraft vulnerability measures are computed in the vulnerability assessment. The specific charge weights selected are representative of the expected threat warheads which might be encountered. Envelopes are determined for a variety of encounter conditions that account for variations in aircraft speed and altitude, as well as aspect. Aircraft critical components vulnerable to the external blast consist principally of portions of the airframe structure and control surfaces. Threshold kill criteria for the critical components are derived from structural and aerodynamic analyses.

Once the blast pressures and impulse levels required for a component kill are determined for several locations on the aircraft surface, a contour may be plotted corresponding to the detonation distance and the weight of pentolite that will provide the required pressure and impulse level. Two different graphical presentations of the data may be used. The first is a plot of charge weight vs distance for a constant kill level. Several curves can be drawn on the same graph, one for each altitude of interest. A similar graph is required at each azimuth and elevation angle of interest about the aircraft. Figure 5.29a is an example of this type of presentation. The second graphical method, illustrated in Fig. 5.29b, is to construct isocharge weight

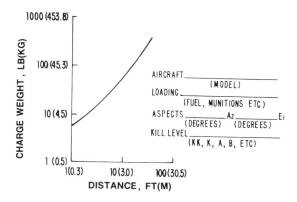

Fig. 5.29a   One type of external blast vulnerability presentation.

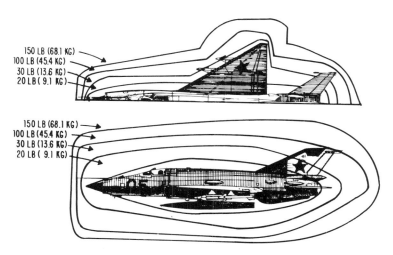

Fig. 5.29b   Typical external blast kill contour data for several weights of uncased pentolite at sea level.

contours about the aircraft for a given kill level and altitude in all planes of interest.

Fragments and penetrators. When a warhead bursts in the vicinity of an aircraft, the fragments or penetrators are usually ejected uniformly around the missile axis and begin to propagate outward in a divergent spherical-like spray pattern at a velocity that is the vector sum of the initial fragment ejection velocity from a static warhead detonation and the missile velocity. (Since the discussion that follows holds for both fragments and penetrators, except for the continuous rods, which are a special case, only the fragments will be referred to.) The fragment at the front of the warhead is assumed to propagate outward at the leading spray angle, and the fragment at the tail end of the warhead is assumed to propagate along the trajectory at the trailing spray angle, as shown in Fig. 5.28. All of the other fragment trajectories lie between these two spray angles and make up the fragment spray. As the fragments propagate outward, the aircraft moves in space, and eventually some of the fragments may strike the aircraft. Whether or not any of the fragments hit the aircraft and where they hit depend upon the relative positions, velocities, and attitudes of the warhead and the aircraft at the time of detonation (the encounter conditions), and the fragment static velocities and static spray angles.

The damage inflicted on the aircraft depends on the number and the location of the fragment impacts and on the terminal effects parameters, such as the fragment mass and impact velocity. The probability of an aircraft kill due to the burst of a specific warhead for a particular set of encounter conditions, $P_{K/D}$, is dependent upon how many fragments hit the aircraft and the aircraft's vulnerability to the multiple hits. This probability can be estimated for a horizontally moving aircraft assuming the entire presented area of the aircraft is hit with a uniform density spray of fragments as shown in Fig. 5.30. The fragments are assumed to travel on parallel paths and to hit the aircraft in a random manner. In this situation, the number of hits, n, on the aircraft presented area at the aspect under consideration, A_p, is given by

$$n = \rho A_p \qquad (5.35)$$

where ρ is the average number of fragments per unit area of fragment spray, known as the fragment spray density. If the fragments are assumed to have uniform velocity and to be uniformly spread over a spherical segment between the leading and trailing fragment dynamic trajectories ϕ_1 and ϕ_2 with respect to a stationary target, as shown in Fig. 5.30, the fragment spray density at a distance s from the detonation point is given by

$$\rho = \frac{N}{2\pi s^2 (\cos \phi_1 - \cos \phi_2)} \qquad (5.36)$$

where N is the total number of fragments in the warhead. The equation

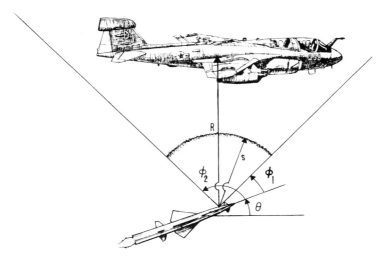

Fig. 5.30   Assumed encounter with a horizontally moving aircraft.

defining the angles ϕ_1 and ϕ_2 is

$$\phi_i = \arctan\left[\frac{V_m\sin\theta + V_f\sin(\theta + \alpha_i)}{V_m\cos\theta + V_f\cos(\theta + \alpha_i) - V_t}\right] - \theta, \qquad i = 1, 2 \quad (5.37)$$

where V_t is the target horizontal speed, V_m is the speed of the missile, θ is the elevation angle of the missile, V_f is the average fragment speed with respect to a stationary warhead, and α_1 and α_2 are the leading and trailing fragment spray angles from the axis of a static warhead detonation, respectively. (The α_i can range from a low of 45 deg to a high of 135 deg, depending upon the design of the warhead.) The fragment spray density when the fragments reach the aircraft is computed using $s = R$, where R is the distance from the detonation point to the aircraft, and Eq. (5.35) is used to compute n. (There is a difference between R and the actual distance the fragments travel due to the aircraft displacement between the time of warhead detonation and the time when the fragments hit the target. This difference is neglected here.) The $P_{K/D}$ due to the n hits is analogous to the $\overline{P}_{K/H}^{(n)}$ derived in this chapter for n random hits from one direction. Thus, $P_{K/D}$ can be estimated using cumulative probability of kill curves similar to the one shown in Fig. 5.21. Simplified equations for $P_{K/D}$ in terms of the aircraft vulnerable area and the n hits are derived below.

The probability the aircraft is killed given the jth random hit by a single fragment, $P_{K/H}^{(j)}$, can be determined using the procedure described in this chapter. The probability that the aircraft is killed by the n independent, random hits from the detonation, $\overline{P}_{K/H}^{(n)}$, is given by Eq. (5.26b). Therefore,

$$\overline{P}_{K/H}^{(n)} = P_{K/D} = 1 - \prod_{j=1}^{n}\left(1 - P_{K/H}^{(j)}\right) \qquad (5.26b')$$

It can be shown that for small $P_{K/H}^{(j)}$

$$\prod_{j=1}^{n} \left(1 - P_{K/H}^{(j)}\right) \simeq \exp\left(-\sum_{j=1}^{n} P_{K/H}^{(j)}\right)$$

Furthermore,

$$\sum_{j=1}^{n} P_{K/H}^{(j)} = \sum_{j=1}^{n} A_V^{(j)}/A_P$$

Hence, $P_{K/D}$ can be given in the form

$$P_{K/D} \simeq 1 - \exp\left(-\frac{\rho}{n} \sum_{j=1}^{n} A_V^{(j)}\right)$$

according to Eq. (5.35). If $A_V^{(j)}$ is assumed to be a constant value for all hits, $P_{K/D}$ simplifies to

$$P_{K/D} \simeq 1 - \exp(-\rho A_V) \qquad (5.38)$$

An example of the computation of $P_{K/D}$ for one encounter is given in Table 5.9.

The assumption has been made in this estimation that the fragment spray covers the entire presented area of the aircraft. For this to be possible, the fragment spray length, $R(\phi_1 - \phi_2)$, must be larger than the presented length

Table 5.9   Example of the Computation for $P_{K/D}$

Static warhead parameters	Spray angles, $\alpha_1 = 50$ deg, $\alpha_2 = 120$ deg Number of fragments, $N = 1000$ Fragment velocity, $V_f = 7000$ ft/s
Encounter parameters	Missile speed, $V_m = 1500$ ft/s Missile angle, $\theta = 30$ deg Detonation distance, $R = 80$ ft Aircraft speed, $V_t = 1000$ ft/s

Aircraft parameters	Aircraft presented length = 50 ft
	Aspect vulnerable area, $A_V = 25$ ft^2
	   (to fragment sizes and striking velocity under
	   consideration)

Fragmentation dynamic spray angles	$\phi_1 = \arctan(7644/1515) - 30$ deg $= 48.8$ deg $\phi_2 = \arctan(4250/-5763) - 30$ deg $= 113.6$ deg
Fragment spray density	$\rho = \dfrac{1000}{2\pi \times 80^2 \times 1.059} = 0.0235$ fragments/ft^2
Probability of kill	$P_{K/D} \simeq 1 - \exp(-0.0235 \times 25) = 0.44$

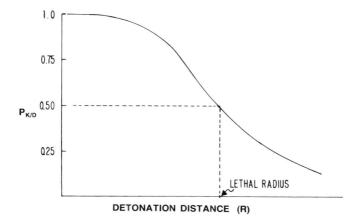

Fig. 5.31   Typical $P_{K/D}$ function.

of the aircraft. If this is not the case, or if only a portion of the spray meridian hits a portion of the aircraft, A_P in Eq. (5.35) must be reduced to the actual area that is struck by fragments. The extent of the fragment spray that does strike the aircraft, the number of fragment hits, the fragment approach directions, and where the hits occur are dependent upon the encounter conditions. For example, a detonation directly below the center of the aircraft in a head-on encounter will have a different result than that from a detonation in the same place for a tail-chasing missile due to the difference in the relative closing velocity. Furthermore, changing the elevation angle of the missile at the time of detonation will change the results.

Consequently, there is no unique value for $P_{K/D}$ for a warhead detonation at a specific location with respect to the aircraft. Similarly, $P_{K/D}$ will be different for detonations at the same distance, but at different locations around the aircraft. Nevertheless, the aircraft's vulnerability to an externally detonating warhead is often indicated only with respect to the distance of the detonation from the aircraft.

A typical curve relating $P_{K/D}$ to the detonation distance R is given in Fig. 5.31. This curve is referred to as the kill function given a detonation; and the radius at which $P_{K/D}$ is equal to 0.5 is called the lethal radius of the warhead. The value of $P_{K/D}$ specified for each value of R could be the average of the $P_{K/D}$ computed for several different encounters at R, or the $P_{K/D}$ values could be weighted with respect to the expected probability of encounter occurrence in order to obtain a weighted average. For example, if a certain missile only approaches the aircraft from the rear aspect, only $P_{K/D}$ values for that type of encounter would be computed.

Vulnerability to Lasers

Because a laser beam must hit the aircraft to damage it, and because no HE charge is involved, the methodology for assessing the vulnerability of aircraft to lasers consists of essentially the same procedures as used in the assessment of aircraft vulnerability to the single nonexplosive penetrator. Those critical components that are vulnerable to the laser-caused damage are examined, and the total aircraft vulnerability to the laser is determined based upon the contribution of the individual critical components. This methodology is currently in development.

Computer Programs for Vulnerability Assessment

The determination of an aircraft's vulnerability can be a complex and time-consuming task. When done manually, many simplifications and assumptions are made, the results are subject to interpretation, and the output is usually limited in scope. Consequently, an extensive number of computer programs or models have been developed by the US military and industry for assessing aircraft vulnerability. These programs can be divided into four major categories: shotline generators, vulnerable area routines, internal burst programs, and endgame programs. Programs in the first two categories are used for the penetrator and single fragment damage mechanisms. Those in the third category are used for internally detonating HE warheads, and those in the fourth category are for the proximity-fuzed HE warhead. (The reader is cautioned that just because a computer is used, the results are not to be treated as sacrosanct. The output is no more valid than the assumptions that were used to develop the model and the input data.)

Shotline generators. These programs generate shotline descriptions of aircraft targets for use as input data to the codes that calculate vulnerable areas. The programs usually model the aircraft external surface and the individual internal and external components either with a set of geometric shapes or with surface patches. Shotline descriptions are obtained by superimposing a planar grid over the target model and by passing parallel shotlines or rays from the attack direction (normal to the grid) through the individual grid cells, as shown in Fig. 5.32. One shotline is randomly located within each cell. The programs trace the path of a shotline through the aircraft and generate sequential lists of components and fluid and air spaces

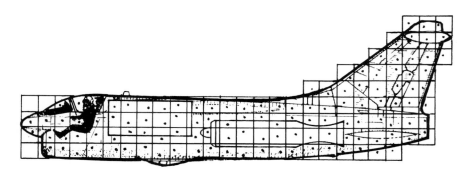

Fig. 5.32   Grid for the shotlines.

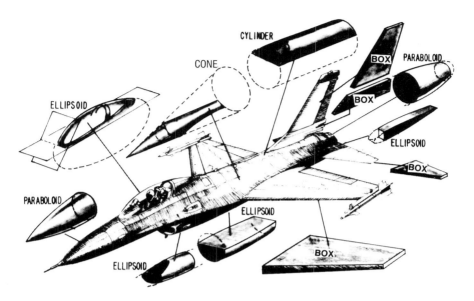

Fig. 5.33   Combinatorial geometry model of an aircraft.

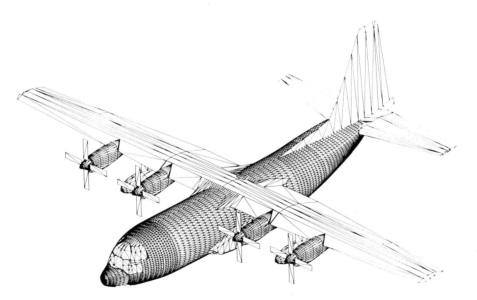

Fig. 5.34   External view of a triangular patch aircraft model (courtesy of the Lockheed-Georgia Co.).

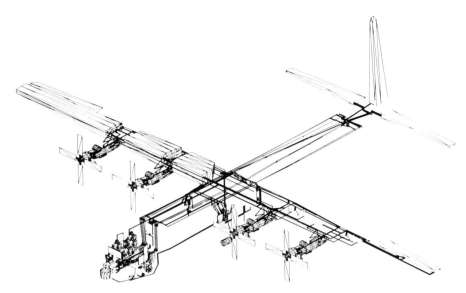

Fig. 5.35 Internal view of a triangular patch aircraft model (courtesy of the Lockheed-Georgia Co.).

encountered along the shotline. Specific component data, such as thickness and shotline obliquity, are also recorded. This procedure is repeated for all shotlines originating from the selected attack directions.

Two families of shotline generator routines have been developed. They are the MAGIC, GIFT family and the SHOTGEN, FASTGEN family. The MAGIC and GIFT codes were developed at the US Army Ballistic Research Laboratory, Aberdeen Proving Ground, Md. These codes use the combinatorial geometry approach, with basic body shapes such as spheres, boxes, cylinders, ellipsoids, and cutting or bounding planes, to describe components. GIFT is an improved version of MAGIC, with simpler input requirements, more efficient computation, and computer-generated graphic displays. Figure 5.33 shows the external view of a model built using the combinatorial geometry approach. The second family, SHOTGEN and the more recent FASTGEN and FASTGEN II, is somewhat similar to the other family, but typically uses the flat triangular patch method to describe the component surfaces. SHOTGEN was developed by the Naval Weapons Center, and FASTGEN and FASTGEN II are improved versions of SHOTGEN sponsored by the Air Force Aeronautical Systems Division (ASD). Figures 5.34 and 5.35 show the external view and some internal components of a flat triangular surface patch model.

Vulnerable area routines. These programs generate component and total aircraft vulnerable area tables for a single penetrator or fragment. The vulnerable area routines can be divided into two groups, the "detailed," or analysis routines, which use the shotline approach to compute the vulnerable area, and the "simplified," or evaluation routines, which use simplified approaches to determine the vulnerable area. The routines in the analysis group are usually used for problems requiring in-depth studies. However, they have the potential for use in early design studies in which only a limited amount of technical description data is available. The evaluation routines are more appropriate for problems in which a cursory analysis is desired.

(1) Analysis routines. The programs VAREA, VAREA02, and COVART belong to the detailed group. Inputs to these programs include the shotline descriptions of the target model generated by the shotline programs, probability of kill given a hit data for the individual components, empirical ballistic penetration data, and weapon characteristics data. Component and aircraft single hit vulnerable area data are output in tabular form.

VAREA is the oldest and least comprehensive of the three routines in this group. It was developed in 1965 by the Naval Weapons Center to conduct vulnerability analyses of systems subjected to fragmenting-type threats and uses the THOR penetration equations to compute penetrator mass and velocity decay due to penetration through the components along the shotline. VAREA02, completed in 1973, evolved from the VAREA program. Its added capabilities include a projectile penetration mode, an air gap fire model, a redundant components model, and an option to use the DRI penetration equations instead of the THOR relations.

COVART (Computation of Vulnerable Area and Repair Time) currently represents the state-of-the-art in vulnerable area routines. It incorporates all of the features of the VAREA02 program and the helicopter vulnerable area routines from the HART program and includes a battle damage repair time model. The procedure used by COVART to compute single hit vulnerable areas is essentially the same as that described in this chapter for the single nonexplosive penetrator or fragment. The component vulnerable area of each grid cell is the product of the cell presented area and the probability of component kill for the shotline in that cell. The vulnerable area of each component is the sum of the component vulnerable areas computed for each grid cell whose shotline passes through the component. The total aircraft vulnerable area is the sum of all of the cell vulnerable areas, considering only the nonredundant critical components and any redundant critical component overlap. Both true and incremental vulnerable areas are available for the overlapping components. Redundant critical components that do not lie along the same shotline do not contribute to the aircraft vulnerability.

(2) Evaluation routines. The computer program COMVAT is representative of the routines that belong to the other group, the simplified codes. These routines were developed to fulfill the need for relatively quick methods for computing vulnerable area. They are intended to be used in

situations when use of the more sophisticated routines may not be feasible or timely, such as during early conceptual design studies. The simplified routines are not as accurate as the detailed routines, but they should require considerably less effort and computer run time to use.

COMVAT was developed specifically to compute the vulnerable areas of aircraft components to projectile threats. It is based upon the same principles as the detailed routines, but it does not use shotline descriptions of the aircraft; instead, it computes component vulnerable areas on the basis of input data describing average shielding conditions on the components. The THOR penetration equations are used to model projectile velocity decay. Secondary effects such as spalling, projectile yawing motions, and projectile breakup are ignored.

Internal burst programs.   Several programs for computing the vulnerability of aircraft to internally detonating HE warheads have been developed under the direction of the JTCG/ME. These programs are sometimes referred to as point burst programs, and the best known program is the POINTBURST program. This program uses the second approach described in the section on vulnerability to internally detonating HE warheads.

Endgame programs.   The endgame refers to the terminal events in an encounter between an aircraft and an HE warhead with a proximity fuze. Just how the warhead got to the vicinity of the aircraft is irrelevant to the endgame analysis. The endgame events may include target detection by the fuze, and usually do include the warhead detonation, blast propagation, and fragment flyout, impact, and penetration through the aircraft. The numerical value for the $P_{K/D}$ is then determined for the given set of encounter conditions and warhead and aircraft characteristics. This procedure is usually repeated for many different sets of encounter conditions and warhead detonation points, and $P_{K/D}$ is established as a function of the detonation distance. Four endgame programs currently in use are SESTEM II, SCAN, ATTACK, and REFMOD or MECA. A fifth program, SHAZAM, is nearing completion.

(1) SESTEM II.   This program was developed in 1977 by the US Air Force Aeronautical Systems Division to evaluate the terminal effectiveness of missiles with nonnuclear blast and fragmentation warheads against aerial targets. The $P_{K/D}$ is computed with respect to a direct hit, fragment damage, and blast. The program has the capability to simulate several fuzing options and a general terminal encounter geometry. The fragment spray angles and density, and fragment average mass, static velocity, cross-sectional area, and coefficient of drag are input data. The target is represented as a collection of shapes that are either single fragment vulnerable, masking, or fuzing components. The external shapes (wing, fuselage, etc.) are modeled using ellipses; and rectangular parallelopipeds are used for the internal components, such as fuel tanks and electronics. The vulnerabil-

ity of the components is represented by vulnerable area tables. The program can be used to generate iso-$P_{K/D}$ contours.

(2) SCAN. SCAN was developed in 1976 under the supervision of the US Navy Pacific Missile Test Center (PMTC) for the JTCG/AS. The objective of SCAN is to predict the probability that an aircraft will survive an attack by a missile armed with a warhead. Aircraft kills due to direct hit, fragment damage, and blast are evaluated. A few fuzing options are considered, as well as a general terminal encounter geometry. The warhead is divided into polar and radial zones and different fragment sizes, shapes, and materials can be specified within each zone. The target is modeled using the combinatorial geometry approach, and component vulnerability to single fragments is expressed by

$$P_{k/h} = C_1 + C_2(\text{mass}) + C_3(\text{velocity})$$

where mass and velocity refer to the fragment mass and velocity. The energy density and area removal kill criteria are also options for use with components such as major structures. Each component is given a material and thickness and is linked to a subsystem, system, or aircraft kill by a logical kill expression, thus allowing the consideration of redundancy. SCAN also has graphics capabilities for evaluation of the input geometric model and output fragment impact data.

(3) ATTACK. ATTACK is a Naval Weapons Center revision of an endgame methodology developed at the Naval Missile Center, Point Mugu. The object of ATTACK is to predict the ability of a missile to detect and destroy an airborne target. Direct hit, blast, and single fragment (component), and multiple fragment (structural) kills are considered, and a general terminal encounter geometry is provided. The warhead in ATTACK uses the concept of polar and radial fragment spray zones and fragment weight classes. A large number of fuze options are available. The program requires four target models, one for each type of damage, and one fuze model for each encounter. The components in the single fragment model are physically represented by spheres at specified locations, and the vulnerability of each component is contained in vulnerable area tables that depend upon aspect angle, fragment mass, and fragment impact velocity. The multiple fragment model uses a segmented cylindrical target representation, and the vulnerability of each segment is specified by a critical level of fragment energy density.

(4) REFMOD (MECA). The REFMOD program, developed in 1981, was intended to be a reference model to be used for computing the effectiveness of externally detonating weapons against moving targets. (It was later renamed Modular Endgame Computer Analysis, or MECA.) The model was developed under the auspices of the JTCG/ME Anti-Air Missile Evaluation Group. REFMOD has been assembled by incorporating meth-

odologies from many other existing endgame programs, including some significant additional features that enable it to work with a wide variety of vulnerability models and to evaluate warhead-target combinations that were previously too cumbersome to assess. The warhead types considered include the continuous rod, divergent fragment spray, convergent fragment spray, focused fragment controlled motion, and an aimable warhead in which the fragment spray density is nonuniform about the missile axis. Several fuze routines are available, and the option exists for the specification of fuzing data from flight tests. The target model and vulnerability employed depend upon the damage mechanism selected. These include direct hit, blast, fragment, and continuous rod. Component vulnerability types for fragments include both vulnerable area and a $P_{k/h}$ kill criterion that is a function of mass, velocity, and density. For the vulnerable area model, components can be described as spherical, linear, cylindrical, or planar in shape, and the component vulnerable area tables generated by COVART can be used. The $P_{k/h}$ vulnerability model employs cylindrical components, and the component kill criterion is given by

$$P_{k/h} = C_1(\text{mass})^{C_2}(\text{velocity})^{C_3}$$

with lower and upper threshold values. By inputting different values for C_1, C_2, and C_3, a variety of kill criteria can be employed. For example, when $C_1 = 0.5$, $C_2 = 1$, and $C_3 = 2$, the energy density criterion is specified.

(5) *SHAZAM.* This code was developed at the Air Force Armament Laboratory (AFATL/DLY) for the evaluation of air-to-air missile effectiveness. The program sequentially assesses the possibility the target aircraft is directly impacted by the missile, the effect of blast overpressures upon the target structures, and the cumulative effect of warhead fragment impacts on the target structure and critical components. The size, shape, and position of the target body and internal components are described by discrete surfaces, and each surface can be vulnerable to a direct hit, to blast, or to fragments. The criteria used to define the kill of each component/surface are supplied by the user. The program utilizes as much of the aircraft descriptions that are prepared for the SHOTGEN and VAREA programs as is economically feasible. A sufficiently large number of encounter conditions are assessed to generate a single shot probability of kill that has converged to a user specified confidence level.

5.4 VULNERABILITY REDUCTION

Vulnerability Reduction Concepts

Vulnerability reduction refers to the use of any design technique or piece of equipment that controls or reduces either the amount or the consequence of damage to the aircraft caused by the damage mechanisms. In other words, vulnerability reduction means controlling or reducing the vulnerability measures of the aircraft and its components. The potential kill modes of each system of the aircraft identified in the DMEA must be examined when considering vulnerability reduction, with particular attention given to those systems that combat data analyses and vulnerability assessments have shown to be the most vulnerable. There are many and varied ways to accomplish this reduction. Some of them involve the design, layout, and location of the various systems; others require special equipment. Some add weight, others are simply the results of good design practice and may actually reduce weight, and some also enhance the safety of flight. In general, each of the techniques for reducing vulnerability is a specific application of one of the six vulnerability concepts introduced in Chap. 1. These six concepts are (1) component redundancy (with separation), (2) component location, (3) passive damage suppression, (4) active damage suppression, (5) component shielding, and (6) component elimination. When considering the possible kill modes of each aircraft system, these six vulnerability reduction concepts, described in some detail below, should be examined to see how they can effectively be applied to prevent the loss of that system.

Component redundancy (with separation).   The employment of multiple devices, structural elements, parts, or mechanisms in combination for the purpose of enhancing survivability is known as redundancy. (Redundancy is often specified for safety of flight reasons alone.) Redundancy can be employed at the component, subsystem, or system level, and may be one of two general types: (1) total redundancy, in which each redundant element is fully capable of performing the essential function, and (2) partial redundancy, in which each element independently performs some portion of the function. If the redundancy is achieved through the use of similar sets of components in which each set performs identical functions, the system is said to have actual redundancy. Functional redundancy is achieved through the use of different sets of components to perform the required functions. Examples of total redundancy are dual power control hydraulic subsystems, two sump tanks, and multiple engines (with one or more engines out capabilities). Partial redundancy is a copilot who can fly but not land the aircraft, and functional redundancy is the use of a speed brake as a backup control surface. Inherent in the assumption that redundancy actually exists after damage occurs is the requirement that redundant components be effectively separated such that one hit will not directly or indirectly kill both components. For example, the engines in a twin-engined aircraft should be separated so that one hit by a damage mechanism will neither directly kill both engines, such as a penetrator striking and killing both engines, nor indirectly kill them, such as a penetrator causing a fire in one engine that spreads to the adjacent engine, eventually leading to a failure of both engines.

Component location.   The type of vulnerability reduction that is achieved by positioning critical components in a manner that reduces the probability that a damage mechanism will produce lethal damage is referred to as component location. Component location design techniques include: (1) positioning noncritical or tougher components to provide shielding for critical components, (2) effectively separating redundant components to ensure true single hit redundancy, (3) compactly grouping or overlapping critical components to reduce the aircraft vulnerable area or to present the least vulnerable aspect to a damage mechanism, and (4) locating or isolating components such that the possibility of cascading damage is reduced or eliminated. Examples of location are the placement of each set of mechanical flight control rods and cables of a dual controls subsystem on opposite sides of the aircraft, the location of a tail rotor servoactuator in the tail rotor gearbox, and the location of the hot air bleed line such that fuel or other combustible mixtures will not leak from punctured lines or containers on to the hot line.

Passive damage suppression. The term passive damage suppression describes any design technique that reduces vulnerability by incorporating a feature that, after the impingement of a damage mechanism, tends to either contain the damage or reduce its effect. These passive features have no damage-sensing capability. There are several passive damage suppression techniques to consider.

(1) Damage tolerance. Damage-tolerant design techniques provide for the construction of aircraft structure and internal components that will accept a degree of mechanical damage without impairing their functional capability. This is accomplished, for example, by providing redundant load paths in critical structural elements, such as multispar wings, by using high-fracture-toughness materials to limit crack propagation, and by using large-diameter, thin-wall control rods that can function with perforations caused by projectiles and fragments. Dual, tandem hydraulic power actuators can be made with rip-stop construction to prevent cracks in one power cylinder from propagating to the other power cylinder and causing a loss of both power control hydraulic subsystems.

(2) Ballistic resistance. Ballistic resistance is a design technique involving the use of high-strength materials in components for the purpose of preventing the total penetration of an impacting penetrator or fragment. For example, the casing around a hydraulic actuator or gearbox can be made ballistically resistant.

(3) Delayed failure. The delayed failure technique reduces vulnerability by using elements that continue to function for a prolonged period of time during and after a damage process, such as penetration or fire. For example, some recent helicopter transmissions and gearboxes have been designed to operate long after a loss of lubrication. Another example is the selection of high-temperature-tolerant materials to serve as a fire barrier in areas where

critical components may be exposed to fire from burning fuel, hydraulic fluid, or torching from a damaged engine combustor or hot air bleed line.

(4) Leakage suppression.   Leakage suppression is a technique that uses self-sealing materials that are designed to accept a degree of ballistic damage and to subsequently allow little or no leakage from the fluid container. Self-sealing materials are beneficial not only because they retain the fluid for continued use, but also because they stop the leakage of the fluid to areas where combustion could occur. Leakage suppression techniques seal off sensitive or ignition-producing areas and also provide for the drainage of combustible fluids. Self-sealing fuel tanks and lines are common examples.

(5) Fire and explosion suppression.   Fires and explosions result from a combustion process requiring three basic elements: oxygen, a flammable material or vapor, and an ignition source. Suppression or prevention of fires and explosions requires either the prevention of ignition or the suppression of the flame front propagation once ignition has occurred. For flammable fluids and vapors, ignition can be prevented by techniques that do not permit the ratio of fluid vapor and air that will support combustion to occur. For example, forced venting of the internal spaces and voids of an aircraft where a fire may occur, such as the engine compartment, is one method of accomplishing this prevention. Inerting the ullage of fuel tanks with nitrogen or partially filling fuel tanks with a flexible foam that hampers propagation of a flame front are also effective methods.

(6) Fail-safe response.   This design technique provides critical systems with components that will revert to a marginally operable condition for a specified or indefinite period of time after damage. Examples include an engine fuel control device that is designed to revert to a predetermined setting if the throttle control linkage is severed and control surfaces that become locked in a flyable position in the event of a total loss of hydraulic power to or control of the surface actuator.

Active damage suppression.   Active damage suppression describes any technique that reduces vulnerability by incorporating a sensor or other device that, upon the impingement of a damage mechanism or the occurrence of a damage process, activates a function that either tends to contain the damage or reduces its subsequent effects. The most common example of an active system is a fire detection and extinguishing system that uses a detector to sense an ignition source or high-temperature areas. Following detection, the system may automatically dispense an inerting fluid, or extinguishing gas, or it may alert the pilot, who may then take appropriate action. Another example is an override switch that allows the pilot to disengage a damaged component, such as a jammed control rod that has frozen the control column.

Component shielding. Shielding of components is achieved with the use of coatings or platelike materials that tend to resist or absorb the damage mechanisms. The shielding can be armor material that may or may not be an integral or load-bearing part of the aircraft structure. The armor is called parasitic if it is attached to bulkheads or other structural elements and serves only a shielding function. This is often the only choice available in a retrofit situation. A better technique is to use integral armor that is incorporated early in the design and is a functional part of the structural system. Shielding may also be provided for the crew members in the form of body armor. However, since the crew member is already encumbered with flight gear, the increased stress and fatigue associated with body armor often makes its use impractical. A blast and fragment shield can be used in the cockpit to effectively separate a pilot and copilot so that an explosion of an HE projectile inside the cockpit does not kill or injure both crew members. Shielding can also be used to protect components from the radiation damage mechanisms.

Component elimination. Vulnerability can be reduced by completely eliminating a particular critical component or by replacing the component with a less vulnerable component that accomplishes the same function. For example, replacing a fuel feed boost pump with a fuel feed suction device can reduce vulnerability by eliminating the possibility of pumping fuel through damage-caused holes in fuel transfer and feed lines and into void spaces where a fire may start. Replacing mechanical flight control rods and linkages with redundant and separated electrical wires or optical fibers can also reduce vulnerability.

Ballistically tolerant techniques vs ballistically resistant techniques. Ballistically tolerant techniques are those techniques that are intended to "bend" with the damage, whereas the ballistically resistant techniques are designed to "repel" the damage mechanism. When the effectiveness of each of the various reduction concepts described here is evaluated for application to a particular aircraft, the ballistically tolerant techniques usually reduce the vulnerability with significantly less weight penalty than that associated with the ballistically resistant techniques.

Aircraft Design for Reduced Vulnerability

The major systems on an aircraft have been described in Chap. 2. These include the fuel system, the propulsion system, the flight control system, the crew system, and the structural system. A brief description of the vulnerability reduction techniques and technology for each of these systems is presented below. The components of the system are defined, and the possible kill modes described in the DMEA are listed. General design guidance and some specific vulnerability reduction techniques are then presented for each possible kill mode. The reader who is interested in delving deeper into this subject should refer to the survivability handbooks described in Chap. 1.

The fuel system. The fuel system is defined as those components that store and deliver fuel to the engine. The system includes, but is not limited to, the following subsystems and components: storage tanks (internal and external), distribution (lines, pumps, valves, controls, and filters), refueling/ dumping, and indicating. The fuel tankage and distribution subsystems usually represent the largest subsystems of the aircraft and are vulnerable to almost all of the damage mechanisms. If unprotected, the fuel system is likely to be the primary contributor to aircraft vulnerability. However, proper design of the fuel system can provide a significant degree of system protection. A high priority assigned to the design of the fuel system to reduce vulnerability will therefore be extremely effective in increasing the survivability of the aircraft.

(1) The kill modes. Fuel system damage-caused failure modes are fuel supply depletion, in-tank fire and explosion, void space fire and explosion, sustained exterior fire, and hydraulic ram.

(2) Design guidance and vulnerability reduction techniques. Development of aircraft fuel systems with protection against the higher levels of nonnuclear weapon effects can only be achieved if the most effective survivability enhancement techniques are incorporated into the basic design concept. Inherent vulnerability reduction features are relatively easy to incorporate in conceptual or preliminary design when the location and geometry of the fuel system are established, but are very difficult to add to an existing design when tank locations, sizes, and other basic airframe configurations are frozen. This is why it is so important to consider survivability in conceptual and preliminary design. Weight gain and fuel volume loss penalties for modifications of existing designs usually result in reduced payloads and reduced combat range. Nevertheless, although the penalties and installation problems may not be insignificant, improvements to the fuel systems of current production aircraft and to those already delivered should be seriously considered.

(a) General principles: The fuel tanks should be located to minimize presented areas in primary threat directions. The fuel tanks, fuel lines, and other fuel system components should be located in such a way that damage to one element does not cascade into other systems. The tanks should be located so as to take advantage of structural masking and to minimize fuel line runs and exposures. All fuel system components containing fuel should be located so that potential leakage or vapors from combat damage neither flows nor is drawn into engine inlet ducts or into contact with possible ignition sources, such as hot engine components, armament, oxygen systems, engine hot air bleed lines, and electrical and electronic equipment. Conversely, fuel containers and lines should not be located where they might be exposed to sparking from severed electrical lines or to hot gases from such sources as torching from perforated engine combustors and hot air bleed lines. Fuel management systems should minimize aircraft center-of-gravity displacement problems if fuel transfer capability is lost.

(b) Prevention of fuel supply depletion: Preventing or minimizing fuel leakage is essential for the prevention of fuel supply depletion. It also significantly reduces the probability of fires, explosions, and engine fuel ingestion as a result of ballistic and hydraulic ram damage. Design techniques to minimize fuel leakage include the use of self-sealing fuel tanks and lines in conjunction with the use of a low ullage pressure when the aircraft is in combat areas to promote good sealing and to lower the weight requirements of the self-sealing materials. The system should also be designed for tolerance to hydraulic ram. The fuel flow configuration and management sequence should be designed in such a way that the maximum amount of fuel is available to the propulsion system by gravity feed. Multiple, separated sump tanks should be used with feed redundancy provided by crossovers in the fuel transfer lines to each engine, and redundant or damage-tolerant supports for the fuel lines should be used. A suction fuel feed system should be considered in lieu of a boost system, and the length of lines outside of tanks should be minimized. The entering and exiting lines, connectors, and closures should be located in the ullage portion of the tanks to minimize the possibility of leakage outside of the tanks, and pumps and other transfer components should be located so they are shielded by the fuel or major structure. Fuel gaging systems should provide quantity difference indications sufficiently sensitive to permit detection of fuel loss from specific tanks. Fuel flow management should have the capability of bypassing damaged components using crossfeed lines and shielded shut-off valves to conserve the fuel supply and minimize leakage. Compartmentalized fuel tanks should be used to minimize fuel loss resulting from ballistic damage. Leakage drain holes should be located to avoid long leakage paths to the exit from the aircraft and leakage of liquid fuel and fuel vapors to hazardous compartments.

Most fuel tankage is either metal or bladder. The metal or wet tanks obviously leak when punctured. In general, the bladders do not seal any punctures and may or may not be tear-resistant. Tear-resistant bladders do reduce the rate of fuel leakage due to penetration below that of nontear-resistant bladders. Self-sealing a metal or bladder tank consists of the application of one or more sealant layers reinforced with coated fabrics of various configurations. Exposure of the sealant, such as uncured rubber, to the fuel as a result of a puncture results in a swelling of the sealant and closure of the wound. Self-sealing tanks are often used in conjunction with a backing board, which provides additional support to the tank walls. The backing board suspends the tank away from the aircraft structure and minimizes metal petaling into the tank, which would degrade the self-sealing effectiveness. Fuel tanks designed to be crashworthy are relatively easy to seal because of their resistance to cracking and petaling. There are limitations to the protection provided by the self-sealing technique, such as the inability to seal against large HE threats and very high-velocity penetrators and fragments, and leakage after penetration of fittings, doors, and corners. There can also be increased maintenance problems. The weight penalty incurred by the use of self-sealing construction can range from 0.4 to 2.5 lb/ft^2, depending upon the level of protection. If the fuel is not in contact with the upper portions of a tank during combat, weight may be saved by using a tear-resistant bladder construction without a sealant in this area. Reduced sealant thickness may also be used where ullage and fuel pressures are low.

Liquid pressures in fuel lines and hoses due to hydraulic ram or penetration by a projectile or fragment can cause cracking, tearing, shattering, or petaling of the walls. A liquid pressure pulse can increase the size of perforations, and subsequent leakage in the line can interfere with the sealing function of any self-sealing material. Leakage from pressurized lines can be minimized by proper selection and application of self-sealing hoses and line covers. Self-sealing coverings should also be applied to suction feed fuel lines to maintain the vacuum in the event of a penetration and to improve performance.

(c) Suppression of fires and explosions: For many years, protection of an aircraft against fire has usually meant engine fire walls, engine compartment venting, and fire detection and possibly extinguishing in the engine compartments and crew stations. These protection measures were primarily installed to combat the peacetime fire safety problems that occur in engine compartments. However, studies of the combat data over the past 25 years have revealed that fires and explosions can occur in other areas, such as fuel tank ullages and the void spaces around the tanks, and that these fires are a major contributor to aircraft attrition rates. Consequently, a mature technology for the suppression of fires and explosions has been developed over the past 15 years or so. (Protection of fuel tanks is not a new idea. In World War II, the Russians pumped the engine exhaust gas into the fuel tanks in the IL-2; and the F-4U used fuel tank inerting in the wing tanks of the early models.) There are many suppression techniques currently available, and in order to appreciate how each one works, the reader should know what fires and explosions are and what causes them.

Fires and explosions in fuel tank ullages, aircraft dry bays, and on the exterior of the aircraft are manifestations of a process known as combustion. Combustion can be defined as a sustained, exothermic chemical reaction of the form

$$C_N H_M + O_2 + N_2 \rightarrow H_2O + CO_2 + N_2 + \text{other products} + \text{energy released}$$

where $C_N H_M$ is a hydrocarbon fuel, O_2 are oxygen molecules, N_2 are nitrogen molecules, H_2O is water, and CO_2 is carbon dioxide. The energy released is the heat of combustion. Combustion will only occur in a gaseous mixture when the concentrations of fuel vapor and oxygen are within certain limits that depend upon the temperature and pressure of the mixture. Fuel concentration, defined as the number of fuel molecules per unit volume, is measured by the fuel vapor pressure. In the partially full fuel tank, the vapor pressure in the ullage is dependent only on the steady-state temperature of the fuel and ullage gas. The higher the temperature, the higher the number of fuel molecules the gas can hold, and the higher the fuel vapor pressure. The total pressure in the ullage gas mixture is the sum

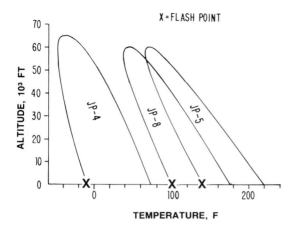

Fig. 5.36 Flammability diagram.

of the fuel vapor pressure and the air pressure. The air pressure governs the amount of oxygen molecules in the mixture and is dependent upon altitude in vented tanks. The relationship between the air pressure (oxygen molecules) in the mixture and the temperature (fuel molecules) determines whether combustion will take place. This relationship can be expressed by the flammability diagram shown in Fig. 5.36. Note that there is only a certain region of temperatures and altitudes (pressures) where combustion will occur given an ignition source. The extent of this region is defined by the flammability limits, and the lowest temperature at which combustion can occur at sea level is known as the flash point.

For example, aircraft ascent will result in a lower ullage pressure in the fuel tanks as the air in the ullage is vented to reduce the difference between the ullage pressure and the atmospheric pressure, and hence the ullage oxygen content will be reduced. This, in turn, can create a mixture in the tank ullage that is too rich, that is, there are too few oxygen molecules for the available fuel molecules. Aircraft descent can create the opposite condition where the mixture is too lean; there are too many oxygen molecules for the available fuel molecules. This explanation assumes the liquid fuel and the ullage gas are in steady-state equilibrium. Penetration of fragments and penetrators into the fuel, fuel sloshing, and fuel tank vibration may produce flammable fuel mists and vapors for some portions of the ullage for almost all flight profiles, and the detonation of an HE warhead in the ullage can significantly increase the flammability limits due to the energy released by the detonation.

Given an ignition source in a flammable mixture, the flame front starts at the source and propagates throughout the mixture until either a solid boundary or a mixture that will not support combustion is reached. The velocity at which the flame front travels depends upon the amount and rate of energy released. A relatively large and rapid energy release by the combustion process causes a supersonic wave or flame front with a rapid

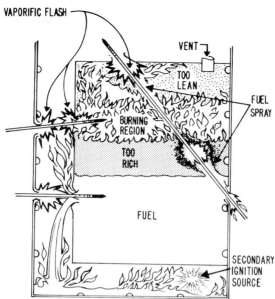

Fig. 5.37 Possible combustion incidents in and around a fuel tank.

rise and large increase in the pressure, called the overpressure. This phenomenon is referred to as a detonation. A relatively small and slow energy release causes a subsonic flame front with a slow rise and low increase in the overpressure. This is called a deflagration. Aviation fuels typically deflagrate with overpressures normally less than 200 psi. Detonations and deflagrations may or may not lead to a fire. When the combustion overpressure is sufficiently large enough to damage or destroy portions of the aircraft structure, the combustion process is referred to as an explosion.

Figure 5.37 illustrates several possible combustion conditions for different penetrator or fragment shotlines. In this situation, fresh air has entered the vent due to aircraft descent and fuel transfer from the tank, and hence the upper part of the ullage is assumed to be too lean. The lower region of the ullage is assumed to be too rich because of its proximity to the sloshing fuel. Only the middle region will support combustion. Shotline 1 shows the direct encounter of a penetrator with the flammable vapor in the ullage. The small clouds along the shotline are typical ignition sources. For incendiary projectiles, these flashes represent burning incendiary mixtures. These incendiary clouds may also be locations of flashes caused by the high-speed impact of a penetrator or fragment upon metal tank surfaces. For HE and HE-I projectiles, the location of each detonation and incendiary flash is determined by the fuze delay employed and the impact conditions. For this particular shotline, the flammable region could be ignited, and an in-tank fire or explosion could occur.

For shotline 2, the flashing external to the tank is caused by effects similar to shotline 1. Although no combustion can occur within the liquid fuel itself, the hydraulic ram can grossly increase the wall damage and fuel leakage. Another possibility with this shotline is the ignition of the fuel that is spurting from the entry hole by either an incendiary or a metal impact flash. An independent hazard is indicated by the lower fire, where leaking fuel and vapor have found an onboard secondary ignition source. These primary and secondary void space fires and explosions caused by shotline 2 can be the most prevalent means by which the smaller incendiary projectiles can cause fuel-system-related aircraft kills.

Shotline 3 is an impact upon a fuel tank wall that is integral with the airframe skin. Even though fuel escapes into the atmosphere through the entry hole, the slipstream may prevent a sustained exterior fire on the tank wall. However, if there is severe petaling, the jagged edges could act as flame holders, and a sustained exterior fire could occur. The second flash along shotline 3 in the ullage denotes the delayed detonation of an HE round or the delayed activation of an incendiary round. The third flash is caused by penetration or impact with the top of the tank. As a result of the fuel spray caused by the penetrator or fragment exiting the liquid surface, a substantial mist is generated that follows the shotline and may reach the incendiary flash at the exit. The mist may convert the too lean zone into a just-right zone for combustion to occur.

Techniques for the suppression of in-tank and void space fires and explosions are based upon the following procedures:

(i)   Removal of the energy supporting the combustion process by the absorption of heat.

(ii) Interference with the combustion mixing process.

(iii) Dilution of the oxygen concentration.

(iv) Breakdown of the long combustion chain reaction.

There are many suppression techniques available that use one or more of these procedures. Probably the most widely used technique is the installation of either flexible or rigid lightweight safety foam in spaces where flammable mixtures could occur. For example, flexible, reticulated (porous) polyurethane foam can easily be installed in the ullage inside a fuel tank. As the fuel is drawn from the full tank, some of it will adhere to the foam. When ignition occurs in the ullage, the wetted foam significantly reduces the combustion overpressure by rapidly absorbing and transferring heat away from the ignition point. The foam is also a locally rich zone, and the small pores interfere with the normal turbulence and mixing action that is characteristic of a flame front. The flexible polyurethane foam is currently available in five types: the orange, yellow, and red polyester types (I, II, and III); and the dark-blue and light-blue polyether types (IV and V). The density of the orange foam is 1.8 lb/ft^3, and the density of the other four types is about 1.3 lb/ft^3. The orange foam is the most porous with 10 relatively large pores per inch (ppi), the yellow and dark blue have 15 ppi, and the fine pore red and light blue have 25 ppi. The foams typically displace 3% of the fuel by volume, and approximately 2% will adhere to the foam skeleton.

The primary reason for installing the reticulated foam in the fuel tanks is to prevent large ullage overpressures following ignition of the flammable vapor. The entire tank does not need to be filled with the foam to accomplish this reduction. Optimization of internal foam installations can be achieved by installing only the volume of foam required to keep the combustion overpressure below the strength of the surrounding structure. It is possible to prevent excessive overpressures with much less than 50% of the ullage volume filled with the finer pore foam. Somewhat more of the larger pore foam would be required. This procedure is referred to as gross voiding.

Associated with the use of the polyester foams is a problem called hydrolytic instability. When used in fuel tanks under conditions of high temperature and humidity, the early polyester foams lost strength, became brittle, and eventually deteriorated to the point that they deposited debris in the fuel system. This problem has been extensively researched, and improvements in foam compositions, in particular the introduction of the polyether foam, appear to have virtually eliminated this problem.

The foam provides excellent suppression at all times and under all conditions, including multiple hits. It is passive, there are no moving parts, no sensing devices, and may require only minimum logistic and maintenance support. It can be cut and fitted into awkward configurations. It mitigates fuel surging and sloshing, and may reduce the effects of hydraulic ram. However, gross voided foam could be scrambled by the fuel during hard maneuvers.

Both a rigid, closed-cell (nonporous) ballistic foam and the flexible, reticulated foam can be installed in the void spaces or dry bays adjacent to fuel tanks and in other locations where flammable mixtures could accumulate. The rigid foam is an effective system that works for all threats. Typical weights are 1.5 to 2.5 lb/ft^3. It can be installed in individual molded blocks or it can be sprayed in place. If lines or other equipment are located in the dry bays, cutouts must be provided, and areas where cooling or ventilating airflow is required cannot be totally filled. The main function of the rigid foam is to prevent the ignition source and the flammable mixture from coming in contact. It works best if the voids are completely filled, but thicknesses greater than several inches may provide some protection. The foam usually is covered with a metallic or fabric material. The flexible foam is more advantageous in those dry bays where the rigid foam is difficult to install, but it may be of limited effectiveness against the stronger ignition sources because it normally is dry in this application.

Lightweight fibrous fillers (similar to angel hair) and expanded aluminum foil batts (known as EXPLOSAFE) have also been developed for installation in ullages and voids to suppress fires and explosions. These void fillers suppress the combustion overpressure in much the same way as the foams do. They are chemically stable in hot fuel and can have a fuel displacement and retention of about 3%. They can be used to completely fill the ullage or they can be installed in a voided pattern, depending on the allowable combustion overpressure. The expanded aluminum foil batts may be hard to remove from an ullage if internal tank inspection is required.

An alternative to the installation of foam, fibers, or expanded aluminum batts is the introduction of an inert gas, such as nitrogen, in the ullages and void spaces. Inerting systems prevent the initiation of combustion by reducing the oxygen concentration of the gaseous mixture to below the combustion limit; they make the fuel-air mixture too rich to support combustion. There are three different types of inerting techniques that have been designed for fuel tanks using nitrogen as the inerting agent: the dilution or closed-vent technique, the purging or open-vent technique, and the scrubbing technique. The dilution technique feeds nitrogen into the closed tanks as fuel is consumed or as decreases in altitude require a flow of air into the tanks to balance the increasing external atmospheric pressure. The purging technique sweeps out the fuel-air mixture in the ullage and replaces it with nitrogen. The scrubbing technique introduces fine bubbles of nitrogen into the fuel near the tank bottom. As the bubbles rise to the top, they scrub the fuel of dissolved oxygen. The tank ullage and vents are then purged. Three supply systems for the nitrogen exist. They are the bottled cryogenic liquid, the bottled high-pressure gas, and the onboard nitrogen generation, known as the onboard inert gas generating system (OBIGGS). The systems typically require a supply reservoir, pressure regulators, relief valves, a pressure demand feed control, and the necessary plumbing required for distribution to the fuel tanks and void spaces.

The parameters of mission profile, volume of void space, and tank ullage condition and volume in the combat environment play an important role in sizing a nitrogen inerting system. The mission profile dictates the number of excursions to altitude, and thus the quantity of nitrogen lost through the pressure and vent sequences. The tank ullage volume during combat is also defined by the mission profile. Another factor that must be considered when rendering a fuel tank system inert by nitrogen is the fuel itself. If oxygen is introduced into the tank ullage through the pressure and vent system during aircraft flight, the fuel will absorb an amount of air that is dependent upon the total ullage pressure. As the aircraft gains altitude, some of the dissolved air will be expelled from the fuel into the ullage. When this occurs without nitrogen dilution of the expelled gases, the oxygen concentration may exceed the safe level.

The nitrogen inerting system can provide excellent fire and explosion protection at moderate weight, with no fuel loss, and in crowded ullages and voids dispersed throughout the aircraft, as long as the oxygen concentration can be maintained below the flammability limit. However, with very large ignition sources, combustion can occur, and the overpressure will vary depending on the ignition level, mixture volume, and oxygen concentration. Furthermore, multi-hit capabilities may be limited because of leakage of the nitrogen through battle damage holes.

Logistics and maintenance requirements are relatively high for the liquid and gaseous systems because facilities for the supply of the nitrogen are required at each air base, and periodic checks of the equipment are necessary to ensure operational capability. Also, nitrogen inerting cannot be used in habitable compartments. The initial and life cycle costs are usually relatively high, and the liquid system may require periodic filling when the aircraft is in an alert status.

The full-time, onboard generation of nitrogen appears to eliminate many of the disadvantages of the stored liquid and gaseous nitrogen systems. Nitrogen can be obtained from an air supply, such as pressure and temperature conditioned engine bleed air, by absorption, by catalytic combustion, or by diffusion processes. The absorption or sorbent-bed fuel tank inerting technique uses the phenomenon of oxygen absorption from air by fluomine, a metal chelate. The catalytic reactor generates an inert gas by reducing the oxygen content in the air by catalytic oxidation of jet fuel at low temperature. Two candidate diffusion systems have been examined, a module composed of many hollow fiber membranes and a molecular sieve. The diffusion type of inerting system appears to be very effective when the volume requirements of the inert gas are not too large, such as on a helicopter.

Introduction of a HALON gas, such as HALON 1301 (CF_3Br), into ullages and voids during periods of potential combat is another suppression technique that is similar to nitrogen inerting, except that it does not replace the oxygen. Instead, the HALON is there to react with the transient, intermediate combustion products to break down the combustion process. The HALON is stored in liquid form in high-pressure bottles and is introduced as a noncorrosive, low-toxicity gas into the void spaces and ullages by the crew just prior to entering the combat area. A short burst fills the ullages and voids, and this is followed by a steady, low flow rate to replace the HALON that becomes dissolved in the fuel and lost in the voids. A potential problem is the possible stratification of the HALON in deep ullages.

Other suppression concepts for dry bays are the powder pack and the purge mat. Both the pack and the mat are located within the voids. When they are perforated by a penetrator or fragment, they spill their contents which suppress any possible combustion from taking place. The powder pack contains a dry fire suppression material, whereas the purge mat contains a high-pressure inerting gas, such as nitrogen.

Another technique for ridding the void spaces of flammable vapors is to provide a continuous flow of air through the space. The air can be obtained from the inlet duct air or from ram-air ducts on the exterior surface of the aircraft. Flowing air is often used in engine compartments to both cool the engine and vent any flammable vapors.

The use of a special "antimisting" fuel is another technique for preventing combustion. Antimisting fuel is aviation fuel that contains an additive, such as a polymer powder called FM-9, that prevents the development of fuel mists. Although the additive may be very effective in preventing combustion, both in flight and during a crash, it can have some disadvantages. For example, jet engines can only burn fuel that is injected into the combustor as a mist, which is precisely what the additive is supposed to prevent. Consequently, the fuel must be treated by shearing or chopping the polymer chains prior to injection into the combustor. This fuel may also cause problems in the pumps, filters, and other distribution components where a gel could form under certain conditions, causing a blockage of the fuel flow. Furthermore, the properties seem to change with the environmental conditions, and the additive may have to be blended with the fuel at the aircraft fueling station due to storage stability problems. Nevertheless, the antimisting fuel is a potential survivability enhancement technique, and a large-scale study on its use in commercial aviation has been underway for several years. The most effective use of the antimisting fuel will probably require the development of propulsion systems that have been specifically designed to use this type of fuel.

Small volume, lightweight, active fire and explosion suppression systems have also been developed for fuel tank ullages and voids. This type of system operates by first detecting the onset of a damage process, such as the presence of an ignition source or flame front, and then rapidly dispersing a chemical fire-suppressing agent, such as HALON 1301 used in the COBRA system, from high-pressure containers before the combustion process can build up. The detector may utilize an infrared sensitive lead sulfide photoelectric cell or an ultraviolet sensitive tube. Since radiation sensors are line of sight type detectors, complex voids and multicell tanks may require more than one detector and possibly multiple dispensers. The radiation detectors must also be shielded from all stray light to ensure that the system is not inadvertently triggered. Detectors that sense the hydraulic ram pressure on the wall of a penetrated tank have also been developed. The tank ullage and the void spaces around the penetrated tank are filled with the suppressing agent when the detector is triggered by the pressure.

The active type of fire suppression systems are ineffective if the peak combustion overpressure is reached before the chemical agent is dispensed. Furthermore, the logistics support for the bottle storage systems can be high because the bottles must be replaced after each activation. Periodic inspection of the bottles may also be required to ensure that inadvertent activation has not occurred, and a deactivation circuit is required for routine maintenance. Toxicity and corrosive properties of the gaseous and the dry chemical suppression agents used must also be considered.

The fire-extinguishing systems used on aircraft put out the fire rather than prevent it from occurring, as do the suppression systems. A temperature sensor registers an overheat condition and an extinguishing agent, such as HALON, is dispensed into the compartment with the fire in one or more shots.

Fire containment within aircraft dry bays is a major requirement when it is neither possible to prevent the fire from occurring nor possible to extinguish it. Fire migration throughout an aircraft can create many problems that were unforeseen in the early development stages. Exposure of components and structure to high thermal environments can circumvent many excellent survivability features. Recent developments have resulted in various insulating foams, ablators, and intumescent coatings to provide improved fire containment.

A summary listing of some of the current techniques for preventing fires and explosions in aircraft is given in Table 5.10.

**Table 5.10   Listing of Some Current Techniques
for Preventing Fires and Explosions**

Passive Techniques

Flexible, reticulated polyurethane (polyester and polyether) foam
Rigid, closed-cell ballistic foam
Fibrous filler
Expanded aluminum batts
Nitrogen inerting (liquid, gaseous, or onboard generation)
HALON inerting
Antimisting fuel
Powder packs
Purge mats
Void space venting with air
Fire walls

Active Techniques

Ignition source/flame front detection and combustion suppression
Hydraulic ram detection and combustion suppression
Fire detection and fire extinguishing

(d) Hydraulic ram protection: There are a number of design techniques that have been developed to provide varying degrees of protection against hydraulic ram. For example, the volume of fuel in each tank should be maximized since the liquid pressure pulse attenuation is dependent upon the fuel mass available to absorb it. Small (low-volume) tanks, if unavoidable, can be made more survivable provided they are shallow and are not totally filled when hit. Smooth, simple tank contours with shapes and structures designed to resist the internal pressure should be used, and narrow, complex tank shapes, and abrupt section cutouts should be avoided. Crash-resistant tank and structural designs using energy-absorbing and tear-resistant construction can significantly reduce the effects of hydraulic ram. Particular attention should be given to any engine inlet duct/fuel tank and engine compartment/fuel tank interfaces. Techniques for minimizing the damage to the tank wall include the use of tear-resistant and energy-absorbing materials and the use of concentric dual-walled tanks next to the inlet duct and engine compartment, with depletion of the interstitial fuel before entering the combat area. The fuel distribution components should also be designed to withstand any internal and external hydraulic ram pressures, and external drop tanks should maintain their structural integrity when penetrated.

The propulsion system.   The propulsion system is usually considered to be made up of the engine(s), the inlet(s) and exhaust(s), the lubrication subsystem, and the controls, accessory drives, and gearboxes. The vulnerability of the propulsion system is highly sensitive to the specific system design and the damage mechanisms. Consequently, gas turbine design requirements have become increasingly more demanding in recent years, not only in terms of performance, but also in terms of survivability requirements. For example, a major program is currently underway within the Advanced Technology Engine Study (ATES) on the development of a multiple application core engine (MACE). A follow-on to the ATES/MACE program is the propulsion assessment for tactical systems (PATS). Such items as the engine cycle selection, engine configuration, component design, and component vulnerability are to be examined with respect to their contribution to the vulnerability of the propulsion system itself as well as to the survivability of the aircraft. In general, the latest engines under development have higher rotating speeds and higher peak gas temperatures and pressures, which make them appear to be more vulnerable. However, they are also smaller, with fewer stages, and lighter, with cooler casing temperatures and lower specific fuel consumption. These improvements in size, weight, and efficiency contribute to making the aircraft a smaller target with reduced fuel requirements and, consequently, more survivable.

(1)   The kill modes.   The possible damage-caused failure modes of the propulsion system are fuel ingestion, foreign object ingestion, inlet flow distortion, lubrication starvation, compressor case perforation or distortion, combustor case perforation, turbine section failure, exhaust duct failure, and engine controls and accessories failure.

(2)   Design guidance and vulnerability reduction techniques.   The design of the propulsion system is a highly specialized effort performed by only a few organizations. As a consequence, only a few of the more general vulnerability reduction techniques are described here.

(a)   General principles: The propulsion system should be configured to minimize the probability of a complete loss of thrust caused by a single hit from a specified projectile or fragment. Protection of critical engine components should be provided against the damage mechanisms using the shielding provided by structural members, other equipment, or, if nothing else is available, armor. The engine mounting system should be redundant and not fail because of a single hit. Redundancy of components should be considered, and the engine should be located out of the expected line of fire and isolated from the fuel tanks as much as possible. Secondary hazards from damaged engines, such as hot gas torching and broken blades, should be contained. Measures should be taken to prevent engine fires from spreading beyond engine compartments or nacelles. The engine compartments or nacelles should be drained and vented, and means should be provided for shutting off the flow of flammable fluids into or through the compartments. A highly reliable and survivable fire detection device and fast-acting fire extinguishers with one or more dispensing shots should be installed in each engine compartment.

A major system redundancy can be provided by the use of multiple engines. For multiple-engined aircraft, the engines should be physically separated or protected, including thermal insulation if required, to prevent complete loss of thrust due to a hit from a single propagator. Design techniques should be incorporated to prevent or minimize the probability of combat damage, such as fire propagating from one engine to another engine and causing a total loss of thrust or severely degraded performance. The engines should be completely independent, with separate fuel and oil tankage, feed lines (with crossovers), pumps, and controls, and the controls should have a fail-safe response if damaged.

(b) Prevention of fuel and foreign object ingestion: The cracking and petaling of common fuel tank and inlet duct walls due to penetration and hydraulic ram can allow chunks of metal and large quantities of fuel to be ingested into the engine. Elimination of fuel and foreign object ingestion by eliminating the fuel tank/inlet duct interface completely, or by reducing the inlet duct damage due to hydraulic ram, are the most important design techniques for reducing the probability of engine failure due to ingestion. Techniques for reducing the damage due to hydraulic ram include the special construction described above, the use of duct materials that are ballistically tolerant and yield very little debris when either impacted by penetrators or subjected to hydraulic ram, and a fuel consumption schedule that ensures that fuel in the tanks adjacent to the inlet ducts is used prior to entering hostile areas. When engines are damaged by ingested metal, secondary damage mechanisms can be created that are more lethal to the aircraft than the primary damage mechanisms. Generation of penetrators, such as broken turbine blades, as a result of damage to high-speed rotating components may be reduced by the incorporation of engine fan, compressor, and turbine blade containment or shielding measures.

(c) Prevention of inlet flow distortion: Air inlet distortion can be the result of the large petaling of the inlet duct walls caused by hydraulic ram or by a detonation of an HE projectile near the duct wall. Construction techniques that mitigate hydraulic ram damage should reduce the probability this failure mode will occur.

(d) Prevention of lubrication starvation: One of the most important techniques for the reduction of propulsion system vulnerability is a fail-safe lubrication subsystem. The relatively large presented areas of the components, their ease of perforation by relatively small damage mechanisms, and the short time the pilot has to act after loss of lubrication make protection of this subsystem vital. The probability of continued operation can be enhanced by the proper location of the components, by redundancy, and by damage-tolerant and fail-safe design. Oil sumps and lines should be self-sealing, shielded, or armored. Bypass lines that isolate damage or leaking lines should be considered, and provision for the manual override of an automatic shutdown of the engine after loss of oil should be available to allow escape from the immediate hostile area.

The flight control system. The flight control system consists of the controls, the control surfaces, and the hydraulic subsystems. Because maintaining aircraft stability and control is one of the most critical factors affecting safety of flight as well as the combat survival of the aircraft and crew, much attention is given to the design of the control system to ensure that there is no unacceptable degradation of functional capabilities due to one or more component failures. Many of the safety of flight features, such as independent hydraulic subsystems and backup controls, can also cause a reduction in vulnerability, provided they are properly designed into the aircraft considering the effects of combat damage. Two independent hydraulic subsystems that have lines running side by side through the aircraft may increase the safety of flight but not the combat survivability, because of the likelihood that a single hit by a damage mechanism can kill both subsystems, leading to a loss of the aircraft.

(1)   The kill modes.   The possible damage-caused failure modes of the control system are the disruption of the control signal path, the loss of control power, the loss of aircraft motion sensor data, damage to the control surfaces and hinges, and hydraulic fluid fires.

(2)   Design guidance and vulnerability reduction techniques.
(a)   General principles: The flight control system should be designed to prevent the loss of flight control due to a single hit by a damage mechanism anywhere on the system; that is, there should be no single point failure possibilities. To accomplish this, techniques such as multiple, independent, and widely separated control signal paths, motion sensors, control surfaces, and control power systems should be used; and no component failure should result in a hard-over signal to a control surface actuator. Jam protection or override capability should be included in the design, and heat-resistant materials and/or fire suppression techniques should be used to protect those control components located in areas where fires or hot gas impingement could occur.

For highly complex flight control systems, such as fly-by-wire, the implementation of redundancy after damage may be difficult. The flight control components that have been damaged or killed must be identified and the undamaged components reconfigured according to the control law selected. A thorough analysis of the multiple combinations of possible combat damage effects must be evaluated in order to select the most effective component arrangement. Surface management is a recently developed functional redundancy technique in which the surviving control surfaces on an aircraft are reconfigured to fly the aircraft after damage to one of the surfaces. The aircraft automatic flight control system contains a hierarchy of control laws consisting of a primary control mode, which utilizes all of the control surfaces, and various reversion control modes, which utilize all flyable subsets of the control surfaces. The AFCS should be structured such that if any one of the control surfaces on the aircraft is disabled, thereby defeating the primary control mode, the aircraft can remain controllable by reconfiguring to one of the remaining reversion modes.

(b)   Control signal path continuity: Two major procedures used to maintain continuity of the control signal path are to reduce the vulnerability of the individual components and to add additional components for redundancy. The vulnerability of the individual components can be reduced by reducing their size (miniaturization) and/or by increasing their damage tolerance, or $P_{k/h}$. Small components are less likely to be hit and have the added advantage of usually being lighter. An example of this is the use of a fly-by-wire electrical signal transmission subsystem to replace a mechanical signal transmission subsystem. The reduction in $P_{k/h}$ is accomplished by good design and by proper location. For example, mounting the servovalve assembly of a servoactuator on the top of the barrel of the power cylinder reduces the probability of a severed feedback link from the cylinder to the valve because of the shorter length and the protected position of the link. Servoactuators can also jam when penetrated by a ballistic damage mechanism. These jams can be freed by several design techniques, such as the use of a frangible piston or malleable internal steel barrel. Jamming of the cockpit controls caused by a jam along one of the mechanical signal paths can be prevented by the use of cartridge springs between the mechanical linkages and by self-aligning bearings for torque tubes. Ballistically tolerant mechanical linkages, such as bell cranks and quadrants, have been designed that can accept multiple hits and remain functional. These components can be constructed of low-density, nonmetallic composite materials with redundant load paths that allow projectiles to core out material with minimum structural damage to the component. Locating the control components out of the line of fire, behind major structure, and out of potential fire areas also helps to ensure their continued operation.

One of the most basic and obvious ways to enhance the survivability of a flight control system is to provide either a backup system providing a "limp-home" capability or one or more additional subsystems providing flight control functions identical to those provided by the primary subsystems. Adequate separation of the redundant control signal paths is required, and redundant fly-by-wire systems should consider the use of more than one flight control computer. Separation of the redundant control paths should be accomplished in such a way that masking is provided by intervening structure and equipment. Statically unstable aircraft using stability augmentation to maintain control require that the backup systems also have stability augmentation in addition to the control power necessary for survivability.

A simple example of the total redundancy concept is the replacement of a single component with a configuration consisting of two components of the same kind connected in parallel, such that a malfunction of one component will not disable the other component. An example of this type of application is the use of two sets of cables and rods to transmit control signals from the stick to the actuators, with one set running along each side of the fuselage. Functional control redundancy consists of providing a backup capability to a system by using a second functionally equivalent but physically different system. Nearly all backup flight control systems (BUFCS) fall into this category. A specific example is the use of a fly-by-wire control augmentation system to back up the primary mechanical control signal transmission system.

(c)   Reduction of control power loss and effects: The major concern here is the prevention or suppression of hydraulic fluid leaks from the reservoirs, plumbing, and servoactuators. One way this can be accomplished is by the addition of logic elements to the hydraulic subsystem. These logic elements detect the leaks and then isolate the damaged portion before a sizable loss of fluid occurs. Fluid in the other branches of the subsystem is preserved, permitting the operation of actuators outside of the damaged portion. The two most common types of hydraulic logic elements are hydraulic fuzes and reservoir level sensors (RLS). Hydraulic fuzes, also known as flow difference sensors, operate on the principle that the return flow must vary in direct proportion to the supply flow in a properly functioning hydraulic subsystem. A difference from the normal ratio between the return flow and the supply flow is interpreted as a leak, and that part of the system monitored by the fuze is disconnected from the rest of the system. The reservoir level sensor is used in subsystems that have two or more independent circuits supplied by one reservoir. The sensor detects a reduction in the level of hydraulic fluid in the reservoir and alternately disconnects the circuits from the reservoir, one at a time, until the level ceases to drop. The damaged circuit has now been disconnected from the rest of the system, thereby conserving the remaining hydraulic fluid for the other circuits.

Another power component that requires attention is the servoactuator. The actuator can be made ballistically resistant to the damage mechanisms using either dual-hardness steel or electroslag remelt (ESR) steel for the power barrel. The design of the servoactuator with respect to the location of important features, such as the control valve and sensitive linkages, is also important. Dual, tandem actuators can use rip-stop body construction. This technique employs separate sections of the cylinder body that are fastened together at the junction between each power system in such a manner as to prevent the propagation of a rip or crack from one power chamber of the actuator to a location where the hydraulic fluid would be lost from both chambers of the unit, leading to a total loss of power. A major change to this subsystem would be the use of electrically powered, self-contained actuators. This change could eliminate the need for much of the hydraulic plumbing used in contemporary aircraft.

When the total loss of either control power to, or control of, a control surface is a possibility, provision should be made to allow the surface to transition or fail to a safe position. For example, aircraft that incorporate either unit or differential horizontal tails should have some way of capturing the tail and preventing it from going hard-over when the power or control is lost, so that controlled flight may be maintained as long as possible.

(d)   Motion sensor data availability: Continuity of aircraft flight data can be provided to the AFCS in the event of the loss of either a motion sensor or the connecting signal path by using redundant, effectively separated sensors. The concept of analytic redundancy (the use of analytical relationships to determine certain parameters given a set of other parameters) utilizing a digital filter has been developed to maximize the amount of redundancy for a given set of sensors. Alternatively, this concept can also be used to reduce the number of sensors required to meet survivability and reliability specifications, offering a savings in cost and weight. In addition, some indirect improvements in survivability may be possible through the use of analytic redundancy to automatically detect failures of other electronic equipment, a job usually delegated to the pilot.

(e)   Control surface and hinge vulnerability reduction: All components in the flight control system should be fail-safe. Consequently, the hinges and control surfaces should be made damage-tolerant, and redundant load paths, such as multiple hinges, should be used.

(f)   Prevention of hydraulic fluid fires: The previous standard aircraft hydraulic fluid, MIL-H-5606, is highly flammable and can be ignited upon exposure to hot surfaces and gunfire, particularly the incendiary projectiles. Consequently, a less flammable hydraulic fluid, MIL-H-83282, has been developed. The fluid has been flight tested and found to be suitable for aircraft operational environments and interchangeability with the existing standard fluid and parts. It has met or exceeded the high-temperature range for MIL-H-5606 and is compatible down to $-40°F$. The fluid is now being incorporated in some operational aircraft. Navy tests have indicated that MIL-H-83282 is acceptable (at least to $-40°F$) in hydraulic devices such as landing gear shock struts and control surface dampers, even though these devices are not connected into the aircraft hydraulic systems and do not benefit from the warming effects associated with hydraulic circulation.

The power train and rotor blade / propeller system.   The power train system consists of a series of transmissions, gearboxes, and connecting drive shafts that transmit power from the engine(s) to the rotor blades or propellers.

(1)   The kill modes.   The kill modes of the power train and blade system are loss of lubrication and mechanical or structural failure.

(2)   Design guidance and vulnerability reduction techniques.
(a)   Prevention of the loss of lubrication effects: The loss of lubrication in transmissions and gearboxes can be prevented by incorporating a backup or emergency lubrication subsystem or by making these components damage-tolerant. Damage-tolerance techniques to delay or prevent failure due to lubrication subsystem damage can provide significant benefits for little or no penalties if incorporated into the initial design. Minimizing the probability of lubrication subsystem failures has been researched and studied extensively during the past decade. There are many different types of power train lubrication subsystems, such as the rotor shaft cooler and the integral oil-air system, and the specific damage-tolerant design selected will be dependent upon the type of primary subsystem used. Less vulnerable lubricating techniques include the use of solid lubricants, high-temperature grease, and oil additives and formulations. High-temperature steel bearings and cages and improved bearing geometry allow prolonged operation at elevated temperatures.

(b)   Prevention of mechanical or structural failure: For those portions of the transmission and gearbox housing where penetration by a damage mechanism cannot be tolerated, masking should be used if possible;

otherwise ballistic-resistant construction or armor shielding must be employed. Rotor blade and drive shaft designs must provide for safe operation after damage. The use of large, thin-wall shafts can prevent total severance and are less prone to low-cycle fatigue failure due to ballistic damage than small, thick-wall shafts. Shaft couplings and intermediate shaft supports or hangers must also be damage-tolerant. The main rotor shaft should be designed to allow autorotation of the main rotor in the event the shaft is severed or the transmission or engine seizes. The prime consideration in the survivability of the rotor blades is to keep them intact. The secondary consideration is to maintain sufficient blade stiffness after damage. Redundant and separated load paths, in conjunction with damage-tolerant materials, are required to accomplish these two goals. Considerable progress has been made in the development of helicopter rotor blades that can withstand hits by HE projectiles.

The crew system.   Many types of combat damage effects can be harmful to aircraft crew members, either directly by penetration or indirectly by smoke, fire, loss of oxygen, or other effects that make the aircraft inhospitable. Vulnerability reduction techniques in the crew stations are mostly a function of shielding, using either nonessential components or armor. The installation of armor falls into three categories: airframe, seat, and body.

When practical, airframe armor should be integral with the structure. Testing of spaced armor systems has shown that HE-I projectiles may be defeated by a two-plate (trigger and backup) system. Protection against AP-I projectiles can be attained by the use of monolithic metal or ceramic armors with a woven fiberglass or Kevlar backing. An acceptable level of protection can be provided by certain canopy materials against small arms projectiles. The use of spall curtains in the crew compartments can prevent secondary damage, and a transparent blast shield between the pilot and copilot can prevent the loss of both crew members to one internal detonation of an HE warhead. Aircrew seat armor should provide protection from both penetrators and crashes. In some aircraft, attack helicopters for example, body armor may be required for the crew's survival.

Protection of the crew from the secondary damage effects of smoke and fire consists mainly of minimizing the amount of combustible or toxic materials in the crew compartments and preventing smoke and toxic fumes from entering the compartments.

The structural system.   The structural system consists of all of the components or members used to establish the configuration of the aircraft and to transmit and react all inertial and aerodynamic loads. The structure consists of the fuselage, the wing, and the empennage subsystems.

(1)   The kill modes.   The structural damage-caused failure modes are structural removal, pressure overload, thermal weakening, and penetration.

(2) Design guidance and vulnerability reduction techniques. The vulnerability reduction of the structural system is largely dependent upon the construction type and material selection, factors that are also critical to modern aircraft from weight and cost considerations. Fiber-reinforced composites, such as boron or graphite fibers bonded within epoxy resins in both sandwich- and solid-layered configurations, are now being proposed as major load-carrying structures on several aircraft currently in design. As a consequence of the increase in the structural applications of composites, in particular the fiber-reinforced composites, and the fact that the behavior of these new materials is significantly different in many aspects from the more conventional aluminum structures, investigation of the vulnerability of composite structures is mandatory.

Of prime importance when selecting aircraft structural materials is the selection of materials with qualities that prevent or minimize the propagation of damage. The aircraft structure itself should be designed to be as damage tolerant as practical to minimize the vulnerability of the system to the damage mechanisms. It should be of a fail-safe design, achieved through the use of multiple load paths and crack stoppers to reduce the probability of catastrophic structural failure due to battle damage. Sufficient strength and redundancy to permit evasive maneuvers to the limit load following the occurrence of damage should be provided, if practical.

Secondary thermal effects should be minimized throughout the entire airframe. These thermal effects include the burning of fuel, hydraulic fluid, oil, or other combustible material, and the torching from a damaged engine or hot air bleed line. The design of the structure should also minimize the secondary effects from exploding ordnance.

The other aircraft systems. The other systems on combat aircraft, such as the avionics system, the armament system, the launch and recovery systems, the electrical system, and the environmental control system, must also be considered when designing for survivability. In general, the vulnerability reduction techniques for these systems are similar in concept to those described above. These include the six major concepts of component redundancy (with separation), component location, passive and active damage suppression, shielding, and component elimination.

Selected Bibliography

Edney, B. E. et. al., "Ballistic Test Facility Guide," JTCG/AS-76-D-001, Sept. 1976.

Hogan, D. T., "Survivability Design Guidelines for Fly-by-Wire Flight Control Systems Development," Master's thesis, Naval Postgraduate School, Monterey, Calif., Dec. 1983.

Remers, R. T., "Design for Reduction of Aircraft Vulnerability," *Proceedings on Aircraft Operational Experience and Its Impact on Safety and Survivability*, AGARD Conference Proceedings No. 212, May 31–June 7, 1976, pp. 19-1 to 19-23.

Snow, R., "The Application of Markov Processes to Vulnerability and Effectiveness Analysis," to be published by the JTCG/ME as 61-JTCG/ME-82-7.

Squire, T. B., "Self-Sealing Fuel Tank Preactivated Sealant Program," JTCG/AS-74-T-007, July 1975.

Wyeth, H. W. G., "Fuel System Protection Methods," AGARD Lecture Series No. 123, Aircraft Fire Safety, pp. 4-1 to 4-15.

6. SUSCEPTIBILITY

6.1   WHAT IS SUSCEPTIBILITY?

Susceptibility refers to the inability of an aircraft to avoid being damaged in the pursuit of its mission, to its probability of being hit. The level or degree of susceptibility of an aircraft in an encounter with a threat is dependent upon three major factors: the scenario, the threat, and the aircraft. The scenario includes the physical environment in which the encounter takes place, the threat deployment and activity, and the aircraft flight path and tactics, including any supporting forces. The important features of the threat are its characteristics, its operations, and its lethality. The aircraft observables or detectable signatures, any countermeasures used, and the aircraft performance capabilities and self-protection armament are the important factors associated with the aircraft itself.

To illustrate the many and varied features of an encounter between one aircraft and one threat, a one-on-one encounter, consider a utility helicopter attempting to deliver troops on a bright, sunny day to a location near the forward edge of the battle area. As the helicopter nears the FEBA, it drops down into a valley to take advantage of terrain masking. However, a self-propelled, radar-directed AAA system is in the vicinity and detects the helicopter with its scanning radar. The observer inside the AAA vehicle looks at the approaching helicopter through an optical tracker and identifies the aircraft as an enemy. The AAA radar is then switched to the target tracking mode. Meanwhile, the radar warning receiver in the helicopter has detected the scanning signal from the AAA radar and alerted the pilot as to the type, location, and status of the threat. The pilot immediately ejects chaff, attempts to break the lock of the tracking radar by maneuvering his helicopter, and searches for some terrain or vegetation to hide behind. The AAA radar receiver sees the chaff and starts to track it rather than the helicopter. However, the observer on the AAA platform has been watching the helicopter through an optical tracker and redirects the tracking radar back to the helicopter. A short time later, after a fire-control solution has been obtained, contact-fuzed HE and AP-I projectiles are fired toward the maneuvering aircraft. One or more of them might hit the helicopter. The more likely it is that a projectile does strike the helicopter, the more susceptible is the helicopter.

The modeling and quantification of the individual events and elements in such an encounter is referred to as a susceptibility assessment. In the assessment, each important event and element, such as the radar signature of the helicopter, the radar detection of the helicopter, the effectiveness of

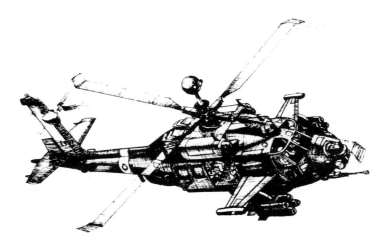

the chaff in decoying the radar tracker, and the effects of the helicopter maneuvers, is modeled, and numerical values are determined for the model parameters. Susceptibility reduction, like vulnerability reduction, is the procedure in which the susceptibility of an aircraft is reduced to its lowest possible value within the design constraints of cost, performance, weight, maintainability, and the other aspects of aircraft effectiveness.

Because susceptibility is so dependent upon the capabilities of the non-terminal threat elements, and because many of the nonterminal elements use either radar or i.r. for aircraft detection and tracking and for missile guidance, a knowledge of radar and i.r. fundamentals is very helpful to the understanding of susceptibility and the techniques for susceptibility reduction. Consequently, background information on radar and i.r. fundamentals is given in Appendix B.

6.2 IDENTIFICATION OF THE ESSENTIAL ELEMENTS AFFECTING SUSCEPTIBILITY

Obviously, there are many diverse factors that influence susceptibility, many of which are difficult to model and to quantify. In order to determine which of the factors or events and elements are the most important and which ones are of lesser importance, an essential elements analysis (EEA) should be conducted. In the EEA, the timewise sequence or chain of events in the encounter to be assessed is examined in detail, starting with the final undesired event and proceeding to the initial event. There is a close parallel between the use of the EEA to determine the essential elements in the scenario and the use of the fault tree analysis to determine the critical components for vulnerability. Both analyses start with an undesired event and then determine what events either can or are required to cause the undesired event.

To illustrate the EEA, consider an encounter between a friendly strike aircraft and an enemy interceptor carrying an air-to-air, infrared homing missile. The enemy aircraft will normally launch the i.r. missile from a position behind the target aircraft, because that's where the i.r. signature is usually the most intense. The missile will then home in on the i.r. radiation emitted and reflected by the target. When the missile gets close enough to the target, the proximity fuze will detonate the warhead. The final (and undesired) event in the susceptibility portion of the encounter is when the blast wave and fragments from the detonated warhead strike the aircraft. In the EEA, this encounter is examined by starting with the final event and working backwards in time.

In order for the blast wave and fragments to strike the aircraft, the warhead must detonate within a certain distance from the aircraft. That distance depends upon the fragment velocities and spray angles and the relative velocity vectors and attitudes of the aircraft and the missile. In order to detonate the warhead, the fuze must first detect the target and then initiate the detonation chain. In order to have an opportunity to fuze, the missile motor must ignite inside the maximum range of the missile to the target, and the guidance system must function properly. In order for the guidance system to function properly, the i.r. seeker must be locked on to the proper i.r. source, such as the target's engine hot parts or exhaust plume, not some other spurious i.r. source or decoy, such as a flare. In order to achieve lock-on, the i.r. source must be within the tracking system's field of view. In order to place the target within the tracking system's field of view and inside the missile's maximum range, the enemy fighter must be maneuvered to come within a certain launch region with respect to the target. This requires performance capabilities on the part of the enemy fighter aircraft, such as speed and turn radius and rate, and acquisition of the target aircraft by the fighter crew with their onboard sensors (radar, visual, etc.). In order to detect the target, the fighter must be within the limits of the onboard sensors, which are influenced by the signatures of the target aircraft.

The chain does not end here, but this example is enough to illustrate the process which should be continued back to the point where the friendly aircraft first enters the hostile airspace. A summary of the EEA for this encounter is given in Table 6.1, and some questions associated with each event and element are listed. There are, of course, practical limits to the degree to which the chain should be broken down. The EEA should, however, be sufficiently precise to allow the identification of each important event and element. In particular, it is important to note those elements that the friendly forces have control over, for those are the ones that should be examined for the possibility of reducing the susceptibility. Table 6.2 contains many of the essential elements and events that are applicable to most encounters.

6.3 SUSCEPTIBILITY ASSESSMENT

Modeling and Measures

A susceptibility assessment is a modeling of the sequence of events and elements in the encounter between the aircraft and the threat until one or more hits on the aircraft occurs. Those events and elements that were

Table 6.1   EEA Summary

Events and Elements	EE?	Questions
1. Blast and fragments strike the A/C.	Yes	How many fragments hit the A/C and where do they hit?
2. Missile warhead detonates within lethal range.	Yes	Can the onboard ECM suite inhibit the functioning of the proximity fuze?
3. Radar proximity fuze detects A/C.	Yes	Will chaff decoy the fuze?
4. Missile propelled and guided to vicinity of A/C.	Yes	Can the target A/C outmaneuver the missile? Are i.r. flares effective decoys?
5. Missile guidance system functions in flight.	Yes	Are i.r. flares effective decoys?
6. Missile motor ignites.	Yes	
7. Missile guidance system locked on to target's engine i.r. radiation.	Yes	Are i.r. flares effective decoys? Is the engine's i.r. suppressor effective in preventing lock-on?
8. Target's engines within missile's field of view.	Yes	Are the engine hot parts shielded?
9. Enemy fighter maneuvers to put target into field of view and within maximum range.	Yes	Does the enemy fighter have a performance edge? Does the target A/C have an offensive capability against the enemy fighter?
10. Target acquired by enemy fighter's onboard sensors.	Yes	Does the onboard ECM suite inhibit acquisition by the fighter's radar? Do the tactics place the target outside sensor limits? Is the camouflage paint scheme effective against visual acquisition?
11. Enemy fighter given steering by ground control intercept (GCI) net to acquire target.	Yes	Does the onboard or stand-off ECM suite have a communications jamming capability? Is a fighter escort available?
12. Target A/C designated to enemy fighter and fighter launched.	Yes	Does the onboard or stand-off ECM suite have a communications jamming capability?
13. Fighter available to launch against target.	Yes	Are there any supporting forces to destroy the enemy fighter on the ground?
14. Enemy C^3 net functions properly.	Yes	Does the stand-off ECM suite have a communications jamming capability?
15. GCI picks up track on target A/C.	Yes	Is the target A/C easily detected and tracked by radar? Is the stand-off ECM suite effective against search radars?
16. Target designated hostile by enemy commander.	Yes	Does the stand-off ECM suite have IFFN countermeasures?
17. Early warning net detects and establishes track (course and speed) of target A/C.	Yes	Is the target A/C easily detected and tracked by radar? Is the stand-off ECM suite effective against search radars? How much do the tactics expose the target A/C to the detection sensors?

Table 6.2 Some Essential Elements for a Susceptibility Assessment

Threat	Scenario	Aircraft
Command, control, and communication capabilities (C^3)	Weapons locations	Countermeasures Threat warning
A/C detection capabilities	Terrain	Signatures
A/C tracking capabilities	A/C flight path and tactics	Performance
Fire-control procedures and ballistic projectile characteristics	A/C detection and tracking	Armament
	Propagator launch/firing and flyout	
	Warhead detonation	
Missile guidance and performance capabilities	Supporting forces	
Warhead and fuzing characteristics		

identified in the EEA as important should be included in the model. In general, the events can be divided into two categories. The first category consists of those events that are associated with the detection, tracking, fire control, and either the launch and guidance of missiles or the firing of ballistic projectiles or radiation beams. Large-scale modeling of the elements and events in this category is usually done on an analog or digital computer and is referred to as a simulation or flyout model. Small-scale modeling usually consists of relatively simple equations that provide estimates or evaluations of each of the portions of the encounter.

The output from the model consists of one or more susceptibility measure predictions. One of the most important susceptibility measures is the closest point of approach (CPA) of a missile, projectile, or radiation beam to a particular location on the aircraft. The CPA is also called the miss distance. In general, the smaller the miss distance, the more likely the aircraft will be hit. The probability that the aircraft is hit, measured by P_H, depends upon the miss distance and upon the physical size of the aircraft presented to the propagator. Other important susceptibility measures are the probability the aircraft is detected and the errors associated with the tracking system. Because the probability of detection, the tracking errors, and the effectiveness of countermeasures are so strongly dependent upon the size of the signatures of the aircraft, the determination of the aircraft signatures is an essential part of any susceptibility assessment, and the sizes of the signatures are important susceptibility measures.

The second assessment category consists of those events and elements that are associated with the detonation of a proximity-fuzed warhead and includes the terminal encounter geometry between the missile and the aircraft, the fuzing capability and logic, and the damage mechanism genera-

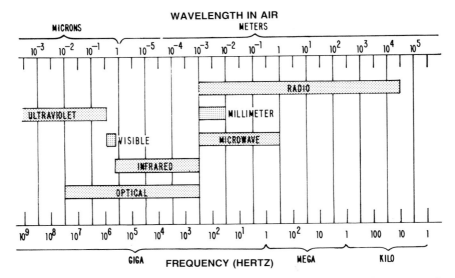

Fig. 6.1 Location of the electromagnetic signatures within the electromagnetic spectrum.

tion and propagation toward the aircraft. When the vulnerability of the aircraft to the impacting damage mechanisms is included in the second category, this part of the assessment is referred to as the endgame analysis. Because the endgame analysis excludes the propagator flyout but includes the vulnerability of the aircraft, it is described in Chap. 5. Assessments that include the events in both categories (flyout and endgame) are referred to as survivability assessments. These assessments are described in Chap. 7.

Aircraft Signatures

The characteristics of the aircraft that are used by the threat nonterminal elements for detection and tracking are called the aircraft signatures or observables. Aircraft have many different kinds of signatures, such as the radar signature, the infrared signature, and the aural signature, but all of the signatures, except for the aural signature, are electromagnetic in origin. Figure 6.1 shows the location of the three major electromagnetic signature bands (the radar, the i.r., and the visible) within the electromagnetic spectrum. (Most lasers operate at a wavelength in the i.r. band.) In addition to these three signatures, any intentional or inadvertent electromagnetic emissions from the aircraft, such as the aircraft's navigation radar, can be used by the threat detection, tracking, and guidance elements.

Radar signature.

(1) Radar cross section. When a radar antenna radiates an electromagnetic pulse or continuous wave in the direction of an airborne aircraft or

target, the power in the signal beam is spread out in space as the signal travels toward the aircraft. The intensity of the signal at any point in the beam can be expressed in terms of the power density, which is the signal power per unit surface area of the beam. When the signal strikes and passes over the aircraft surface, a portion of the incident energy may be absorbed as heat, another portion may pass completely through parts of the aircraft, and the remainder is reradiated in many different directions by the various electrically conducting surfaces on the aircraft. This reradiated electromagnetic signal is caused by any oscillating surface currents (or charges) induced by the impingement of the oscillating electric and magnetic fields of the radar signal on the target and is usually referred to as the scattered or reflected signal.

Some of the reradiated signal may be in the direction of other conducting surfaces on the aircraft, causing multiple reflections. The total portion of the impinging signal eventually reflected in the direction of the receiving antenna is, of course, the portion of interest. This portion is known as the aircraft echo and is the aircraft's radar signature σ. The size of the signature is referred to as the aircraft's radar cross section (RCS). When the radar transmitter and receiver are collocated, as is the case for monostatic radars, the RCS is referred to as the backscatter RCS. When the two are not collocated, the RCS is referred to as the bistatic RCS. One unit of measurement of σ is the square meter, and another is the decibel (dB), where the reference level is usually 1 m^2 (dB_{sm}).

There is not just one value of σ for an aircraft. The RCS depends strongly upon the direction from which the signal arrives and the direction of the receiving antenna. The size of the aircraft, its configuration and materials, and the wavelength and polarization of the signal also affect the RCS. For most types of aircraft, the radar cross section does not bear a simple relationship to the physical projected area. In fact, σ is a very complex parameter.

(a)   RCS of simple shapes: In theory, the reradiated or scattered field, and thus the radar cross section, can be determined by solving Maxwell's equations with the appropriate boundary conditions for the given target shape, which is called the scatterer. However, this can be accomplished only for the most simple of shapes, such as a perfectly conducting sphere, and even the simple shapes exhibit several complex phenomena. For example, Fig. 6.2 shows the variation of the normalized farfield, backscattered RCS of a perfectly conducting sphere of radius a with respect to the radius to radar wavelength ratio a/λ. (The term farfield implies that the impinging signal is a plane wave and that the receiver is located at a relatively long distance away from the scatterer.) Note that there are essentially three distinct RCS regions in Fig. 6.2: the Rayleigh region, where $\lambda \gg a$ and the RCS monotonically increases with decreasing λ; the resonance region, where $\lambda \approx a$ and the RCS oscillates as λ decreases; and the optical region, where $\lambda \ll a$ and the RCS is independent of λ. All three regions can be pertinent to the RCS of an aircraft, where the various scattering surfaces may vary from much larger to much smaller than the radar wavelength.

In the Rayleigh region, where the sphere is small with respect to the radar wavelength, σ is approximately equal to $9(2\pi a/\lambda)^4(\pi a^2)$. In the resonance

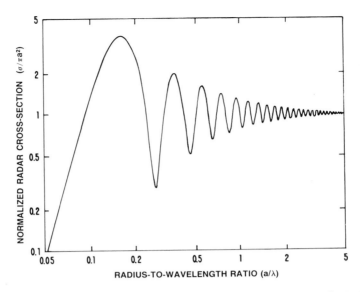

Fig. 6.2   Radar cross section of a sphere of radius *a* vs the wavelength λ (Ref.: L. V. Blake, "Calculation of the Radar Cross Section of a Perfectly Conducting Sphere," Naval Research Laboratory, Rept. NRL-MR-2419, April 1972).

region, where the sphere and wavelength are of the same order of magnitude, there is no simple relationship between σ and λ.

The optical region, where the scatterer is large with respect to the radar signal wavelength, is often the major region of interest for aircraft-radar encounters, particularly when the radar wavelength is very short. In this region, the scattering phenomena can be approximated by the theory of geometrical or ray optics and of physical or wave optics, and the reradiation or reflection of the impinging signal from smooth surfaces is referred to as the specular reflection. In the theory of geometrical optics, an incident plane electromagnetic wave (or ray) is reflected from a smooth convex surface such that the angle between the direction of propagation of the incident signal and the direction of propagation of the reflected signal is bisected by the normal to the surface at the point of contact, as shown in Fig. 6.3a. The specular backscatter RCS in the direction of the normal to a smooth, second-order conducting surface is $\pi \rho_1 \rho_2$, where ρ_1 and ρ_2 are the principal radii of curvature of the surface at the reflection point. Thus, when a plane wave strikes a sphere, $\rho_1 = \rho_2 = a$, from any direction, nearly all of the signal will be reflected away from the normal direction, as shown in Fig. 6.3b, and the backscatter RCS is equal to the physical cross-sectional area of the sphere, πa^2, which is independent of the signal wavelength. The nonbackscatter or bistatic RCS for the sphere is also equal to πa^2 for a large range of aspect angle. On the other hand, when a signal strikes a perfectly conducting, perfectly flat plate of area A that is normal to the direction of signal propagation, all of the impinging signal is reflected

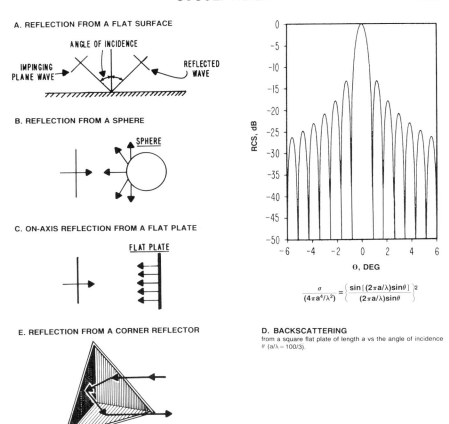

A. REFLECTION FROM A FLAT SURFACE

ANGLE OF INCIDENCE

IMPINGING
PLANE WAVE

REFLECTED
WAVE

B. REFLECTION FROM A SPHERE

SPHERE

C. ON-AXIS REFLECTION FROM A FLAT PLATE

FLAT PLATE

E. REFLECTION FROM A CORNER REFLECTOR

$$\frac{\sigma}{(4\pi a^4/\lambda^2)} = \left(\frac{\sin\left[(2\pi a/\lambda)\sin\theta\right]}{(2\pi a/\lambda)\sin\theta}\right)^2$$

D. BACKSCATTERING
from a square flat plate of length a vs the angle of incidence
θ (a/λ = 100/3).

Fig. 6.3   Scattering from different bodies.

directly backwards, as illustrated in Fig. 6.3c. Because $\rho_1 = \rho_2 = \infty$ for the flat plate, the theory of geometric optics gives an infinitely large RCS, which is, of course, unreasonable. This theory is not valid in this limiting case. Consequently, the theory of physical or wave optics is used to determine the RCS of the flat plate.

According to the theory of physical optics, the flat plate backscatter RCS is equal to $4\pi A/\lambda^2$, which is dependent upon the wavelength and which can be an extremely large value compared to the backscatter RCS of a sphere of the same cross-sectional area. For example, if the cross-sectional area of both the sphere and the flat plate is 1 m², the sphere RCS is also 1 m² (0 dB$_{sm}$), but the flat plate RCS is 13,963 m² (41.45 dB$_{sm}$) for a 3-cm wavelength signal. However, if the direction of propagation of the imping-ing wave is not normal to the flat plate, most of the wave is reflected away from the approach direction, as shown in Fig. 6.3a. Figure 6.3d shows the backscatter RCS of a 1-m² square flat plate of length a, normalized with respect to the peak value, as a function of the angle of incidence of the 3-cm impinging signal. Note that the backscatter RCS is down by approximately 14 dB for very small angles of incidence and by much more than that for larger angles of incidence. Thus, the flat plate is said to be highly specular because its backscatter RCS changes so drastically with respect to the direction of propagation of the impinging signal. (The backscatter RCS pattern with respect to the angle of incidence is analogous to the gain pattern from an antenna. Both exhibit a strong main lobe with much smaller sidelobes.) Of course, the bistatic RCS of the plate in the direction of the reflected signal can be very large.

If two flat plates are joined together along one edge, forming a dihedral, they will have a very large backscatter RCS not only for the aspects normal to each plate, but also for a region of aspect angle between the two plates where the reflection from one plate is subsequently reflected from the other plate back in the direction of the receiver. This is known as retroreflection, and the two plates form a dihedral retroreflector. Three orthogonal plates joined together form a corner reflector. The retroreflection from a corner reflector, shown in Fig. 6.3e, is very large over a relatively large region of aspect angle due to the multiple reflections.

Theoretical values of the peak backscatter RCS due to specular reflection are given in Table 6.3 for several "simple" scatterers. The scatterers with the largest RCS are usually those whose RCS is inversely proportional to the wavelength.

Other contributions to the RCS of a body in the optical and upper resonance region can come from the diffraction of the signal by edges and tips on the body and from creeping and traveling waves on the surfaces. Creeping waves are caused by the currents that exist on those surfaces that are not directly impinged by the incident wave. These surfaces are referred to as shadow surfaces. The creeping wave starts at the shadow boundary, propagates over the shadow surface, and emerges at another shadow boundary, thus contributing to the RCS. The traveling wave occurs in long thin bodies, such as wires and ogives, that are illuminated by a wave traveling essentially parallel to the axis of the body. The contribution of the

Table 6.3   Maximum Specular Backscatter RCS Values for Several Scatterers

Body	Maximum Backscatter RCS	Comments
Sphere	πa^2	Radius a
Curved surface	$\pi \rho_1 \rho_2$	Normal to a surface with principal radii of curvature ρ_1 and ρ_2
Flat plate	$4\pi A^2/\lambda^2$	Normal to the surface
Triangular corner reflector	$4\pi L^4/(3\lambda^2)$	Side length L
Large cylinder	$2\pi L^2 a/\lambda$	Normal to the axis; radius a, length L

traveling wave to the RCS can have large values, depending upon the polarization, that appear to emanate from the rear of the body.

(b)   Effects of materials and polarization on RCS: The RCS values given in Table 6.3 are for bodies composed of materials that are perfect electrical conductors. Aircraft metals, such as steel, aluminum, and titanium, fall into this category.

When the material of the scatterer is not a perfect conductor, the RCS will be reduced from that of the perfect conductor due to the reduced reradiated electromagnetic field. In this situation, some of the incident signal will pass into and possibly through the body. In general, the amount of reduction in RCS is strongly dependent upon the wavelength and the type and thickness of the material. Just because a scatterer is made of a nonmetallic material does not necessarily mean that there is a significant reduction in RCS. For example, the return from a relatively thick fiberglass laminate may be down from that of a perfect conductor by only 6 dB over a wide range of wavelengths.

The polarization of the impinging signal also affects the RCS. The extent of the influence of polarization on σ is dependent upon the relative sizes of the scatterer and the signal wavelength, on the configuration of the body, on the aspect, and on the material.

(2)   Aircraft RCS.   An aircraft is composed of many individual conducting surfaces or scatterers, each with different scattering properties that vary as the viewing or striking angle changes. In addition, multiple or sequential reflections of the reradiated signal may occur between the various scatterers. These features can strongly affect the resultant value of σ for the following reasons. As the signal is scattered from the many conducting surfaces on the aircraft, as shown in Fig. 6.4a, some of the individual surface echoes will propagate directly away from the aircraft toward the radar receiver, and some will impinge on other conducting surfaces on the aircraft, causing multiple reflections. Some of the multiple reflections will also be in the direction of the receiving antenna. The resultant RCS is the vectorial combination of all of these individual returns. Because of the many different path lengths, the phases of the individual singly and multiply scattered signals will differ. Consequently, the amplitudes of the individual surface echoes (which are electromagnetic waves) may add (in phase) to give a relatively large σ, or they may subtract (out of phase), resulting in a relatively small σ. This is known as constructive and destructive interference, respectively.

In general, the typical behavior is somewhere between maximum enhancement and total cancellation of the aircraft echo. The superposition of the individual echoes, in conjunction with the highly specular return from the various flat surfaces and retroreflectors and the possible depolarization of the scattered field, can cause a widely varying echo amplitude with relatively small changes in the viewing angle. The large amplitude fluctuation of σ with respect to small changes in the viewing angle is referred to as scintillation. In general, the amount of scintillation decreases as the wavelength increases. This interaction of the individual surface returns can also cause the apparent "centroid" of the aircraft RCS as seen by the radar

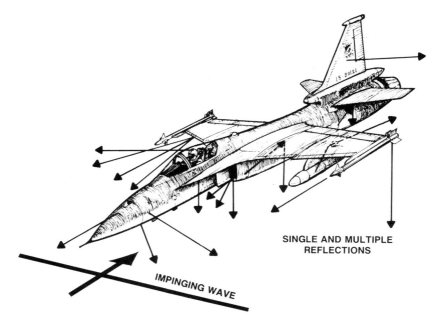

Fig. 6.4a   Various scattering surfaces on an aircraft.

tracker to wander in angle due to very small changes in viewing angle, a phenomenon known as target glint or bright spot wander. For example, on one pulse the return from the nose of the aircraft may be the dominant part of the echo, whereas on the next pulse the return from the tail may be dominant because the returns from the scatterers in the nose are out of phase and cancel each other out.

A typical plot of an aircraft backscatter RCS in one plane with respect to aspect is shown in Fig. 6.4b for a microwave radar signal. Note the scintillation. Sometimes the many different RCS values over a small interval of viewing angle, such as 10 deg, are averaged, and the resultant average σ is plotted at the midpoint of the interval. The average σ values for each interval midpoint are then connected by straight or smooth lines. This procedure is known as aspect smoothing, and it eliminates the appearance of the scintillation in the RCS. For most contemporary aircraft, the RCS can vary from less than 1 to more than 1000 m^2 (0 to 30 dB) at microwave frequencies over all aspects.

Because flat plates, dihedrals, and corners exhibit such a relatively large RCS, those surfaces on the aircraft that are either somewhat flat or whose intersections form dihedrals or corners can be sources of a strong echo. These surfaces are referred to as flare spots. Relatively flat surfaces usually occur on the sides of some fuselages, on the vertical tail, and on the upper and lower surfaces of the wing and horizontal tail. Consequently, the RCS of most aircraft are largest when the aircraft is viewed from the sides and from directly above and below. Dihedrals and corners typically occur

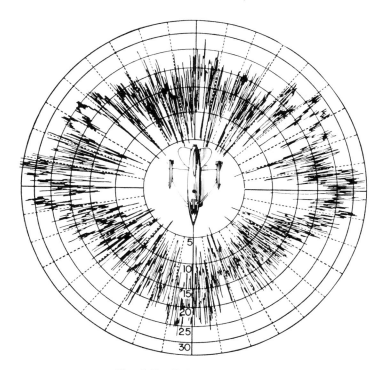

Fig. 6.4b Polar plot of RCS.

around jet engine inlets and nozzles, the fuselage-wing intersection, and
weapon pylon-wing intersections. The cockpit can be a major contributor to
the echo from the forward aspect due to the passage of the radar signal
through the canopy and the impingement on the bulkheads and other flat
surfaces in the cockpit itself. Antenna compartments in the aircraft and in
any external stores can also be sources of a strong return due to the possible
signal gain caused by the antenna itself and to the flat bulkheads in these
locations. Helicopter blades, propellers, and engine fan blades can also be
strong sources, and they have the additional feature of providing a Doppler
effect, which can be utilized by the threat radar system to enhance detection
and tracking capabilities. Figures 6.4a and 6.5 illustrate some of the typical
radar flare spots on a fixed-wing aircraft and a helicopter, respectively.

   (3) RCS prediction and measurement. The accurate prediction and
measurement of the RCS of a specific aircraft as a function of viewing angle
or aspect for a given radar are very difficult tasks for many reasons. Looking
at the RCS plot shown in Fig. 6.4b, it is very difficult to tell what the RCS
value is at any one aspect angle, and is that specific value important
anyway? Because the aircraft is in motion, its aspect with respect to the
radar is bound to vary by some small amount on every scan of the target,
and this variation can cause a significant fluctuation in the magnitude of σ

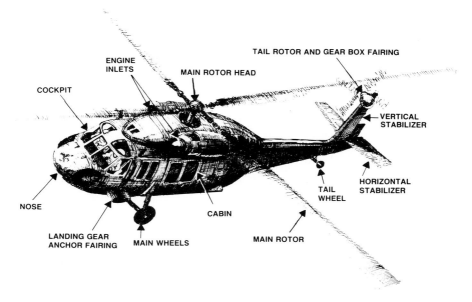

Fig. 6.5   Typical radar flare spots on a helicopter.

seen by the radar (the scintillation phenomenon). In actual fact, radar echoes from aircraft do fluctuate, and this fluctuation has an important effect upon the probability the aircraft is detected and the accuracy with which it is tracked. The "Swerling" distribution models define several possible cases of RCS fluctuation.

(a)   RCS computation: The backscatter RCS value at a given aspect is usually assessed by considering the aircraft to be made up of a collection S of the most important scatterers, such as the flat plates, dihedrals, corners, antennas, edges, etc. Each of these S scatterers has a backscatter RCS in the aspect and polarization of interest σ_s. If the relative path length of the return from each of the S scatterers l_s (the distance from a reference plane perpendicular to the radar line of sight to the sth scatter) is known, the composite echo is the vectorial sum of the individual waves, and the RCS is proportional to the square of the electric field strength of the composite wave. Thus, σ is given by

$$\sigma = \left| \sum_{s=1}^{S} \sqrt{\sigma_s} \exp(i4\pi l_s/\lambda) \right|^2 \tag{6.1}$$

where $i = \sqrt{-1}$. A simpler approach is to assume that the individual scattered waves are randomly distributed in phase. In this random phase method, the approximate RCS of the aircraft at the aspect of interest is just the sum of the backscatter RCS from each of the scatterers

$$\sigma = \sum_{s=1}^{S} \sigma_s \tag{6.2}$$

The upper bound on the backscatter RCS occurs when the returns from all of the scatterers are in phase and is given by

$$\sigma = \left(\sum_{s=1}^{S} \sqrt{\sigma_s} \right)^2 \tag{6.3}$$

Several digital computer programs have been developed to predict aircraft RCS values. These programs have the capability to predict RCS values for a variety of target geometries, including the external surfaces of aircraft (fuselage, wings, nacelles, empennage, etc.) and certain types of engine cavities. A computer model of the target is developed using planar, quadric, and superelliptic surfaces. An appropriate scattering technique is selected for each flare spot.

(b)   Experimental techniques for determining RCS: Values for aircraft RCS can also be obtained experimentally, either dynamically or statically. The dynamic experimentation method is a flight test in which an aircraft flies a set flight path, and the RCS for that specific aircraft configuration is measured. This method has the disadvantages of requiring precise aspect control and range calibration, of the inability to identify the contributions of the individual scatterers, and of the difficulty of incorporating proposed RCS reduction designs. The elevation angles are also usually limited to a narrow elevation band below the plane of the wings.

Static testing consists of illuminating a stationary, rotatable target from various aspects. It can be done on models ranging in size from small to full size. Small models are used in anechoic chambers, while large-scale testing is done on outdoor ranges. Basically, an aircraft model is mounted on a spindle at varying degrees of roll angle. The spindle is then rotated through 360 deg of azimuth, and the RCS data are recorded for specific aspect angles while the aircraft is illuminated by a stationary test radar. This gives a great circle roll or orange slice of the RCS. The advantages of static testing with reduced-size models are reduced measurement range, ease of handling and storage, reduced material costs, reduced target size and weight, the target support system is simplified, and the variability caused by wind conditions is reduced. The disadvantages are the high-frequency radar equipment required (due to the requirement to have the same target dimension-to-radar wavelength ratio in the scale-model test as that in the actual situation), the tolerances are difficult to maintain, the model materials must have the same radar reflective properties as those on the actual target, and the target echo-to-background clutter ratio is decreased.

Another static experimental technique that has some utility for identifying the flare spots on an aircraft for very short wavelength radars is flare-spot photography. In this technique, a small, shiny aircraft model is illuminated by a light source. The experiment is conducted in an enclosed chamber, and the walls are covered with a nonreflecting material. A photograph is taken of the illuminated model. The illuminating light is analogous to the radar signal, and the bright spots on the illuminated model indicate the locations of the flare spots on the actual target where the specular return can be expected to be large.

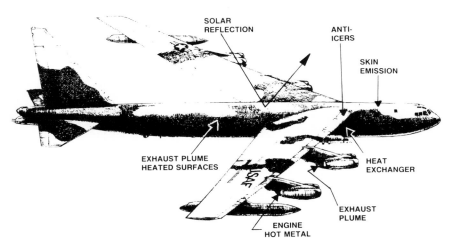

SOLAR
REFLECTION

ANTI-
ICERS

SKIN
EMISSION

EXHAUST PLUME
HEATED SURFACES

HEAT
EXCHANGER

EXHAUST
PLUME

ENGINE
HOT METAL

Fig. 6.6 Typical major i.r. sources.

Infrared (i.r.) signature. An aircraft i.r. signature is composed of radiation emitted by and reflected from the aircraft in the 0.77- to 1000-μm band of the electromagnetic wave spectrum shown in Fig. 6.1. The major sources of this signature are the radiation emitted by the hot parts of the airframe and the propulsion system, the reflected solar radiation incident on the aircraft, and the radiation emitted by the hot engine exhaust gas or plume. Figure 6.6 illustrates the typical major i.r. sources. These solid and gaseous surfaces emit and reflect i.r. radiation with an intensity that varies as a function of the radiation wavelength λ and source temperature T. The wavelength associated with the peak spectral radiant emittance can be estimated using Wein's displacement law, $\lambda(\mu m) = 2893/T$ (K). Typically, the hot solid surfaces emit radiation in the 2- to 5-μm band, and the higher the temperature, the shorter the wavelength emitted. Reflected solar i.r. radiation is normally in the 0.77- to 3-μm band. Radiation from the engine exhaust plume occurs at several discrete wavelengths or lines, such as 2.7 and 4.3 μm, that depend on the plume gas species. The intensity of the total radiation from the aircraft integrated over all of the wavelengths (the radiant flux) is proportional to the temperature to the fourth power. However, the peak intensity within a small band of wavelengths where the energy is concentrated can be proportional to the temperature to a higher power. The relative contribution of each of the major sources to the total i.r. signature depends upon the aircraft materials, surface conditions and coatings, components and configuration, the aircraft operating condition, and the viewing angle.

(1) Airframe contributors. The airframe is a continuum radiator and emits radiation from aerodynamically heated surfaces and from hot parts, such as the heat exchanger and the oil cooler. At subsonic speeds and

medium to high altitude, the radiation due to aerodynamic heating is usually negligible. However, for aircraft flying either supersonically or high subsonically at low altitude, the skin i.r. emission can be significant, depending upon the intensity of the radiation from the other sources and the emissivity of the skin. Reflected solar radiation off of the airframe, including the canopy, is known as sun glint and can also be a significant source of i.r. radiation. The spectral distribution of the reflected radiation resembles that of the solar radiation at 6000 K, and the magnitude depends upon the incident illumination, the angles between the sun, the aircraft, and the observer, and the shape, condition, and reflectivity of the surface.

(2) Propulsion system contributors. The propulsion system contributes i.r. radiation from the engine and exhaust nozzle hot parts and from the hot exhaust gas. The maximum intensity of radiation from the engine and exhaust hot parts normally occurs tail on, where the hot parts are easily seen. The radiant intensity is significantly less when viewed from the sides and front of the aircraft where most of the hot parts are usually hidden from view. The plume i.r. signature is composed mainly of radiation from the hot carbon dioxide (CO_2) and water vapor (H_2O) in the exhaust gas. Most of the plume i.r. radiation is due to the CO_2 and occurs at 4.3 μm with a typical bandwidth of approximately 0.4 μm. The plume radiation may possibly be seen from all directions around the aircraft, particularly when an afterburner is used.

(3) Atmospheric absorption. The i.r. radiation propagating away from the aircraft through the atmosphere is absorbed by the various gases in the atmosphere at several discrete wavelengths. Those wavelength bands where the atmospheric absorption is small are called windows. The absorption is typically concentrated at 1.4 and 1.9 μm (H_2O), 2.7 μm (CO_2 and H_2O), 4.3 μm (CO_2), 5 to 8 μm (H_2O), and 14 to 16 μm (CO_2).

(4) Aircraft i.r. signature pattern. A typical infrared radiation signature at several locations around a jet-engined aircraft at some arbitrary distance away may have the appearance shown in Fig. 6.7a. The magnitude of the signature is usually expressed as the thermal power per unit solid angle per unit wavelength (watts/steradian/micron), the spectral radiant intensity. Note the change in the scale of intensity in Fig. 6.7a for the different aspects. When the aircraft is viewed from the front and the sides, the plume radiation is the primary source of the i.r. signature. Note that the radiation is most intense at the two wings of the CO_2 radiation line centered at 4.3 μm. The radiation from the plume in the center portion of this line has been absorbed by the cooler CO_2 gas in the atmosphere. When viewed from the tail, the engine hot parts become the major i.r. source. The absence of radiation from the hot parts at 2.7 and 4.3 μm shown in Fig. 6.7a is due to the atmospheric absorption by the H_2O and CO_2 molecules. A helicopter typically exhibits the same type of i.r. radiation as a fixed-wing aircraft. However, the pattern may differ from that shown in Fig. 6.7a if the engine

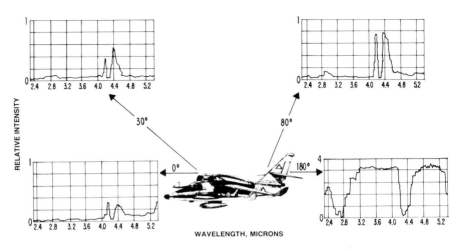

Fig. 6.7a   An i.r. signature around an aircraft.

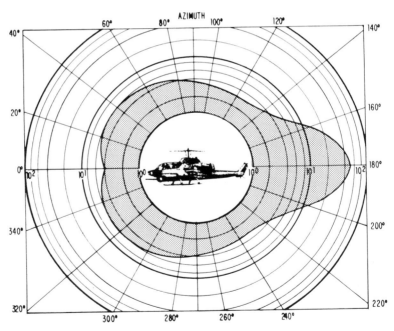

Fig. 6.7b   Polar plot of the radiant intensity (watts / steradian) from a helicopter in a given wavelength band.

does not exhaust to the rear. A polar plot of the radiant intensity from a rear-exhaust helicopter within a limited wavelength band is given in Fig. 6.7b.

(5) Infrared signature prediction and measurement. Several i.r. signature prediction computer models are currently available. These models are based upon the underlying physics of thermal radiation, reflection, and transmission. In one of the programs, the i.r. prediction method is broken down into groups of computational steps or modules. Each module has a particular functional capability. One module models the airframe surface areas, emissivity, and temperature as viewed from specified aspect angles. A second module is used to model the engine exhaust system areas, temperatures, and radiant interchange between these areas and the ambient environment. A third module models the spatial distribution of engine exhaust products, such as H_2O and CO_2, as they mix to lower temperature and concentrations with the ambient air. A fourth module models the i.r. emission and attenuation of the exhaust and atmospheric gases in the path between the aircraft hot components and exhaust gases and the observer location in space. Other modules are available to calculate an i.r. missile's utilization of this incident radiant energy. The input data for the program are obtained from the aircraft design. Typical input quantities are the airframe geometry, the engine interior geometry, the engine exhaust temperature profile, and the H_2O and CO_2 concentrations.

Experimental measurement of the i.r. signature of aircraft is conducted at several facilities in the U.S. Radiometers are used to determine the total radiation over a band of wavelengths, and spectrometers are used to measure the spectral distribution of the radiation from the target. A guidebook, "The Aircraft Infrared Measurements Guide," JTCG/AS-81-C-002, has been prepared by the JTCG/AS as a reference source for the infrared measurement community.

A special center, known as the Infrared Information and Analysis Center (IRIA), has been set up by the Department of Defense as a focal point for the collection of infrared and electro-optical information. The IRIA is a DLA-administered Department of Defense Information and Analysis Center operated by the Environmental Research Institute of Michigan (ERIM) under contract to the Office of Naval Research. Its mission is to collect, analyze, and disseminate to authorized recipients information concerning infrared and electro-optical research and development. Accordingly, the IRIA Center publishes and distributes IRIA Annotated Bibliographies, the Infrared Newsletter, the Infrared Handbook, IRIA Data Compilations, and the Proceedings of the Infrared Information Symposia (IRIS), the proceedings and/or minutes of the meetings of the six specialty groups of IRIS, IRIA State-of-the-Art Reports, and proceedings of the DoD conferences on laser technology. The center serves as a national reference library in military infrared technology, offering assistance and advice to visitors having the appropriate clearances and need-to-know. Special bibliographies and searches are prepared for IRIA-IRIS members upon request. All IRIA-IRIS publications up to Feb. 1, 1971 are available from the Defense Technical

Information Center (DTIC). Since that date, publications are available only from the IRIA Center on a service charge basis. Membership is available by annual subscription and includes receipt of documents as they are published. Inquiries concerning the annual subscription plan should be directed to: IRIA Center, Environmental Research Institute of Michigan, P.O. Box 8618, Ann Arbor, MI 48107. Telephone: (313) 994-1200, ext. 214.

Department of Defense agencies desiring to join IRIA should write: Office of Naval Research, Chicago Branch Office, 536 South Clark Street, Chicago, IL 60605. Telephone: (312) 353-6069.

Visual signature. A large number of combat aircraft lost in the Southeast Asia conflict were hit by projectiles from visually directed weapons. In many cases, the enemy simply aimed a barrage in the direction of the visual observables of the aircraft, such as a smoke trail, before the aircraft itself could be observed. In addition to smoke, visual observables from sources on or near the aircraft include contrails and, at night, the engine exhaust glow and cockpit lighting.

In general, the visual detectability of an aircraft is dependent upon the difference between the background and the aircraft. There are four parameters that influence the detectability of the visual signature. These are luminance, chromaticity, clutter, and movement. Of these four, the most important is the aircraft luminance contrast with the background luminance. Luminance is the radiance (the power/unit solid angle/unit area) of an object weighted by the luminosity function of a standard observer. Aircraft luminance is the sum of the luminance of any onboard luminance sources, such as exterior and cockpit lighting and the glowing exhaust nozzle, and the luminous reflection from the aircraft exterior surfaces. Aircraft detection can occur when the aircraft luminance is too low compared with its background (the aircraft appears as a dark spot in a bright background) or when the aircraft luminance is too high with respect to the background (a bright aircraft is easily observed against a dark background).

For aircraft that have a low luminance contrast with the background, the chromatic contrast between the aircraft and the background can become the dominant detection feature. An aircraft painted with a brown and green camouflage scheme for protection from attacks from the air while parked will be quite visible from above when it is flying over sand or water. Since color sources may differ in hue (a chromatic characteristic), as well as their luminance, the term color encompasses both luminance and chromatic contrast.

Clutter contrast also affects visual detectability. Examples where clutter contrast is important are helicopter nap-of-the-Earth flight profiles and low-altitude flight paths of fixed-wing aircraft. In these situations, the observer attempts to discriminate between the moving aircraft and a changing background of confusing forms. For many observers, detection is immediately achieved, once fixation in the general direction is achieved, when the target luminance contrasts with the background clutter.

Movement is the fourth parameter that influences the visual detectability of an aircraft. Movement is more easily observed when there is a strong luminance, chromatic, or clutter contrast between the aircraft and the background. In the case of rotary-wing aircraft, one movement that may be detected is the rotation of the rotor blades. Against a background of relatively high luminance, such as the sky, the rotating blades may present a negative contrast or a flickering stimulus. Under some illumination conditions, the rotating blades exhibit a glint-flicker signature that is a highly detectable cue due to the high luminance associated with the glint combined with the temporal enhancement due to flicker.

Aural signature. Aircraft are often heard before being seen by ground observers, primarily as a result of engine and/or rotor blade noise. For example, low-flying helicopters can sometimes be heard as early as 30 s before they become visible because of rotor blade noise. (Under battlefield conditions, however, background noise from tanks, guns, and other aircraft may prevent or delay aural detection.)

The factors which determine aural detectability include the intensity and the spatial pattern of the noise generated by the aircraft, the frequency spectrum and real time character of the noise, the distance between the noise source and the receiver, the atmospheric attenuation of the noise, the scattering effects due to atmospheric winds, the atmospheric temperature gradient and turbulence, the noise attenuation (absorption and scattering) due to terrain, the level and frequency of the background noise in the vicinity of the receiver, and the sensitivity of the receiver to the noise. Although these factors have been identified as significant contributors to aural detection by enemy ground observers, they also influence undersea detection of aircraft. In this situation, the aircraft-generated noise passes through the atmosphere, across the atmosphere-to-water interface, and along ocean bottom-reflected paths. The aural signature, if detected, could be used by a submarine to launch an air-defense missile, if available, or to take evasive maneuvers.

The noise from an aircraft comes from many sources, which can include propeller/rotor blade rotational and vortex noises, engine inlet, combustion, exhaust, and rotary noises, and airframe aerodynamic noise. For gas turbine powered rotary-wing aircraft, the rotors are usually the principal noise source. In the case of propeller driven aircraft, aerodynamic boundary-layer noise may exceed the noise from the propellers. Engine cycle type is a significant factor that determines the percentage of engine noise to the total aircraft noise. Aircraft utilizing high-bypass turbofan engines have a reduced noise level from that of turbojet engines of equivalent thrust and aircraft type. The noise from all of these sources is usually highly spectral in content, with much of the intensity concentrated within specific narrow frequency bands.

Aircraft Detection and Tracking

Air-defense systems utilize several procedures to detect, identify, and track aircraft. These procedures are usually based upon a timewise progression of accuracy of aircraft location starting from a warning that an aircraft is approaching from a general direction and ending with a relatively accurate determination of the aircraft's location in azimuth, elevation, velocity, and range as a function of time. Each threat system, whether it be a radar-directed AAA, an air-to-air i.r. homing missile, or an infantryman with a rifle, usually follows this sequence of events in one form or another. However, the specific techniques used to accomplish the detection, identification, and tracking are dependent upon the type of threat system. The three major types of detection and tracking systems are the radar-directed, the infrared, and the visually directed systems.

Radar-directed systems.

(1)   *Detection.*   Air-defense radars fall into two broad categories: detection or surveillance radars and weapon- or fire-control radars. Surveillance radars are used to detect the presence of aircraft at long ranges and to provide the general view of the overall situation in the air. They usually are pulse radars.

(a)   Maximum range: The maximum distance a surveillance radar antenna at a height h_{ant} can see an aircraft flying at an altitude h_{ac} is limited by the radar horizon R_h, which is given by

$$R_h = 1.23\left(\sqrt{h_{ant}} + \sqrt{h_{ac}}\right) \text{ (n. mi.)} \qquad (6.4)$$

where h_{ant} and h_{ac} are given in feet. (This equation assumes a standard refraction of the radar wave of 4/3 due to the Earth's atmosphere. When horizontal ducting of the radar signal occurs due to atmospheric conditions, the actual maximum distance can be much further.)

The range to the target R is determined by measuring the elapsed time between the transmission of the pulse and the return of the echo Δt. Thus,

$$R = c\Delta t/2 \qquad (6.5a)$$

where c is the velocity of propagation of the radar wave. The maximum range at which a radar operator can recognize an aircraft as a target R_{max} is given by the radar range equation. This equation can be given in the form

$$R_{max} = \left(\frac{P_r G_r^2 \lambda^2}{(4\pi)^3 L_s} \frac{\sigma F^4}{\xi_{min} N L_a}\right)^{\frac{1}{4}} \qquad (6.5b)$$

where P_r is the peak power of the radar, G_r is the gain of the antenna, λ is the radar wavelength, and L_s represents the radar system losses ($L_s \geq 1$). The aircraft radar cross section is σ, and F is the relative electrical field strength of the echo at the receiving antenna, which can vary from 0 to 2, depending upon the amount of multipath interference. N is the noise taken in by the system during the detection process and includes the internal receiver noise, any background clutter from rain or surface features in the range resolution cell, the return from reflected paths off of a glistening surface, and any electronic countermeasure noise. L_a represents the signal and echo loss due to radar transmission through the atmosphere ($L_a \geq 1$), and ξ_{min} is the signal-to-noise ratio associated with a specified probability of detection and of false alarm.

For pulse radars with multiple or repeated pulse transmissions, the maximum unambiguous range R_u is given by

$$R_u = c/2f_r \qquad (6.6)$$

where f_r is the pulse repetition rate or frequency (PRF). A return from a target beyond this range could be erroneously interpreted as a return from a closer target due to the multiple pulses. The limiting detection range is related to the three ranges R_h, R_{max}, and R_u.

(b) Probability of detection: During each scan of the target by the radar beam, a large number of pulses will be transmitted and echoes received. The receiver either will process these echoes individually, or several of the echoes will be summed or integrated to improve detection performance. The performance improvement is in the form of a larger probability of detection and/or a smaller probability of false alarm for the same peak power. The signal-to-noise ratio for a specified probability of detection and of false alarm, ξ_{min}, is based upon the number of integrated pulses. For the sth scan of the target, there will be a certain probability of detection $P_D(s)$ based upon the actual signal-to-noise ratio, which can be determined from the radar equation and is a function of target range and radar cross section, both of which can vary with each scan. Thus, $P_D(s)$ is generally a function of time. The probability of detecting a target as time passes (after several scans) is a cumulative phenomenon, and the probability that the target has been detected after S scans, $\bar{P}_D^{(S)}$, is given by

$$\bar{P}_D^{(S)} = 1 - \left(1 - P_D^{(1)}\right)\left(1 - P_D^{(2)}\right)\left(1 - P_D^{(3)}\right)\ldots\left(1 - P_D^{(S)}\right)$$

$$= 1 - \prod_{s=1}^{S}\left(1 - P_D^{(S)}\right) \qquad (6.7a)$$

If $P_D(s)$ is essentially a constant value for each scan, P_D, then Eq. (6.7a) simplifies to

$$\bar{P}_D^{(S)} = 1 - \left(1 - P_D\right)^S \qquad (6.7b)$$

(2) Tracking. When the decision is made that the aircraft is a threat and is within the range of a weapon-control radar, the current aircraft or target information is passed to the assigned weapon-control radar. Weapon-control radars are usually pulse radars and normally operate over a small volume of space and handle relatively few targets. They mechanically or electronically move the radar beam using circular, spiral, sawtooth, helical, or raster types of scanning. The output from the fire-control radar is

used to determine the target's flight path, and a prediction of the target's future position is then made, usually by a computer, so that the threat platform or propagator can be pointed in the correct position to cause a propagator intercept. The fire-control radar usually must obtain an accurate measurement of the target location in both range and angle in order to generate a small propagator miss distance. Velocity or Doppler tracking is sometimes used in place of, or in addition to, range tracking.

There are two general techniques used by weapon-control radars to track the target in angle: single-target tracking and track-while-scan (TWS). Two often-used single-target tracking techniques are the conical scan and monopulse.

(a) Conical scan tracking: A conical scan tracker may use a feed horn that moves or nutates in a circular path around the boresight of a parabolic dish antenna. This nutation causes the pencil beam from the parabolic antenna to scan a small volume of space around the boresight of the antenna, as shown in Fig. 6.8a. The echo from a target that is not located on

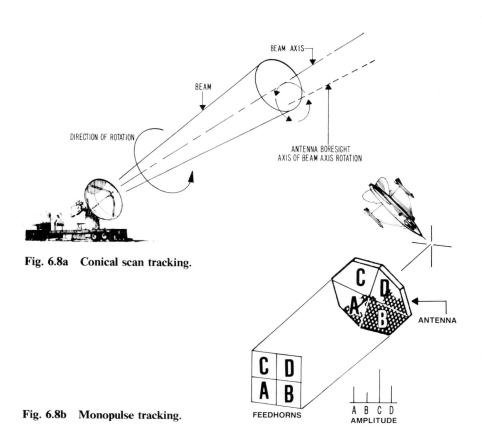

Fig. 6.8a   Conical scan tracking.

Fig. 6.8b   Monopulse tracking.

the boresight will be modulated in amplitude as the horn nutates. Adjusting the antenna angle until there is no modulation of the target echo centers the target in the boresight. (Note the problem that scintillation can cause a conical scan radar.)

(b) Monopulse tracking: Monopulse is a very accurate tracking technique that uses a cluster of several antennas or feed horns, as shown in Fig. 6.8b. A single composite pulse or beam is transmitted by the cluster (A, B, C, and D). Each antenna receives a different echo (as illustrated in Fig. 6.8b) due to the different return path from the target to each antenna. The range to the target is determined using the sum of the returns from each antenna. The direction or angle to the target is determined by moving the boresight of the total antenna until the difference between either the phase or the amplitude of the echoes received simultaneously at pairs of antenna locations is minimized or nulled. Arrangements of four orthogonal antennas or feeds (as shown in Fig. 6.8b) can be used to determine both azimuth and elevation. For the antenna illustrated in Fig. 6.8b, the difference between the sum of the echoes in C and A and the sum of the echoes in D and B is a measure of the azimuth error, and the difference between the sum of the echoes in A and B and the sum of the echoes in C and D is a measure of the elevation error. This method can be much superior in accuracy to the conical scan, and because it does not require repeated pulses to locate the angular position of the target (hence the name monopulse), it is much more difficult to deceive with countermeasures. A less sophisticated version of monopulse, known as lobe-on-receive-only (LORO), transmits a burst of composite pulses and examines the individual echoes in each antenna location (the lobe) one at a time (the first pulse echo is received in A, the second pulse echo is received in B, the third pulse echo is received in C, and so on), as opposed to the simultaneous single echo/multiple antenna processing of monopulse.

(c) Track-while-scan: Track-while-scan weapon-control radars scan a limited angular sector in a regular manner and develop one or more target tracks with data obtained at the sector scan rate rather than continuously, as in the case of the single-target tracking radar. The scan can be accomplished using a single-beam antenna or two orthogonal fan beams. During each scan, the target will be illuminated for a brief period of time. Keeping track of the target's position during each scan provides the history of the target's flight path.

(3) *Accuracy.* The determination of the tracking accuracy of a radar system is a complex problem due to the many influential variables that are continuously changing in time. The tracking accuracy is influenced by such factors as the mechanical properties of the radar antenna and pedestal, the method by which the angular position of the antenna is measured, the quality of the servo-system that moves the antenna, the stability of the electronic circuits, the noise level of the receiver, and the antenna beamwidth and side lobes. These factors are associated with the radar system itself and consequently are usually not affected by the aircraft or its tactics. Other

factors that also influence tracking accuracy, and that can be affected by the aircraft and its tactics, are atmospheric conditions, the presence of clutter and any radar countermeasures, and the radar reflection characteristics and the altitude of the aircraft. Atmospheric conditions can affect the signal strength, and clutter and any countermeasures can contribute external noise and false targets, making the echo more difficult to detect.

The reflection characteristics of the aircraft determine both the RCS level and the amount of RCS scintillation and target glint, all of which affect tracking accuracy. The aircraft altitude can have a major effect on the elevation accuracy of ground-based radars when the aircraft flies low enough to cause the multipath phenomenon to become significant. Because of the indirect return off of the surface of the Earth, the radar "sees" two targets: the actual target whose echo arrives along the direct path and an image of the actual target whose echo arrives along the elevation angle corresponding to the reflected path. (Refer to Fig. B.9a of Appendix B for an illustration of the multipath phenomenon.) Many pulse radars are unable to track aircraft that fly at elevation angles less than some fraction (typically 0.5 to 0.7) of the radar beamwidth due to the multipath phenomenon. Low-flying aircraft are also difficult to track from above due to the Earth clutter.

(a)   Tracking error measures: When a radar system tracks an aircraft, the target coordinates measured by the radar, such as range, angle, and velocity, will typically fluctuate about the true value with time, as illustrated in Fig. 6.9. The tracking error ε is the difference between the true coordinate data and the radar data. Two important measures of the error shown in Fig. 6.9 are its average value, or mean, over a period of time and its variance about the mean. If ε is sampled at N locations along the time axis, the sample mean M is given in terms of ε_i, the error of the ith sample, by

$$M = \frac{1}{N} \sum_{i=1}^{N} \varepsilon_i \qquad (6.8)$$

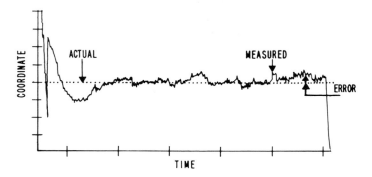

Fig. 6.9   Measured target coordinate vs time.

The variance of the error is one measure of the dispersion of the error about the mean, and the sample variance S^2 (based on the N values of ε_i) is given by

$$S^2 = \frac{1}{N} \sum_{i=1}^{N} (\varepsilon_i - M)^2 \qquad (6.9)$$

where $(\varepsilon_i - M)$ is the deviation error. The square root of the variance S is referred to as the root mean square (rms) of the deviation error. The rms of the deviation error is related to the rms of the error ε_{rms} by the expression

$$\varepsilon_{rms}^2 = \frac{1}{N} \sum_{i=1}^{N} \varepsilon_i^2 = M^2 + S^2 \qquad (6.10)$$

If each of the N numerical values of ε_i is put into one of several classes or finite intervals of error values according to the value of the error, a histogram of the error data is obtained, such as the one shown in Fig. 6.10a.

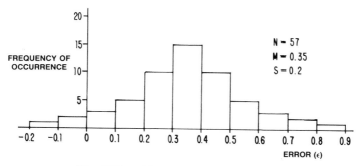

Fig. 6.10a   Histogram of a tracking error.

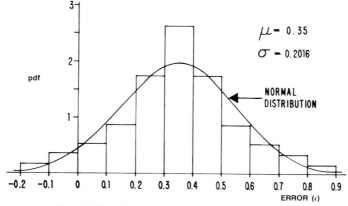

Fig. 6.10b   Normal distribution of the error.

The sample mean and the square root of the sample variance of the error data are indicated in the figure.

The error also can be represented by a distribution known as the probability density function (pdf). The pdf does not give the probability that the error has any specific value, but instead is used to compute the probability that the error falls within an error interval. For example, the probability that the error shown in Fig. 6.10a falls between the interval from 0.2 to 0.3 is given by the integral

$$\text{Probability}(0.2 \leq \varepsilon \leq 0.3) = \int_{0.2}^{0.3} \text{pdf}\, d\varepsilon \qquad (6.11)$$

For the histogram shown in Fig. 6.10a, the probability that the error falls within the interval from 0.2 to 0.3 is known to be 10/57, and hence the unknown variable in Eq. (6.11) is the pdf. Assuming a constant value for the pdf in each of the histogram error intervals, Eq. (6.11) becomes

$$10/57 = \text{pdf}(0.3 - 0.2)$$

Thus, the value for the pdf between 0.2 and 0.3 is 1.754. Computing the pdf values for the entire histogram leads to the discontinuous pdf shown in Fig. 6.10b. Note that the area under the pdf is unity.

For a variety of reasons, the discontinuous pdf is usually replaced or approximated by a smooth or continuous pdf. The continuous distribution most often used in this type of analysis is the normal or Gaussian distribution, $F(\varepsilon)$. The expression for the normal distribution of the error ε is

$$F(\varepsilon) = \frac{1}{(2\pi\sigma^2)^{\frac{1}{2}}} \exp\left(\frac{-(\varepsilon - \mu)^2}{2\sigma^2}\right) \qquad (6.12)$$

where μ is the mean or bias, and σ^2 is the variance. The relationships between the sample mean M and sample variance S^2 and between the normal mean μ and normal variance σ^2 are usually given in the form

$$\mu = M \qquad (6.13a)$$

and

$$\sigma^2 = \left(\frac{N}{N-1}\right)S^2 \qquad (6.13b)$$

although σ^2 is sometimes set equal to S^2, particularly when N is large compared to unity. The square root of σ^2 is called the standard deviation (s.d.), or 1 σ, or rms of the deviation error. The normal distribution for the example error data given in Fig. 6.10a is presented in Fig. 6.10b.

The probability that the tracking error will fall between minus infinity and plus infinity is, of course, unity. Of particular interest in error analysis is the magnitude of the deviation error that bounds the symmetric interval about the mean such that the probability that the error lies within the interval is 0.5. This error is called the probable error (p.e.) and is obtained from the relationship

$$\text{Probability}(-\text{p.e.} \le \varepsilon - \mu \le \text{p.e.}) = 0.5 = \int_{\mu - \text{p.e.}}^{\mu + \text{p.e.}} F(\varepsilon)\,d\varepsilon \qquad (6.14a)$$

This equation has been solved for the p.e. for the normal distribution, and the solution is

$$\text{p.e.} = 0.6745\sigma \qquad (6.14b)$$

Thus, the probability that the deviation error lies between $(\mu - 0.6745\sigma)$ and $(\mu + 0.6745\sigma)$ is 0.5.

(b) Coordinate tracking errors: The tracking error in any one coordinate is the net result of the combination of the errors in that coordinate associated with the different tracking factors. For example, the error shown in Fig. 6.9 could be the net azimuth error caused by the azimuth error due to noise, $\varepsilon_{\text{noise}}$, and the azimuth error due to target glint, $\varepsilon_{\text{glint}}$. Thus,

$$\varepsilon = \varepsilon_{\text{noise}} + \varepsilon_{\text{glint}} \qquad (6.15)$$

Each of the individual errors can also be represented by the normal distribution, with a specific mean and variance associated with each error. The individual error distributions can be combined mathematically into one error distribution such that the mean and the variance of the total error are numerically equal to the mean and variance of the sum of the individual errors. For example, the mean of the azimuth error is given by

$$M = \frac{1}{N} \sum_{i=1}^{N} \varepsilon_i = \frac{1}{N} \sum_{i=1}^{N} \left(\varepsilon_{\text{noise}_i} + \varepsilon_{\text{glint}_i} \right)$$

$$= \frac{1}{N} \sum_{i=1}^{N} \varepsilon_{\text{noise}_i} + \frac{1}{N} \sum_{i=1}^{N} \varepsilon_{\text{glint}_i} = M_{\text{noise}} + M_{\text{glint}} \qquad (6.16)$$

Thus, the mean of the sum of errors is equal to the sum of the individual mean errors. For the variance of the error

$$S^2 = \frac{1}{N} \sum_{i=1}^{N} (\varepsilon_i - M)^2 = \frac{1}{N} \sum_{i=1}^{N} \left(\varepsilon_{\text{noise}_i} + \varepsilon_{\text{glint}_i} - M_{\text{noise}} - M_{\text{glint}} \right)^2$$

$$= \frac{1}{N} \sum_{i=1}^{N} \left(\varepsilon_{\text{noise}_i} - M_{\text{noise}} \right)^2 + \frac{1}{N} \sum_{i=1}^{N} \left(\varepsilon_{\text{glint}_i} - M_{\text{glint}} \right)^2$$

$$+ \frac{2}{N} \sum_{i=1}^{N} \left[\left(\varepsilon_{\text{noise}_i} - M_{\text{noise}} \right)\left(\varepsilon_{\text{glint}_i} - M_{\text{glint}} \right) \right]$$

The term

$$\frac{1}{N} \sum_{i=1}^{N} \left[\left(\varepsilon_{\text{noise}_i} - M_{\text{noise}} \right) \left(\varepsilon_{\text{glint}_i} - M_{\text{glint}} \right) \right]$$

is called the covariance between the $\varepsilon_{\text{noise}}$ and $\varepsilon_{\text{glint}}$ errors. If the two errors are independent from one another (neither one is influenced by the other), the covariance is zero, and the variance is given by

$$S^2 = S^2_{\text{noise}} + S^2_{\text{glint}} \qquad (6.17a)$$

and hence,

$$\sigma = \left(\sigma^2_{\text{noise}} + \sigma^2_{\text{glint}} \right)^{\frac{1}{2}} \qquad (6.17b)$$

Thus, the standard deviation of the sum of errors is the square root of the sum of the squares (rss) of the individual standard deviations.

In general, the individual tracking errors can be categorized either as random errors that may or may not fluctuate about a zero mean or as systematic errors that may or may not fluctuate about a nonzero mean. The zero mean random errors are associated with such factors as receiver noise, tracking jitter, scintillation, and target glint. The systematic errors are caused by factors such as antenna misalignment, servo lags, and multipath. Radar countermeasures can cause both kinds of errors. Estimates of the rms errors due to noise have been made for several different tracking systems. In general, the standard deviation for all coordinates due to noise can be given in the form

$$\sigma_{\text{noise}} = K_n / (S/N)^{\frac{1}{2}} \qquad (6.18)$$

where S/N is the single-look signal-to-noise ratio, and K_n is a constant that depends upon the type of radar system and the specific target coordinate. The signal must be large compared with the noise for this estimate to be valid. For angular measurements, K_n is directly proportional to the antenna beam width.

Another important tracking error is that due to target glint. The standard deviation of a target at a range R due to glint for all coordinates has been estimated to be

$$\sigma_{\text{glint}} = L_x K_g \qquad (6.19)$$

where L_x is the target projected width to the radar, and the coefficient K_g is a constant that depends on the type of radar system and the specific target coordinate. For angular measurements, K_g is inversely proportional to R. The combined tracking error in any coordinate can be obtained using these and other estimates for the individual error measures and the relationships given by Eqs. (6.16) and (6.17b).

(c) Two-dimensional errors: The one-dimensional normal distribution for the coordinate tracking error given by Eq. (6.12) can also be used to determine the normal distribution in a two-dimensional coordinate space, $F(\varepsilon_1, \varepsilon_2)$. For example, if the two orthogonal angular tracking errors ε_1 and ε_2 are independent, the two-dimensional distribution of the angular error is given by the product of the two one-dimensional normal distributions. Hence,

$$F(\varepsilon_1)F(\varepsilon_2)$$

$$F(\varepsilon_1, \varepsilon_2) = F(\varepsilon_1)F(\varepsilon_2) = \left[\frac{1}{(2\pi\sigma_1^2)^{\frac{1}{2}}}\exp\left(\frac{-(\varepsilon_1-\mu_1)^2}{2\sigma_1^2}\right)\right]$$

$$\times\left[\frac{1}{(2\pi\sigma_2^2)^{\frac{1}{2}}}\exp\left(\frac{-(\varepsilon_2-\mu_2)^2}{2\sigma_2^2}\right)\right]$$

$$= \frac{1}{2\pi\sigma_1\sigma_2}\exp\left(-\frac{(\varepsilon_1-\mu_1)^2}{2\sigma_1^2}-\frac{(\varepsilon_2-\mu_2)^2}{2\sigma_2^2}\right) \quad (6.20)$$

where μ_1 and μ_2 are the two angular means, and σ_1 and σ_2 are the two angular standard deviations. This expression is called the bivariate (two variable) normal distribution. The sample mean and sample variance for each coordinate are evaluated using Eqs. (6.8), (6.9), and (6.13) with the corresponding coordinate errors ε_{1_i} and ε_{2_i}.

The bivariate normal distribution is used to calculate the probability that each of the angular errors lies within some specified interval. For example, the probability that the angular error ε_1 lies between -0.2 and 0.3 mrad and that the angular error ε_2 lies between 0.4 and 0.5 mrad is given by

$$\text{Probability}\left\{\begin{array}{c}-0.2\le\varepsilon_1\le 0.3\\0.4\le\varepsilon_2\le 0.5\end{array}\right\} = \frac{1}{2\pi\sigma_1\sigma_2}\int_{-0.2}^{0.3}$$

$$\times\exp\left(-\frac{(\varepsilon_1-\mu_1)^2}{2\sigma_1^2}\right)d\varepsilon_1\int_{0.4}^{0.5}\exp\left(-\frac{(\varepsilon_2-\mu_2)^2}{2\sigma_2^2}\right)d\varepsilon_2$$

When a circular symmetric antenna is used, σ_1 and σ_2 are often assumed to be equal, and the two bias errors are usually assumed to be zero. For this situation, the bivariate normal distribution given by Eq. (6.20) becomes the one-dimensional circular normal distribution for the radial angular error ε, given by

$$F(\varepsilon) = \frac{1}{2\pi\sigma^2}\exp\left(\frac{-\varepsilon^2}{2\sigma^2}\right) \quad (6.21)$$

where $\sigma = \sigma_1 = \sigma_2$, and $\varepsilon^2 = \varepsilon_1^2 + \varepsilon_2^2$. The probability that the angular error lies somewhere within a radial error interval from ε_a to ε_b is given by

$$\text{Probability}(\varepsilon_a \le \varepsilon \le \varepsilon_b) = \frac{1}{2\pi\sigma^2}\int_{\varepsilon_a}^{\varepsilon_b}\int_0^{2\pi}\exp\left(\frac{-\varepsilon^2}{2\sigma^2}\right)\varepsilon\,d\theta\,d\varepsilon$$

$$= \int_{\varepsilon_a}^{\varepsilon_b}\frac{\varepsilon}{\sigma^2}\exp\left(\frac{-\varepsilon^2}{2\sigma^2}\right)d\varepsilon \qquad (6.22)$$

The integrand in Eq. (6.22) is referred to as the Rayleigh distribution. A special case of Eq. (6.22) is when $\varepsilon_a = 0$ and ε_b is that particular value, called the circular error probable (CEP), or circular probable error (CPE), which results in a 50% probability that the error lies within the interval from zero to the CEP. For this case

$$0.5 = \int_0^{\text{CEP}}\frac{\varepsilon}{\sigma^2}\exp\left(\frac{-\varepsilon^2}{2\sigma^2}\right)d\varepsilon$$

Solving this equation for the CEP gives

$$\text{CEP} = 1.177\sigma \qquad (6.23)$$

The CEP for the circular symmetric error distribution is analogous to the probable error for the one-dimensional distribution.

(d) Total tracking error model: The preceding discussion described the distribution and measures of the individual range and angular tracking errors. These coordinate tracking errors can be combined in such a manner as to give a total tracking error model that permits a simple estimate of the overall tracking accuracy. However, this model does not allow the consideration of the component of the total error in a specific direction or coordinate. This total error represents a volume of uncertainty that surrounds the aircraft as illustrated in Fig. 6.11. The aircraft is actually located at the center of this volume (zero mean), but the radar, due to the tracking errors, will place its location somewhere else on each scan. The total tracking error of a target ε_t at a slant range R is given by

$$\varepsilon_t = \left[\varepsilon_R^2 + R^2\left(\varepsilon_{a1}^2 + \varepsilon_{a2}^2\right)\right]^{\frac{1}{2}} \quad \text{(meters)} \qquad (6.24)$$

where the range error ε_R and R are in meters; and the orthogonal angular errors ε_{a1} and ε_{a2} are in radians.

Infrared tracking systems.   Infrared detection and tracking systems are most often used in the guidance of missiles, either by command, by semiactive homing, or by passive homing. Missiles with command guidance may carry an i.r. beacon in the tail. The beacon is passively tracked by an i.r. sensor in the tracking device while the operator attempts to track the

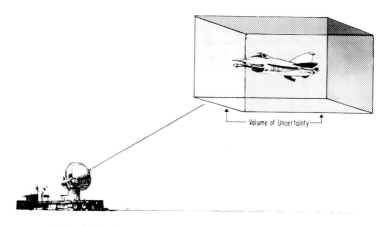

Fig. 6.11 Volume of uncertainty around the aircraft.

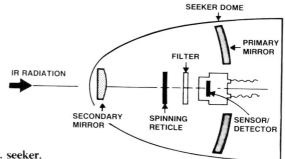

Fig. 6.12 One type of an i.r. seeker.

aircraft, usually with the aid of either direct-view optics or electro-optics. The tracking system notes the difference in the target and missile positions and generates the necessary commands to direct the missile to an intercept. The command-to-line-of-sight navigation technique is usually used when the target range information is not available.

Passive i.r. homing missiles carry the complete detection, tracking, and guidance subsystems on board. The tracker or seeker typically consists of a gimballed platform that contains optical components for collecting and focusing the target radiation, an i.r. sensor that converts the incident radiation to one or more electrical signals, electronics for processing the sensor output signals and converting them to guidance commands, and a servo- and stabilization system to control the position of the tracking platform. One type of i.r. seeker is shown in Fig. 6.12. Infrared radiation incident on the seeker dome passes through the dome and strikes the primary mirror, which redirects the incident radiation to the secondary mirror. This mirror focuses the radiation on a spinning reticle or chopper. When a point source of radiation is on the movable optical axis, the radiation is focused at a spot on the center of the reticle. When the source is off of the axis, the focused spot is off of the reticle center. The reticle periodically interrupts or modulates the incoming radiation or signal for the purpose of target discrimination and tracking. The modulated signal passes through a spectral filter designed to eliminate much of the background radiation to improve the signal-to-background-noise ratio. Finally, the signal impinges upon the i.r. sensor, which in this example is a single detector element. Some passive i.r. systems may use more than one detector element to cover different portions of the i.r. band. These systems are used to enhance tracking and are referred to as multiple color systems. For example, a two-color system could be used to discriminate between a very hot i.r. countermeasure and the cooler aircraft on the basis of the radiation spectral content.

Other types of passive i.r. systems, such as the forward looking infrared radiation device, are used in fire-control systems for initial target acquisition and possibly for tracking. These types of devices may use a two-dimensional planar array of individual elemental i.r. detectors such that the output is a two-dimensional i.r. picture of the target. Finally, pulsed or continuous wave (CW) lasers can be used to illuminate or track targets, providing a source for a semiactive laser homing or a beam-riding missile to track and close on.

(1)   Detection.   The detection of an aircraft by an i.r. seeker occurs when the infrared radiation from the aircraft collected by the seeker reaches the minimum or threshold power level (within the operating wavelength band of the detector) for detection. When detection occurs, the tracking process is initiated, provided the tracking platform is uncaged. When the tracker is continuously and automatically tracking the target, the seeker is said to be locked on. The range at which lock-on occurs is called the lock-on range R_{LO} and is given by

$$R_{LO} = \left(\frac{I}{L \xi_{min}(\text{NEFD})} \right)^{\frac{1}{2}} \qquad (6.25)$$

where I (W/sr) is the aircraft radiant intensity at the aircraft in the direction of the sensor and in the band of the sensor; L (≥ 1) represents the atmospheric loss or attenuation of the signature as it propagates over the distance R_{LO} toward the seeker; ξ_{min} is the minimum signal-to-noise ratio required by the sensor for target lock-on; and NEFD is the noise equivalent irradiance (W/cm^2) at the seeker that produces a signal equal to the internal noise. The NEFD is a performance feature of the seeker design. The lock-on range varies with aspect because the aircraft's signature varies with aspect. The locus of points around the aircraft or the missile that define the lock-on range is called the lock-on envelope or boundary.

The i.r. detectors used in the early i.r. homing missiles employed uncooled detectors, such as lead sulfide (P_bS), with a useful sensitivity in the 1.8- to

2.8-μm, or hot metal emission and reflected sunlight, region. Although homing in on the aircraft-reflected sunlight from any direction is possible with an uncooled seeker, the early i.r. missiles were generally restricted to launches from behind the target aircraft toward the exposed hot engine parts and tail pipe because these were the only parts of the aircraft that were hot enough to be detected. These launches at departing aircraft were often referred to as revenge shots. Cooling the i.r. detectors in advanced missiles may enable the seeker to track the relatively low-level radiation in the 4- to 5-μm band that is emitted by the hot gases in the engine exhaust plume. Because the plume may be observed from all aspects around the aircraft, cooled-seeker i.r. missiles have the potential for detecting the aircraft from almost any direction. Any i.r. missile that can detect, track, and intercept an aircraft after a launch from any direction is referred to as an all-aspect i.r. missile. (The tracking rate can be relatively high when a pro nav missile is launched from the forward hemisphere directly at the target aircraft compared with a rear hemisphere launch. This high tracking rate may prevent a cooled-seeker missile from being an all-aspect missile.)

The outer limit of the effective operation of i.r. missiles depends upon the aircraft i.r. signature, the sensor sensitivity, the intervening atmosphere, and the missile's dynamic launch envelope, which is dependent upon the aircraft's relative flight path and velocity. The projection of the operational range limits of surface-launched missiles upon the ground is referred to as the missile's footprint, as illustrated in Fig. 6.13. The missile is effective only when launched at aircraft located in the overlap of the lock-on region and the missile launch region.

(2) Tracking. Aircraft can be tracked by i.r. seekers by modulating the incident radiation with reticles, by scanning, and by using imaging sensors.

(a) Reticle trackers: A reticle tracker is a seeker that has a reticle placed in front of a single detector. The reticle has a spatial pattern of varying i.r. transmission. The reticle can either be spinning (spin-scan), or it can be

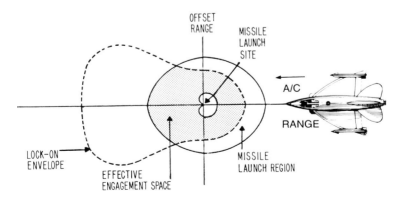

Fig. 6.13   Footprint of an i.r. missile.

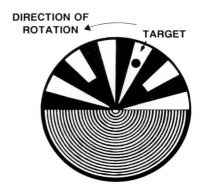

DIRECTION OF ROTATION ← **TARGET**

Fig. 6.14 Pattern for a spinning multiple-frequency reticle.

stationary and the incident illumination is nutated about the center of the instantaneous field of view (con-scan). Both types modulate or chop the incident radiation. This modulation can be used both to track the target in polar angle (and possibly radius) and to exclude the background, thus improving the signal-to-noise ratio.

Spinning reticles are often referred to as amplitude modulation (AM), frequency modulation (FM), or multiple frequency. One simple example of a spinning multiple frequency reticle is shown in Fig. 6.14. The relationship between the angular position of the reticle (with respect to one of the missile's coordinate axes) and time is known. The radiation from the target is represented by the dot. Both halves of the reticle allow approximately 50% of the incoming radiation to pass through. Consequently, the radiation from a uniform background in the instantaneous field of view of the seeker (which is noise to the tracker) will be essentially constant as the reticle spins, whereas the radiation from the target will be chopped or modulated over one-half of the reticle and will be constant over the other half. The radiation on the detector is shown in Fig. 6.15 as a function of time, and hence of the angular position of the reticle. The peak values occur when the target is in the open spaces between the opaque spokes, and the minimum values occur when it is behind the opaque spokes. Only the modulation of the signal is of interest. The steady noise due to the background radiation can be eliminated by signal processing. Although the signal chopping improves the signal-to-noise ratio, it also reduces the efficiency of the seeker because only the modulated signal is available for processing.

For the reticle shown in Fig. 6.14, the directional or polar location of the target with respect to the optical axis (and hence the missile axis) can be determined by noting the timing of the initiation of the sequence of modulations. The radial location can be determined by examining the number of modulations during each revolution. When the target is centered, no modulations occur. The farther away the target is from the center, the larger the number of modulations. Thus, the number of the modulations and their timing determine the angular and radial tracking signal for the

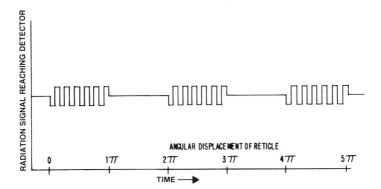

Fig. 6.15   Radiation on the detector vs time.

missile. The tracking platform may be rotated in the attempt to position the target on the optical axis. Thus, the angle between the optical axis and the missile axis becomes the line-of-site angle. More complicated reticles are sometimes used to degrade the effects of countermeasures and to reduce the effects of strong gradients in the background radiation from features such as cloud edges.

(b)   Scanning trackers: A scanning tracker consists of one or more relatively small detectors. Each detector has an instantaneous field of view that is a fraction of the total field of view of the seeker. A tracking logic circuit scans the field of detectors, one at a time. When a detector indicates that the incident radiation has exceeded a threshold value, the logic circuit notes the position of the field of view of that detector. The signal processor accumulates the information from all of the instantaneous fields of view and determines the target polar and radial position within the seeker's field of view during that scan. When the target lies within only one detector's instantaneous field of view, the target location is well defined, and multiple small targets can be resolved. For a large target seen by several detectors, the signal processor can track a particular location on the target, such as an edge or other identifiable point.

One type of scanning tracker is the rosette tracker. The basic rosette tracker uses a single, fixed detector that is illuminated by the radiation incident on an optical device that has a relatively small instantaneous field of view. The optical device scans the seeker field of view using a rosette pattern consisting of a number of loops or petals emanating from a common center. Figure 6.16 illustrates a typical rosette pattern. When the optical device "sees" the target, it directs the target's i.r. radiation on to the detector. The resultant signal from the detector tells the tracking circuit that a source of i.r. radiation is located at the particular instantaneous field of view seen by the optical device (within the seeker field of view). No modulation of the incident radiation is required in this type of tracker. Other types of scanning trackers are the crossed-array trackers (four rectan-

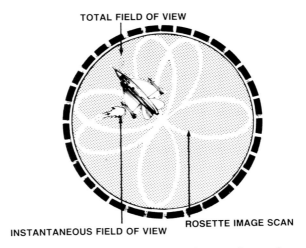

Fig. 6.16   Typical rosette pattern of a scanning tracker.

gular detectors arranged in a cross), and the raster and rotating linear-array trackers (a line of small detectors).

(c)   Imaging trackers: Imaging trackers are the most recent development in i.r. tracking techniques. The devices use hundreds of tiny i.r. detectors arranged in a planar array. The absence of a scanning mechanism allows the tracker to be packaged in relatively small configurations. These trackers have the potential for detecting and tracking specific locations on low i.r. signature aircraft against a strong background.

Visually directed systems.   A visually directed system is one which uses the human eye as the sensor for detecting and tracking aircraft. Many different threat systems use the visual signature of the aircraft for detection, and some use it for tracking, either as the primary signature or as a backup. The gun systems that use the visual signature are usually short to medium range and vary from hand-held and airborne guns to the larger AAA systems. Some short-range missile systems require visual detection prior to tracking using other signatures, and some medium-range missile systems have the capability to detect and accurately track the visual signature. The detection and tracking devices used by visually directed systems include iron sights, direct-view optical telescopes and periscopes with cross-hairs or range rings, and electro-optical imaging equipment, such as low-light-level television (LLTV).

The detection and tracking capabilities of these passive systems vary widely from very poor to highly accurate. Under good visibility conditions, direct-view optical and electro-optical trackers can provide angular tracking data accuracy equal to or better than radar, particularly for low-flying and maneuvering aircraft and when radar countermeasures are employed. The probability of detection and the rms and bias angular tracking errors for visually directed systems can be expressed using the same measures as those used for radar systems. Studies of the actual detection and tracking performance of human operators using visual tracking devices have been conducted by the Air Force Aerospace Medical Research Laboratory, Wright-Patterson AFB, Ohio, as part of the Air Force Manned Threat Quantification (MTQ) Program.

The Miss Distance and Hits on the Aircraft

An aircraft has been detected and tracked for several seconds, and the enemy decides to launch a missile or fire a projectile or a laser beam. Will any of the damage mechanisms associated with these propagators strike the aircraft? The specific equations required to answer that question depend upon the type of warhead. For example, the probability that a small arms projectile hits an aircraft will be evaluated using a different methodology than would be used to evaluate the probability that a fragment from the detonation of an HE proximity-fuzed warhead hits the aircraft. There are, however, certain features in common to each methodology. These features relate to the probability that a threat propagator will arrive at a specific x, y, z location in space relative to the aircraft. This probability depends upon the ability of the threat system to guide or fire a propagator toward an intercept with the aircraft and the ability of the aircraft to avoid that intercept.

The miss distance. The measure of the threat system's ability to position a warhead within the vicinity of the aircraft is the closest point of approach or miss distance of the propagator with respect to the aircraft. This miss distance is basically an error, and consequently it can be expressed by a distribution function of the same form as the tracking error. In general, the miss distance is a function of the three spatial coordinates (x, y, z) whose origin is centered at the aim point on the target. However, in most evaluations the problem is usually simplified to two spatial dimensions (x, y), and sometimes only one dimension (r) is used in simple estimates.

(1) Factors that influence the miss distance. The miss distance for ballistic projectiles is affected by the accuracy of the tracking system, the logic and operation of the fire-control system, the forces acting on the propagator as it approaches the target, and the flight path of the aircraft. For guided missiles, there are several important factors relating to the design of the missile that influence the miss distance. One of these factors is the missile response time. The response time defines the relative ability of the missile to rapidly change direction. Missiles that have a relatively short response time are highly maneuverable, whereas missiles that have a relatively long response time are slow to respond and may continually oscillate about the desired flight path. The missile energy in the terminal phase of the encounter is also an important factor. Generally, short-range missiles have a significant speed advantage over the target aircraft. However, medium- and

long-range missiles may have only a small speed advantage at the beginning of the terminal phase of the encounter, and any last-second aircraft maneuvers will reduce the speed advantage due to maneuver-induced drag on the missile. The missile's maximum turning rate also affects the miss distance. This rate is directly proportional to the maximum load factor of the missile and inversely proportional to the velocity. For example, a missile traveling at Mach 3 (three times the speed of sound) requires a 27 g maneuver capability to have the same turning rate as a target aircraft pulling 9 g's at Mach 1.

The guidance and control laws that navigate many of today's missiles are usually approximations to the proportional navigation law, and these approximations can have a significant effect on the miss distance, particularly for maneuvering targets. The measurement of all of the target coordinates, such as position and velocity, allows the use of more sophisticated navigation laws. However, a loss of one or more of the coordinate data, or a sudden target maneuver, may have a significant effect on the missile's ability to intercept the target when a more sophisticated law is used.

When radar target tracking is used, internal thermal noise and external noise, target glint, and scintillation will cause errors in the measured target coordinates that will contribute to the miss distance. At the beginning of an engagement, the thermal and external noise can seriously degrade missile performance by causing erroneous maneuvers that unnecessarily add to the drag on the missile, slowing it down. When the signal-to-noise ratio is low, the missile can literally chase the noise. Target glint can also be a serious problem, particularly when the missile gets close to the target, due to the fact that it is inversely proportional to the relative range. As the missile approaches the target, the target ceases to be essentially a point target and becomes an area target, possibly with widely separated scatters. Target scintillation is another contributor to the tracking error, and hence the miss distance. This error is independent of range and may be smaller than the larger of the noise and glint errors. Passive i.r. homing missiles also have angular tracking errors. When the seeker tracks the engine exhaust plume, it is tracking a source behind the aircraft, which may cause a bias error toward the aft end of the aircraft.

(2) Miss distance frequency distribution. To illustrate the physical and mathematical features of the miss distance, consider the aircraft shown in Fig. 6.17. Assume that N propagators are launched or fired toward the aircraft and that they all travel parallel paths (relative to a stationary aircraft) normal to the plane of the page. The intercept plane is the plane that contains the miss distance vector from the target aim point to the CPA and is normal to the propagator path (relative to a stationary aircraft). In this example, it is the x, y plane of the page. The N shots intersect the intercept plane at N locations of x, y pairs. The distance from the aircraft aim point (the origin of the coordinate system and normally the aircraft centroid) to any x, y pair is the miss distance for that shot, and the distances x and y are the coordinate errors.

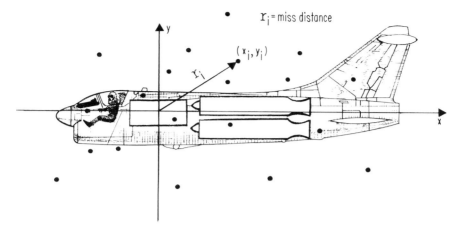

Fig. 6.17   Intercept plane and a target.

The N shots will have a miss distance mean and variance in both the x and y directions in the intercept plane. The sample means M_x and M_y are given by

$$M_x = \frac{1}{N} \sum_{i=1}^{N} x_i, \qquad M_y = \frac{1}{N} \sum_{i=1}^{N} y_i$$

where x_i and y_i denote the x and y location of the miss distance for the ith shot, and the sample variances S_x^2 and S_y^2 are computed using

$$S_x^2 = \frac{1}{N} \sum_{i=1}^{N} (x_i - M_x)^2, \qquad S_y^2 = \frac{1}{N} \sum_{i=1}^{N} (y_i - M_y)^2$$

If there is no correlation between the x and y components of the miss distances, the frequency distribution of the miss distance $\rho(x, y)$ can be expressed by the bivariate normal distribution

$$\rho(x, y) = \frac{1}{2\pi\sigma_x\sigma_y} \exp\left(-\frac{(x - \mu_x)^2}{2\sigma_x^2} - \frac{(y - \mu_y)^2}{2\sigma_y^2} \right) \qquad (6.26)$$

where the means μ_x and μ_y and the standard deviations σ_x and σ_y are related to the sample means and variances according to Eq. (6.13).

If the two means are found or assumed to be equal to zero, and if the two standard deviations are found or assumed to be equal, the bivariate distribution simplifies to the circular normal distribution given by

$$\rho(r) = \frac{1}{2\pi\sigma_r^2} \exp\left(-\frac{r^2}{2\sigma_r^2}\right) \tag{6.27}$$

where r is the radial miss distance from the target aim point, and σ_r is the circular standard deviation, which is equal to both σ_x and σ_y. The circular miss distance within which 50% of the shots fall (the CEP) is given by

$$CEP = 1.177\sigma_r \tag{6.28}$$

according to Eq. (6.23).

The total miss distance model. The miss distance is dependent upon the threat system's ability to accurately track the aircraft and to guide or point the propagator toward an intercept. The system predicts the aircraft will be at a certain location at a certain time and fires or launches and guides accordingly. If its measurement of the current target location is greatly in error, the predicted future target position will most likely be greatly in error. Furthermore, if the propagator cannot reach a correctly predicted target position, the miss distance will probably be large. Thus, the miss distance is dependent upon both the tracking accuracy and the fire-control/guidance accuracy of the system. From a total error point of view, the total miss distance standard deviation σ_m is related to the tracking error variance σ_t^2 and the fire-control/guidance miss distance variance σ_g^2 by the rss relationship when the two errors are independent. Thus,

$$\sigma_m = \left(\sigma_t^2 + \sigma_g^2\right)^{\frac{1}{2}} \tag{6.29}$$

The fire-control/guidance variance relates to the ability of the threat system to get the propagator to where the system thinks the aircraft will be at intercept (based upon the current tracking data), and the tracking error variance relates to the ability of the tracking system to accurately determine the current aircraft flight-path parameters, such as position and velocity.

The expression for σ_m given by Eq. (6.29) can be used to estimate the total rms miss distance based upon the contributions of the individual errors. The tracking error standard deviation is given by Eq. (6.24). The variance of the errors due to the control, guidance, and propagator flight path can also be estimated or measured. Guns have jitter, ballistic rounds have dispersion, and missiles have electronic boxes for receiving and/or transmitting target position data and for controlling the flight path of the missile. The error associated with each one of these features can be represented by a normal distribution with a specific variance. The aircraft flight path also affects the miss distance. However, its contribution to the miss distance is more difficult to estimate due to its variability, and consequently most simple assessments assume a nonmaneuvering aircraft.

If both the angular tracking errors and the fire-control/guidance errors are circular symmetric, and if the range tracking error is neglected, the total radial miss distance standard deviation σ_r is given by

$$\sigma_m = \sigma_r = \left(R^2\sigma_a^2 + \sigma_g^2 \right)^{\frac{1}{2}} \tag{6.30}$$

where σ_a is the standard deviation of the angular tracking error in radians.

The probability a propagator hits the aircraft. For propagators that carry a proximity-fuzed HE warhead, miss distances larger than the aircraft size can result in damage to the aircraft. On the other hand, the propagators with either non-HE warheads or contact-fuzed HE warheads must actually hit the aircraft in order to cause damage. In general, the probability the aircraft is hit by a propagator, P_H, depends upon the shape or extent of the aircraft projected in the intercept plane and the miss distance distribution function. For the general aircraft whose extent in the intercept plane is defined by the two-dimensional function $L(x,y)$, the probability of a propagator hit on the aircraft is given by the integral of the two-dimensional miss distance distribution function over the extent of the aircraft. Hence,

$$P_H = \iint_L \rho(x,y)\,dx\,dy \tag{6.31}$$

If the shape of the aircraft (whose presented area in the intercept plane is A_P) is assumed to be a "shoe box" with side lengths x_0 and y_0, then

$$A_P = x_0 y_0$$

Further, if the bivariate normal is used for the miss distance distribution, and if the aim point of the target is taken to be the centroid of the box, P_H is given by

$$P_H = \int_{-y_0/2}^{y_0/2}\int_{-x_0/2}^{x_0/2} \left(\frac{1}{2\pi\sigma_x\sigma_y}\right)\exp\left(-\frac{(x-\mu_x)^2}{2\sigma_x^2}-\frac{(y-\mu_y)^2}{2\sigma_y^2}\right)dx\,dy$$

$$\tag{6.32}$$

Unfortunately, the integrals in Eq. (6.32) can only be evaluated numerically using tables of the normal distribution.

As a result of the nonavailability of an analytical, closed-form solution for the P_H for the two-dimensional shoe box aircraft, the diffused Gaussian or Carlton function is sometimes used to define the extent of the aircraft. In Eq. (6.31), the aircraft is assumed to be hit only when x and y define a location within the physical extent of the aircraft; locations of x,y pairs outside the aircraft boundary are misses. By introducing a hit function,

$H(x, y)$, that defines the probability that the target is hit given a propagator location x, y, Eq. (6.31) can be rewritten as

$$P_H = \int_{-\infty}^{\infty} \int_{-\infty}^{\infty} \rho(x,y) H(x,y) \, dx \, dy \qquad (6.33)$$

Note that

$$\int_{-\infty}^{\infty} \int_{-\infty}^{\infty} H(x,y) \, dx \, dy = A_P$$

In order for Eq. (6.33) to correspond to Eq. (6.31), $H(x, y) = 1$ when x and y lie inside the aircraft perimeter, and $H(x, y) = 0$ when x and y lie outside the aircraft perimeter. This particular form of $H(x, y)$ is sometimes referred to as the "cookie-cutter" hit function because of its demarcation property. In the Carlton approach, $H(x, y)$ is taken in the form

$$H(x, y) = \exp\left(\frac{-\pi x^2}{x_0^2}\right) \exp\left(\frac{-\pi y^2}{y_0^2}\right) \qquad (6.34a)$$

where the parameters x_0 and y_0 are scaling parameters related to the aircraft presented area by the expression

$$A_P = \int_{-\infty}^{\infty} \int_{-\infty}^{\infty} \exp\left(\frac{-\pi x^2}{x_0^2}\right) \exp\left(\frac{-\pi y^2}{y_0^2}\right) dx \, dy = x_0 y_0 \qquad (6.34b)$$

Both the cookie-cutter and the Carlton hit functions are plotted as a function of x (with $y = 0$) in Fig. 6.18 for a square box aircraft. Note that

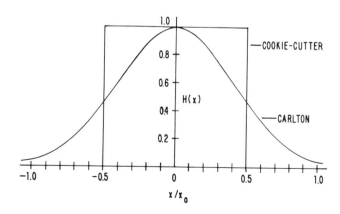

Fig. 6.18   Cookie-cutter and Carlton hit functions.

the Carlton hit function gives a nonzero probability of a hit occurring for miss distances larger than the aircraft size. Also note that the use of the Carlton function eliminates the mutually exclusive feature of the cookie-cutter function. With the cookie-cutter function, the aircraft is either hit, or is not hit, by a propagator; whereas with the Carlton function there is always a nonzero probability the aircraft is hit for all finite miss distances. Substituting Eq. (6.34a) into Eq. (6.33) with $\rho(x, y)$ expressed by the bivariate normal, Eq. (6.26), leads to

$$P_H = \int_{-\infty}^{\infty} \int_{-\infty}^{\infty} \frac{1}{2\pi\sigma_x\sigma_y} \exp\left(-\frac{(x-\mu_x)^2}{2\sigma_x^2} - \frac{\pi x^2}{x_0^2}\right)$$

$$\times \exp\left(-\frac{(y-\mu_y)^2}{2\sigma_y^2} - \frac{\pi y^2}{y_0^2}\right) dx\, dy$$

This expression for P_H can be integrated, and carrying out the integration gives

$$P_H = \frac{A_P}{\left(2\pi\sigma_x^2 + x_0^2\right)^{\frac{1}{2}}\left(2\pi\sigma_y^2 + y_0^2\right)^{\frac{1}{2}}}$$

$$\times \exp\left(-\frac{\pi\mu_x^2}{2\pi\sigma_x^2 + x_0^2} - \frac{\pi\mu_y^2}{2\pi\sigma_y^2 + y_0^2}\right) \tag{6.35a}$$

when Eq. (6.34b) is used. If the assumption is made that the aircraft is square, $x_0 = y_0$, and Eq. (6.35a) becomes

$$P_H = \frac{A_P}{\left(2\pi\sigma_x^2 + A_P\right)^{\frac{1}{2}}\left(2\pi\sigma_y^2 + A_P\right)^{\frac{1}{2}}}$$

$$\times \exp\left(-\frac{\pi\mu_x^2}{2\pi\sigma_x^2 + A_P} - \frac{\pi\mu_y^2}{2\pi\sigma_y^2 + A_P}\right) \tag{6.35b}$$

If the argument in the exponential in Eq. (6.35b) is very small due to relatively small means, or large standard deviations or aircraft presented area, the exponential function is approximately equal to unity. Hence,

$$P_H \approx \frac{A_P}{\left(2\pi\sigma_x^2 + A_P\right)^{\frac{1}{2}}\left(2\pi\sigma_y^2 + A_P\right)^{\frac{1}{2}}}$$

$$\text{provided} \quad \left\{ \begin{array}{c} x_0 = y_0 \\[2mm] -\dfrac{\pi\mu_x^2}{2\pi\sigma_x^2 + A_P} - \dfrac{\pi\mu_y^2}{2\pi\sigma_y^2 + A_P} \ll 1 \end{array} \right. \quad (6.36a)$$

Further, if $\sigma_x = \sigma_y = \sigma$,

$$P_H \approx \frac{A_P}{2\pi\sigma^2 + A_P} \qquad (6.36b)$$

If circular symmetry about the aim point is assumed for the miss distance distribution, and if the aircraft presented area is taken as a circle of radius r_0,

$$A_P = \pi r_0^2$$

and P_H becomes

$$P_H = \int_0^{2\pi}\int_0^{r_0} \frac{r}{2\pi\sigma_r^2}\exp\left(-\frac{r^2}{2\sigma_r^2}\right)\,dr\,d\theta = 1 - \exp\left(\frac{-A_P}{2\pi\sigma_r^2}\right) \qquad (6.37)$$

for the cookie-cutter hit function. For the circular Carlton hit function

$$H(r) = \exp\left(-r^2/r_0^2\right)$$

and

$$A_P = \int_0^{2\pi}\int_0^{\infty} r\exp\left(-\frac{r^2}{r_0^2}\right)\,dr\,d\theta = \pi r_0^2$$

Thus,

$$P_H = \int_0^{2\pi}\int_0^{\infty} \frac{r}{2\pi\sigma_r^2}\exp\left(-\frac{-r^2}{2\sigma_r^2} - \frac{r^2}{r_0^2}\right)\,dr\,d\theta = \frac{A_P}{2\pi\sigma_r^2 + A_P} \qquad (6.38)$$

for the circular Carlton hit function. When r_0 is small compared with σ_r,

Table 6.4 Probability of Hit (P_H) Equations

(x, y)	$\displaystyle\int_{-y_0/2}^{y_0/2}\int_{-x_0/2}^{x_0/2}\frac{1}{2\pi\sigma_x\sigma_y}\exp\left(-\frac{(x-\mu_x)^2}{2\sigma_x^2}-\frac{(y-\mu_y)^2}{2\sigma_y^2}\right)\,dx\,dy$	$x_0 y_0 = A_P$
Shoe box		
(r)	$\displaystyle 1-\exp\left(\frac{-A_P}{2\pi\sigma_r^2}\right)$	$\pi r_0^2 = A_P$
(x, y)	$\displaystyle\frac{A_P}{\left(2\pi\sigma_x^2+x_0^2\right)^{\frac{1}{2}}\left(2\pi\sigma_y^2+y_0^2\right)^{\frac{1}{2}}}\exp\left(-\frac{\pi\mu_x}{2\sigma_x^2+x_0^2}-\frac{\pi\mu_y}{2\sigma_y^2+y_0^2}\right)$	$x_0 y_0 = A_P$
Carlton		
(r)	$\displaystyle\frac{A_P}{2\pi\sigma_r^2+A_P}$	$\pi r_0^2 = A_P$

both the cookie-cutter and the Carlton expressions for P_H simplify to

$$P_H \approx A_P/2\pi\sigma_r^2 \qquad \text{provided } 2\pi\sigma_r^2 \gg A_P \tag{6.39}$$

Table 6.4 contains a summary of the probability of hit equations for the shoe box and the Carlton aircraft.

6.4 SUSCEPTIBILITY REDUCTION

The history of aircraft susceptibility reduction to hostile air-defense systems is mainly a story of reactions to a changed or unanticipated threat situation, most of them conducted on a short-term crash basis in order to keep aircraft losses to an "acceptable" level. As a consequence, this approach to survivability enhancement is often referred to as countermeasures because its purpose is to counter the actions of the threat elements. The development and production of countermeasures systems and techniques, and their application to the enhancement of aircraft survivability, have followed the ebb and flow of immediate military needs and have tended, therefore, to lag the development of air-defense weapons. However, the hard lessons learned in the Southeast Asia conflict, in the Arab-Israeli conflicts, and in the Falklands have given countermeasures the proper credentials to make it a major consideration for survivability enhancement; and susceptibility reduction is now given serious attention over the entire life span of an aircraft, from the earliest conceptual design phase until retirement from the inventory.

The increasing use of electromagnetic radiation and receiving devices for target acquisition and tracking and for the guidance and fire-control of propagators has led to a major emphasis on countermeasures to the electronic threat elements, and the phrases electronic warfare (EW), electronic countermeasures (ECM), and electronic counter-countermeasures (ECCM) have become familiar to anyone even remotely associated with aircraft survivability. Almost all of the threat systems use a particular region of the electromagnetic frequency spectrum shown in Fig. 6.1. The earliest electronic systems used the radio portion for target detection and tracking. These were called radar systems. The many new detection, tracking, and homing devices, such as the electro-optical and laser devices, rely on the entire spectrum, from the lowest radio frequencies through microwaves, infrared, visible light, and out to ultraviolet. Aircraft survivability is now dependent upon countermeasures that must cover this ever-expanding frequency spectrum.

Many different types of countermeasures have been and are being developed to degrade the effectiveness of the various elements of the hostile air-defense systems. For example, it has previously been shown in Chap. 1 that the probability of an aircraft kill could be expressed as the product of a series of individual probabilities in the form

$$P_K = P_A P_{\text{DIT}} P_{\text{LGD}} P_{K/H}$$

All of these terms can be influenced in some manner by countermeasures. The probability the threat is active, P_A, can be reduced by the use of antiradiation missiles and iron bombs to destroy active radar units and other threat platforms and by the use of tactics that catch the enemy off guard or overwhelm him. The probability of detection, identification, and tracking, P_{DIT}, can be reduced by tactics that employ terrain masking to reduce the probability that the threat will have a clear line of sight to the aircraft. The probability of detection can also be affected by passive measures that reduce or disguise the signatures of the aircraft. Countermeasures in the form of onboard or offboard electronic jamming of the enemy's electronic tracking devices may be actively employed to reduce the probability of accurate target tracking. Similarly, the probability of a successful missile launch, guidance to an intercept, and warhead detonation, P_{LGD}, may be decreased by jamming missile command guidance signals or missile down-links, and proximity-fuzed jamming techniques may cause a premature detonation or disabling of the weapon arming system, thus reducing the probability of a successful detonation. The value for $P_{K/H}$ can be reduced by countermeasures that cause an increase in the propagator miss distance. The $P_{K/D}$ for a SAM warhead that detonates 200 ft from the aircraft will most likely be less than the corresponding value for a warhead that detonates 20 ft away. In general, the combined effects of all of these countermeasures techniques are usually synergistic and can significantly enhance the probability of aircraft survival in the hostile environment.

The examples of susceptibility reduction described above illustrate the fact that there are many different kinds of countermeasures available today for reducing the susceptibility of aircraft. These susceptibility reduction features can be grouped into the following six concepts: (1) threat warning, (2) noise jammers and deceivers, (3) signature reduction, (4) expendables, (5) threat suppression, and (6) tactics.

All of these concepts, except some aspects of signature reduction and tactics, involve some piece of equipment, device, or armament that is carried either by the aircraft for self-protection or by another special purpose aircraft in a support role. Specific applications of each of these concepts have been developed for the important portions of the electromagnetic spectrum (radar, i.r., and visual); and in most combat situations, combinations of these concepts are used to degrade more than one aspect of the total air-defense system. Because most of this equipment is referred to by its type designation, Table 6.5 presents the Joint Electronics Type Designation System used for US military electronic equipment.

The words passive and active are often used to describe the various countermeasure techniques. Passive refers to any technique that does not require any action that would alert the enemy as to the presence of the aircraft, whereas active does require such action. For example, threat warning and signature reduction are usually passive techniques, whereas noise jamming, expendables, and threat suppression are usually active techniques.

Threat Warning

Knowledge of the location, type, and status of the threat elements in the vicinity of an aircraft is extremely important to the aircraft's survival. For example, if the pilot knew that a missile was approaching from a particular direction, he/she could make an evasive maneuver in an attempt to significantly increase the miss distance, or if he/she knew that the aircraft was being tracked by a particular type of fire-control system, jamming could be initiated and expendables deployed to cause the tracker to lose "sight" of the aircraft, thus breaking the tracker's lock on the aircraft. Threat warning devices are designed to provide that kind of information. Passive, onboard threat warning devices for many of the hostile radar detection, tracking, and missile guidance systems have been developed and are referred to as radar homing and warning receivers (RHAW), radar warning receivers (RWR), and intercept receivers. The need for similar warning devices for the i.r., visual, and laser tracking and guidance systems and for the warning of a missile launch and approach is becoming increasingly apparent. Not all threat warning is passive. The radio call from a wingman or special observer that a missile is heading toward the aircraft is an active form of threat warning.

Radar warning. Radar warning of the presence of radar-directed air defenses requires two capabilities for maximum effectiveness. They are the timely detection of the radiating threat elements and the accurate location and status of the weapon delivery systems intent on destroying the aircraft. Because of the extent and capabilities of the early warning radar networks, the assumption is sometimes made that the aircraft will be under observation by the early warning radars long before it reaches its destination, and thus there is generally no need to warn the aircrew of this fact. Consequently, the radar warning is usually associated with the tracking and

Table 6.5   Joint Electronics Type Designation System (JETDS)

```
AN  /  A  L  Q  -  99  A
 |        |  |  |      |  └────────── First Modification
Set       |  |  |      └──────────── Model = 99
          |  |  └─────────────────── Purpose = Special or Combination
          |  └────────────────────── Type = Countermeasures
          └───────────────────────── Installation = Airborne
```

Installation	Type	Purpose
A Piloted aircraft	A Invisible light, heat radiation	B Bombing
B Underwater mobile submarine		C Communications
	C Carrier	D Direction finder, reconnaissance and/or surveillance
D Pilotless carrier	D Radiac	
F Fixed ground	G Telegraph or teletype	
G General ground use		E Ejection and/or release
K Amphibious	I Interphone and public address	
M Mobile (ground)		G Fire-control or searchlight directing
P Portable	J Electromechanical or inertial wire covered	
S Water		H Recording and/or reproducing
T Transportable (ground)	K Telemetering	
U General utility	L Countermeasures	K Computing
V Vehicular (ground)	M Meteorological	M Maintenance and/or test assemblies
W Water surface and underwater combination	N Sound in air	
	P Radar	N Navigational aids
Z Piloted-pilotless airborne vehicle combination	Q Sonar and underwater sound	Q Special or combination of purposes
	R Radio	R Receiving, passive detecting
	S Special or combinations of types	
	T Telephone (wire)	S Detecting and/or range and bearing search
	V Visual and visible light	
	W Armament	T Transmitting
	X Facsimile or television	W Automatic flight or remote control
	Y Data processing	X Identification and recognition

fire-control radars, and the basic radar warning functions are to provide the crew with a map of the hostile radar-directed weapons which surround the aircraft and their status. The radar warning receiver provides this map by detecting the radar emissions impinging on the aircraft, and from this information it determines the classification (radar type), location (range and bearing), and status of the weapon system with respect to the aircraft (searching, tracking, illuminating, or actively guiding a missile). A prioritization of the threats based upon their status might also be indicated. The aircrew must then decide what to do with this information, such as attempt to mask the aircraft behind terrain, eject a bundle of chaff, turn on a radar jammer or deceiver, and/or initiate a missile evasive maneuver if a missile is on the way.

(1)   Components.   All RWR systems contain the same basic components to perform the functions of signal detection and identification and of emitter location or direction-finding (DF). These components consist of one or more antennas, a receiver, a signal analyzer, and a display. A control panel for operator input and one or more auxiliary outputs, such as warning lights or audio tones, are often provided.

Most DF systems consist of several receiving antennas distributed around the aircraft in azimuth; typically there is one in each quadrant. Advanced systems may have several antennas in each quadrant, and some DF systems employ a rotating antenna. The gain pattern in each antenna is designed with sufficient overlap to prevent gaps in the coverage. Reception of the aircraft's own electromagnetic transmissions from nearby transmitting antennas can be a problem. The coverage in elevation can vary from a limited region to full spherical coverage, depending upon the requirements. Comparison of the output from each antenna, using either amplitude or phase comparison of the impinging signal, defines the azimuthal bearing of the target radar. The range to the radar can be estimated based on the strength of the signal or computed using a triangulation procedure.

The basic function of the receiver is to detect and convert any low power level pulsed or CW radar signal intercepted by the antennas to a level high enough for the signal analyzer to process. The signal characteristics, such as frequency and pulse width, must be maintained during the processing. Since the antennas will most likely intercept several simultaneous radar signals in a dense air-defense environment, the phase, amplitude, and PRF relationships between the different signals must also be maintained.

A modern signal analyzer consists of two basic sections: a preprocessor and a computer. The preprocessor takes the continuous signal output from the receiver and conditions and converts the signal into the digital format required by the computer. The computer examines the data from each antenna to determine the direction of the radar and compares the data with emitter characteristics that have been stored in the computer memory to determine the type of radar. Pulsed radars are somewhat easier to identify than CW radars because they have several additional characteristics that are associated with the pulse, such as pulse width and PRF. If more than one radar signal is involved, the analyzer must deinterleave (separate) the mixed signals into the individual signals. Once identified, the signal may be prioritized based on the weapon system's known operational modes.

There are two approaches to the signal processing task: the hardware approach and the software approach. In the hardware approach, all functions, processing algorithms, and controls are implemented in specialized circuits. Changes in any of these features are often expensive and time-consuming. In the software approach, all data processing and controls are performed in or under the command of a computer in accordance with special software algorithms. To change one of these features requires only a change in the computer software program. This approach is referred to as software programmable. The early RWRs used the hardware approach. However, except for a limited number of specific systems, most recent RWRs have software programmable signal analyzers. The advantages of this approach are the capability to operate in a wide range of radar environments at high speed and the ability to rapidly change the processing techniques, the signal identification criteria, the display, and the interface with any auxiliary system, at less cost.

The display associated with most RWRs consists of a cathode-ray tube (CRT). In hardware RWRs, the direction to the radar is usually indicated by a strobe or radial line; the type of radar can be denoted by the type of line, such as solid, dashed, or flashing; and a rough approximation of the range to the radar is given by the length of the strobe. Software RWRs typically use symbols to denote the type of radar, and the position of the symbol on the screen may indicate the radar bearing, range, and status. Figure 6.19 illustrates the video display of one RWR. A blinking symbol or audible signal can be used to inform the crew as to the status of the system. The aural output makes it unnecessary for the crew to constantly monitor the CRT because the modulation and volume of the audio signal indicate to the crew the particular status of the threat. For example, when the radar is searching, wide variations in the signal amplitude will take place as the radar beam scans back and forth across the aircraft. This could be indicated by a relatively soft and slowly varying tone. When the radar is in the track

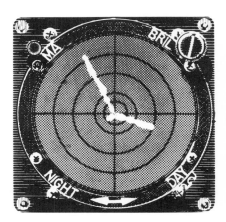

Fig. 6.19   RWR video display.

mode, the signal could be a loud tone with a modulation frequency equal to the PRF of the tracking radar. The fact that a missile is being command guided toward the aircraft could be indicated by a *very loud* warbling tone.

(2) Power management. Because it may be difficult for the crew to react in time to the warning provided by the RWR, and because only a limited amount of electronic power is available for radar jamming, many modern ECM systems incorporate a power management processor. This processor examines the output from the intercept receiver and optimally allocates the available electronic and expendable countermeasures to defeat the threat. The power manager often shares the same physical unit with the receiver to save on costs and space. The primary functions of power management are the allocation of jamming and expendable resources to priority targets, the pointing of any rotatable jamming antennas, the optimization of the jamming by the selection of modulation techniques and frequency setting to match the measured radar characteristics, and a reallocation, if required, based on controlled "look-through" of the jamming signals by the RWR. Furthermore, because the jamming is under complete control of the manager, the jamming duty cycle can be adjusted for both maximum jamming effectiveness and system power consumption. An unmanaged system will attempt to jam all radars, including those that are not a threat to the aircraft. The managed system will jam only those radars that are a threat and, consequently, can use the available power selectivity to jam more of the threat radars. The use of time-gated noise allows the jammer to nearly simultaneously jam several radars in succession, thus controlling the system power consumption without reducing the jamming effectiveness. The power manager can also control the deployment of expendables. Just as in the case of jamming, prestored priority rules can be used by the processor to select the radars against which to deploy chaff, either alone or in conjunction with jamming.

(3) Design considerations. The selection or design of an RWR for a particular aircraft is influenced by the aircraft mission requirements, the aircrew complement and duties, and the aircraft itself. Each mission places certain requirements upon the RWR system. For example, an attack mission may require relatively good emitter location information, particularly in the forward direction. If the aircraft flies very low, the surveillance radars may not interfere. However, for aircraft that operate at higher altitudes, the nonthreatening radars must be sorted out from the actual threats. Strike cover and threat suppression, on the other hand, have the requirement to identify and accurately locate radar systems that are threatening other aircraft. Multimission aircraft may pose a more difficult design problem than single mission aircraft.

The number and duties of the aircrew dictate the degree of automation required for the RWR. In a single-placed aircraft, the RWR must not add appreciably to the pilot's tasks, but it nevertheless must keep the pilot aware of the total threat situation. In aircraft with two crew members, the person not flying the aircraft may have more time to monitor the data from the

RWR. Aircraft with many members may have an electronic warfare officer (EWO) devoted to the survivability problem. This concentrated assignment permits an increased latitude in the automation, the amount of data that can be presented and interpreted, and the degree of control that can be exercised.

The aircraft itself also influences the requirements for the RWR system. The available space and weight are obvious considerations, and the decision whether to centralize or to scatter the various electronic components plays a major role. The location of the antennas is influenced by the aircraft shape and the location of other emitters on the aircraft, such as the jammer and other radars.

Infrared / laser / visual warning.   The need for warning devices for the i.r., laser, and visual detection, tracking, illuminating, and missile guidance systems is becoming increasingly apparent. The laser threat warning receiver operates on the same principle as the radar warning receiver because the laser is an active system; it must transmit radiation. Illumination of the aircraft by a laser for the purpose of determining range or for the guidance of a beam-rider or semiactive homing missile is no different in principle than illuminating or tracking the aircraft with radar, only the signal characteristic values are different.

The determination that a passive i.r. sensor or a direct-view optical or electro-optical device is looking at the aircraft is more difficult, and several detection concepts are currently being investigated.

Missile launch and approach warning.   The determination that a missile has been launched, possibly toward the aircraft, can be made using passive starring or searching sensors that detect the electromagnetic radiation associated with the missile launch and flyout. These sensors can be located around the aircraft or only in the expected missile approach direction. For example, if i.r. homing missiles are expected to approach the aircraft from the rear only, the launch warning system would be installed in the tail of the aircraft. Because there are several common features shared between the target to be detected and the background clutter to be rejected, care must be given to the design of the system to ensure a very low false alarm rate. A warning that a missile is actually approaching the aircraft can be provided by an active missile approach device that uses an active transmitter and receiver to track the missile. Perhaps someday the missile launch and approach warning device may input the appropriate information into a central countermeasures computer, which will then turn on a jammer, deploy expendables, and automatically maneuver the aircraft to avoid the oncoming missile. The pilot just goes along for the ride.

Noise Jammers and Deceivers

One of the most important countermeasures concepts that should be considered in any survivability program is the use of either onboard or stand-off active electronic equipment to degrade the effectiveness of the various nonterminal threat elements. Onboard radiation emission equipment for defensive electronic countermeasures (DECM) is usually referred to as a self-screening or self-protection jammer, such as the Navy's airborne self-protection jammer (ASPJ). Offboard equipment can be carried either by a drone or by a special purpose ECM support aircraft, such as the Navy's EA-6 and the Air Force's EF-111 aircraft.

There are two major radiation emission techniques used to reduce the susceptibility of the aircraft; they are noise or denial jamming and deception. Noise jamming can be described as a "brute force" method in which the jammer simply "outshouts" or masks the echo from the aircraft. Deception techniques are more subtle and complex than noise jammers because they transmit signals designed to fool or confuse the threat system by appearing as one or more false targets. Deceivers are often referred to as deception jammers, which is technically incorrect since they do not "jam," or as deception repeaters, or spoofers. Although jamming and deceiving is normally associated with radar, there are devices for jamming and deceiving in the other portions of the electromagnetic spectrum, such as i.r.

Radar noise jamming. Radar noise jamming consists of the generation and directed transmission of a noise-like signal that has the characteristics of radar receiver noise. The purpose of this noise is to mask or obscure the target echo. The noise may be continuous (CW) or intermittent. The radar operator "sees" the noise on a PPI as a relatively large area of clutter. Figure 6.20 illustrates the effects of CW noise jamming on a surveillance radar PPI for three different jammer power levels. Because the surveillance radar continuously listens for the echo, the CW noise is continuously received, and the noise lights up a strobe on the PPI corresponding to the direction of the antenna when the noise is received. Note that for the low-power jammer, the noise is above the threshold only when the main lobe axis of the antenna is pointing at the jammer. For the medium- and high-power jammers, the jamming effect is much wider because the noise has sufficient power to be "seen" off of the main lobe axis of the antenna. Thus, even though the antenna is not pointing directly at the jammer, noise is received, possibly in the side lobes, and the PPI lights up whenever the threshold is exceeded.

There are several frequency techniques used by radar noise jammers to obscure the aircraft echo. One is called broadband or barrage jamming. It consists of jamming a spectrum of frequencies much wider than the operating bandwidth of the radar. Barrage jamming is normally used when the radar frequency is either unknown or changing, or to cover the operating frequencies of more than one radar. Spot jamming is noise jamming in a relatively narrow frequency band centered at the radar frequency and usually somewhat larger than the radar bandwidth. This type is used when the radar frequency is known. Swept jamming is the rapid, repetitive sweeping of a narrow-bandwidth noise signal across the range of frequencies to be jammed and is sometimes used in place of barrage jamming.

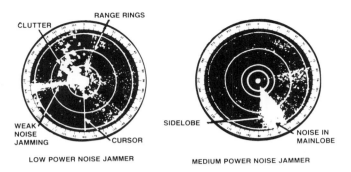

LOW POWER NOISE JAMMER   MEDIUM POWER NOISE JAMMER

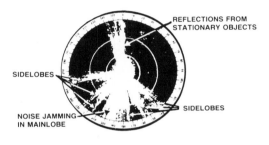

Fig. 6.20 Examples of continuous noise jamming effects on a PPI.

HIGH POWER NOISE JAMMER

(1) Jam-to-signal ratio. One of the most important parameters affecting the effectiveness of noise jamming is the jam-to-signal or J/S ratio. This is the ratio of the power of the noise J to the power of the echo S. The power of the jammer is usually expressed as the product of the jammer power density (the power per unit bandwidth) P_j times the bandwidth of the radar receiver B. For a variety of reasons, the frequency bandwidth of the jammer is usually larger than that of the radar, therefore the product $P_j B$ gives only that portion of the total jammer power intercepted by the radar receiver. The power of the generated noise directed toward the radar is therefore given by

$$J = P_j B G_j$$

where G_j is the gain of the jammer antenna in the direction of the radar receiver. For the self-screening situation, the power in the echo at the target is

$$S = P_r G_r \sigma / 4\pi R^2$$

It is important to note that in the self-screening situation both the reflected echo and the jamming signal travel the same distance from the target to the receiver. Hence, the jam-to-signal ratio is established at the target and remains constant all the way back to the radar. Thus, the J/S ratio at the radar receiver can be given in the form

$$\frac{J}{S} = \left(\frac{P_j B G_j}{P_r G_r}\right)\left(\frac{4\pi}{\sigma}\right)(R^2) \tag{6.40}$$

(2) Burn-through range. Note that the J/S ratio given by Eq. (6.40) is directly proportional to R^2. This means the jammer has a range advantage because the radar signal has to traverse twice the distance traveled by the jamming signal. However, looking at this feature from a different point of view, the echo power S at the aircraft increases as the target approaches the radar receiver (R decreases), whereas the jammer power remains constant. Eventually, a range may be reached where the target echo has increased to the point that it can be detected by the radar operator in the presence of the jamming signal. This distance is called the burn-through range R_B because the echo has "burned through" the jamming signal. If a "camouflage factor" C is defined as the minimum J/S ratio that will just barely conceal the echo in the noise, then substituting C in Eq. (6.40) for J/S and solving for the burn-through range gives

$$R_B = \left(\frac{P_r G_r \sigma C}{P_j B G_j 4\pi}\right)^{\frac{1}{2}} \tag{6.41}$$

In reality, there is no one value for the burn-through range because of the fluctuations in σ and G_j that occur in a typical scenario.

(3) Stand-off jamming (SOJ). Frequently, noise jammers are carried on supporting aircraft rather than on the aircraft to be protected. The supporting aircraft in this case usually stands off at a distance from both the target aircraft and the radar, out of range of the air defenses. There are several advantages in the use of dedicated stand-off jammers compared with self-protection jammers. These are:

(a) A dedicated jammer can protect several attack vehicles.

(b) A dedicated jammer can have higher power.

(c) A dedicated jammer may be able to use one or more directional antenna.

(d) A dedicated jammer may be able to operate at optimum altitude to maximize the jammer-to-radar propagation factor.

(e) Use of stand-off jammers may prevent the use of home-on-jam tracking.

(f) Two or more jammers can sometimes be used simultaneously for maximum protection.

(g) The precise direction to the attack vehicles is not revealed before burn-through.

Disadvantages in the use of stand-off jammers are:

(a) The jammer-to-radar range is relatively large, hence high jamming power is required for a desired J/S.

(b) It may be difficult for the stand-off jammer to provide enough protection by remaining behind the strike aircraft.

(c) The jamming aircraft itself becomes a high-value target, and its loss could be detrimental to the survivability of the aircraft it was supposed to protect.

The use of a remotely piloted vehicle (RPV) as a stand-off jamming platform may eliminate these disadvantages.

The jam-to-signal ratio and burn-through range equation for the stand-off jammer can be derived in a manner similar to that used for the self-protection jammer, except the ratio must also account for the fact that the jammer and the target are not coincident. The J/S ratio for the SOJ situation can be given in the form

$$\frac{J}{S} = \left(\frac{P_j BG_{jr} G_{rj}}{P_r G_r G_r} \right) \left(\frac{4\pi}{\sigma} \right) \left(\frac{R_t^4}{R_j^2} \right) \tag{6.42}$$

where R_t is the radar to target range, R_j is the radar to jammer range, G_{jr} is the gain of the jammer antenna toward the radar, and G_{rj} is the gain of the radar antenna in the direction of the jammer. The burn-through range R_B is obtained by setting $J/S = C$ and solving Eq. (6.42) for R_t. Thus,

$$R_B = \left(\frac{P_r G_r^2 \sigma C R_j^2}{P_j BG_{jr} G_{rj} 4\pi} \right)^{\frac{1}{4}} \tag{6.43}$$

(4) Design and operational considerations. In designing a noise jammer for optimum performance, the burn-through range given by Eqs. (6.41) and (6.43) show that to minimize the burn-through range, the engineer should design for the maximum possible power per unit bandwidth, obtain as much antenna directivity toward the victim receiver as possible, and select a jamming waveform that will minimize the camouflage factor.

Maximum jamming power output may be limited by the ratings of the available devices, by the power supply and environmental limitations (such as the available cooling) on the aircraft, by safety considerations for personnel, and by power limitations of waveguides, antennas, or other components. To maximize the power per unit bandwidth, the jammer bandwidth should be made as narrow as possible (spot jamming), and the spectrum should be matched to the victim receiver bandwidth. In most cases, the jammer bandwidth must be somewhat greater than the receiver bandwidth to allow for frequency set-on tolerances and drift of jammer and receiver, or in order to jam several receivers on different frequencies simultaneously. Normally, the designer tries to obtain as uniform a jamming spectrum over the jammer bandwidth as possible so that jamming effectiveness will not be a function of the location of the receiver bandwidth within the jamming spectrum.

In order to obtain antenna gain greater than unity toward the radar receiver, directional antenna must be used. If either the jammer or the receiver is moving, the antenna beam must be steered. This can be accomplished manually if personnel are available, or it may be accomplished automatically. When designing self-protection jammers, it may be desirable to employ radiating systems that are completely omnidirectional if jamming coverage is required during hard maneuvers.

If the characteristics of the radar receiver were known exactly, it would be possible to select an optimum waveform to use against that receiver. Such an optimum choice is generally not possible for several reasons. Even if the receiver characteristics were known exactly, the enemy might temporarily change the receiver circuitry to reduce the effectiveness of the jamming signal. Moreover, the jammer must be able to operate against several radar systems with receivers having different characteristics, and sometimes two or more systems must be jammed simultaneously.

There are, of course, other problems in designing a jamming system. The enemy radar signals must be detected and identified before they can be jammed. A jamming system could be useless if the user does not know which frequencies need to be jammed. Intelligence information is not enough, for radars can change frequency or go off the air. Furthermore, it would be pointless and possibly dangerous to jam a radar that was not radiating for two reasons. One, a missile with a home-on-jam tracking capability could be on its way; and two, although a nonradiating radar cannot directly measure the range to a target, it can determine the direction to a jammer, and two such radars can obtain a fix on the jammer. Thus, most jammers have an intercept receiver or RWR capability.

Detecting the impinging radar signals while jamming (the "look-through" problem) can be difficult. The received radar signal may be in the order of -35 dBm, while the jammer output may be $+55$ dBm or more. Thus, isolation between the jamming transmitter and the intercept receiver in the order of 90 dB or more is required for detection of the victim signal while jamming. It is not always possible to obtain this degree of isolation, particularly with an omnidirectional transmitting antenna. Alternate solutions to the look-through problem are to either turn the jammer off or to detune it for a very short time.

Threat priorities must be established in order to jam effectively. Electronic support measures (ESM) are therefore needed to obtain up-to-date information on operating radars so that the most dangerous threats can be jammed. The jammer must be set on the radar frequency and jamming initiated at the proper time. These functions can be provided by a power-managed ECM suite. It has previously been shown that the J/S ratio increases as the square of the range. Therefore, the jammer can be detected by the radar at ranges much greater than the range at which the jamming aircraft can be detected by the radar. Thus, the jammer should not be turned on beyond the maximum detection range of the radar. To do so may give the enemy information they could not obtain with their own radar at that range, such as the direction of the jammer.

Sometimes, when a very wide band of frequencies must be jammed, a swept jammer is used. In this case the jamming is swept over the band of frequencies at a relatively slow rate so that each radar is jammed intermittently. Thus, the target aircraft is seen intermittently by the radar, but the blip-scan ratio (the single scan detection probability) is reduced below its values without any jamming. It is also more difficult to determine the direction to the jammer from the radar PPI display, since jamming strobes appear on the display in various directions, depending on the direction the radar antenna is pointing at the times when the jammer signal is received.

All forms of noise jamming are generally most effective if several jammers are scattered geographically and used simultaneously. With several jammers in different directions, the PPI picture can be so confusing that the radar operator has difficulty determining the direction to any one of the jammers. This is particularly true at short-to-moderate ranges where the jamming may enter the radar antenna through the main and the side lobes.

Radar deception.   Deception of a surveillance or weapon-control radar system consists of those electronic techniques that present false target information to the radar. In some cases, it may be possible to cause the break-lock of a tracking radar, causing it to become completely unlocked from the target. The radar must then attempt to reacquire the aircraft. The usual approaches for deception are:

(1)   To generate a large number of false targets that are indistinguishable from the real target and that overload the system by subtle means rather than by brute force.

(2)   To provide incorrect target bearing, range, or velocity information to the radar.

In general, many deception signals may be unmasked by a properly designed radar with ECCM, but they can be very effective if not accounted for by the radar.

(1)   Deception techniques.   There are a great many deception techniques available today, and many more will probably be developed to counter the changing threat environment. In general, they all modify or modulate the echo received by the radar in some manner. Because of the power limitations on self-protection jammers, most self-protection jammers rely heavily on deception for their effectiveness. The deception methods can be divided into the following four categories according to the type of echo modulation used: time, amplitude, phase or frequency, and polarization. Two of the most common deception techniques, range-gate pull-off and inverse con-scan, are described below to give the reader an indication of the nature of this beast.

(a)   Range-gate pull-off (RGPO): This time modulation deception technique, also known as range-gate walk-off and range-gate stealer, is a DECM countermeasure that can work with automatic range tracking pulse radars

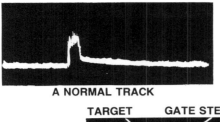

A NORMAL TRACK

TARGET   GATE STEALER PULSE

AGC CAPTURED, NOTE REDUCTION IN NOISE LEVEL

TARGET   GATE STEALER PULSE

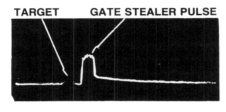

TARGET   GATE STEALER PULSE

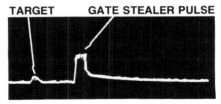

Fig. 6.21   Range-gate pull-off.

using automatic gain control. The procedure and effects of RGPO are illustrated in Fig. 6.21. The pull-off of the range gate is accomplished by first detecting the impinging radar pulse and as quickly as possible transmitting a relatively small deceiving signal as identical to the target echo as possible. The radar then sees both the target echo and the deceiving signal nearly simultaneously. As this superposition procedure continues, the power of the deceiving signal is continually increased until it "captures" the radar's automatic gain control. Now the radar is tracking the stronger deceiving signal, and it cannot see the target echo. Next, the deceiving signal is slowly delayed, causing the automatic range tracking circuit to move the presumed target (the false target) beyond the range of the actual target. The deceiver has now pulled the range gate off of the target. Eventually, the deceiving signal may be shut off, causing the radar to lose sight of the false target.

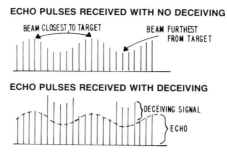

Fig. 6.22   Inverse con-scan.

Because the radar gain control is now so low, and because the actual target is out of the range gate, the radar must go into its acquisition mode to reacquire the target. Its lock on the target has been broken. RGPO is not always effective. An operator watching this spoofing start to happen on a PPI scope may be able to detect the RGPO and prevent it from breaking lock, and there are ECCM techniques that will degrade or eliminate its effectiveness, such as leading-edge tracking. In leading-edge tracking, the range gate always tracks the leading edge of the pulse, and thus the delayed deceiving signal will not capture the tracking gate.

(b)   Inverse con-scan: This is an amplitude modulation technique for deceiving conical scan tracking radars and is illustrated in Fig. 6.22. It works by determining both the scan rate of the radar and when the scanning beam is closest to the aircraft. When the scanning beam is pointed away from the aircraft, the deceiver transmits a relatively strong signal so that the radar sees both the echo and the deceiving signal. As the beam approaches the aircraft, the deceiver stops transmitting so that only the target echo is received. When the combination of the faint target echo and the strong deceiving signal (when the beam is farthest from the target) is stronger in amplitude than the return from the target alone (when the beam is closest to the target), the radar will interpret the inverse modulation pattern to mean that the aircraft is in the direction indicated when the deceiving signals were received, which is of course in the wrong direction. This can cause a break-lock of the radar. There are ECCM techniques to defeat inverse con-scan, such as lobe-on-receive-only, in which the radar lobes only the receiving antenna. With LORO, the jammer does not know the scan rate or when the receiver is looking away from the aircraft. The use of monopulse also defeats this technique because only one pulse is required to determine the angle to the aircraft.

(2)   Comparison of radar noise jammers and deceivers.   The noise jammer is universal in that it can degrade the performance of any radar. With adequate noise, range, and possibly angle, information is denied to the radar. However, relatively high power is required for noise jammers, since they may operate with a 100% duty cycle, and directional information may

not be denied by a single low-power jammer used for self-protection. Furthermore, the noise jammer can serve as a beacon for home-on-jam missiles.

The deceiver for a pulse radar usually requires relatively small average power output, since its duty cycle is comparable to the radar duty cycle. To be effective, its modulation must be carefully tailored to the characteristics of the victim radar. Like the noise jammer, the deceiver can serve as a beacon, although it is somewhat harder to detect. It can be programmed to give false range information and false angular information. However, angular deception against certain types of radars, such as monopulse, is much more difficult.

Radar fuze jamming. Many modern missiles are detonated by some sort of proximity fuze that senses the presence of the target and detonates the warhead at the optimum distance to maximize damage. Proximity fuzes can sometimes be affected by countermeasures. In general, the best countermeasure procedure will cause the fuze to detonate the warhead at a range great enough to reduce the probability of damage to the target and to other aircraft in the vicinity to near zero. When this is not possible, an alternate countermeasure mode is to prevent the operation of the proximity fuze. However, this is of little comfort if the missile scores a direct hit.

Infrared jammers and deceivers. Infrared countermeasure (IRCM) devices that either introduce large amounts of i.r. noise into threat i.r. tracking systems or fool the i.r. trackers by sending false target information can also be important to the survivability of an aircraft. The first type of device is referred to as a saturation jammer. This device generates an amount of i.r. radiation in the bandwidth of the detector that is sufficient to saturate or possibly damage the detector, causing the seeker to go blind.

The second type of device is the smart i.r. jammer or deceiver. One particular example of a deceiver works against reticle trackers and is often referred to as a hot brick. Figure 6.23 presents an illustration of the hot brick installed on a helicopter. This type of jammer may use JP fuel or electricity to heat a ceramic source. The i.r. radiation from the hot source can be mechanically modulated to provide the deceiving signal. The i.r. seeker will see the combination of the relatively steady aircraft signature and the pulses of i.r. energy from the hot brick. Further modulation of the fluctuating incoming signal by the seeker reticle to determine the aircraft's angular location will create false information on that location. The deceiver modulations will be processed with the reticle-caused target modulations, and the computed location of the target will be wrong, causing the missile to go astray.

There are several design considerations for the smart jammer. Besides being light, inexpensive, and reliable, it must have an adequate radiation pattern around the aircraft to deceive missiles approaching from any direction. It must have sufficient signal strength to be seen by the missile in

Fig. 6.23   An i.r. deceiver.

combination with the aircraft signature; it should be capable of operating as long as the aircraft is in the hostile environment; and it should have a filter that removes the visible radiation so the device cannot be seen at night. Its effectiveness against advanced i.r. missiles must be evaluated because, like the radar jammer, it may be a beacon that more sophisticated i.r. trackers can home in on.

Signature Reduction

The ability of a threat system to quickly detect, locate, identify, and accurately track an airborne target has a significant influence upon the survivability of the target. Features that reduce the apparent size of the observables or signatures of the target degrade the ability of the threat system to accomplish these functions. These features are therefore extremely important and should be a major consideration in the design of an aircraft.

There are several detectable parameters utilized by threat systems for target detection and tracking. Currently, they are the radar cross section, the i.r. radiation, the visual signature, and the acoustic signature. The two general methods used to make an aircraft more difficult to be seen by detection and tracking systems are: (1) reduction of the aircraft signature to a level that is below the sensor threshold, and (2) masking of the aircraft signature by minimizing the aircraft-to-background contrast. Both of these methods are passive. The particular method used to enhance survivability depends upon the type of threat system sensors expected to be encountered.

The radar signature.   Briefly, the two major features that determine the RCS of any aircraft for a given radar are its geometry (size and shape) and the electromagnetic properties of the aircraft materials. The major sources of the radar echo from metallic aircraft surfaces are the flat surfaces, which return the signal in a mirrorlike manner, and the intersections of surfaces and the cavities, which scatter the return over broad angular regions. Thus, for fixed-wing aircraft, the return from the fuselage, the fuselage-wing-empennage interfaces, the leading and trailing edges, the cockpit interiors, the antennas and compartments, the engine propellers or inlet and exhaust cavities, the external stores and associated suspension equipment, and any other protuberances should be controlled. For rotary-wing aircraft, additional sources are the fuselage-sponson interfaces, the main rotor mast, hub, and blades, the tail rotor drive, hub, and blades, and the landing gear.

The general method of RCS control is the reduction in the level of the signature. This has the effect of decreasing the signal-to-noise ratio. This reduction can be accomplished in three ways: (1) reflection of the radar signal away from any receiving antenna, (2) "absorption" of the radar signal by attenuation or interference, and (3) active interference with the surface currents.

(1) Reflection. Reflection of the impinging radar signal away from the receiving antenna of a monostatic radar can be accomplished by shaping the conducting aircraft surfaces to eliminate the backscatter from both the large flat surfaces and from the surface intersections and cavities. This approach leads to an aircraft with a smooth, curved shape and blended surface intersections at locations, such as the wing root and the weapon pylon attachments, and to other features, such as the location of engine inlets on the upper surface of the wing or fuselage, removing them from the line of sight to ground-based radars (but possibly putting them in the view of higher-flying aircraft). Radar reflection away from the receiving antenna can also be accomplished by covering radar transparent materials with a thin layer of conducting material that is opaque to the radar signal. This prevents the signal from being backscattered by internal structures, such as bulkheads, and by other components.

The objective of the reflection technique is to reflect the radar signal away from the receiving antenna. This objective presupposes a knowledge of the direction of the receiver. For monostatic radars, the transmitter and receiver are collocated, and consequently the impinging radar signal should be directed away from the approach direction. However, this could actually increase the RCS of the aircraft for a bistatic radar, since the receiver may be in the direction of the reflected signal. In general, shaping is most effective when the radar wavelength is short compared with the dimensions of the individual reflecting surfaces.

(2) Absorption. Absorption of the impinging radar signal is accomplished using special radar absorbent materials called RAM. RAM can "absorb" the echo either by admitting and then internally attenuating the strength of the impinging signal or by internally generating reflections that interfere with the reflection from the front surface. The former type is referred to as attenuating or broadband RAM, and the latter type is known as interference, tuned, or resonant RAM. A number of RAM types have

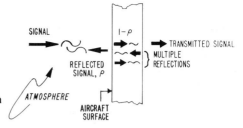

Fig. 6.24   Reflection and transmission of a radar signal.

been developed that provide a selection of weights, thicknesses, costs, and structural properties. These include the attenuating dielectric gradients and magnetics, and the resonant tuned RAM and circuit analogs. The effectiveness of RAM is greatly dependent upon its electromagnetic impedence, which is usually frequency dependent.

When a radar signal traveling through the atmosphere strikes the surface or skin of an aircraft, some of it will be reradiated at the interface by the aircraft material, and the remainder will travel partly or completely through the material, as shown in Fig. 6.24. The strength of the nonscattered portion will decay somewhat as the signal passes through the material until the signal strikes the rear face of the skin. Some of this portion will be reflected at the interface, and the remainder will pass through. The internally reflected portion will again pass through the material, continuing to decay in strength as it propagates, until it reaches the front interface where the reflection-transmission phenomenon occurs again. This process continues until the signal within the material has totally decayed. The backscatter echo is the sum of the backscattered reflection from the front face and the internal backscattered reflections.

The amount of signal that is reradiated by the induced electric charge oscillations on the skin and the remaining amount that passes through the air-skin interface are dependent upon the relative electromagnetic impedances of the air and the skin. The electromagnetic characteristic impedance of a material η is given by

$$\eta = (\mu/\varepsilon)^{\frac{1}{2}}$$

where μ and ε are the permeability and permittivity of the material, respectively. (In materials with nonzero conductivity, ε is a complex number.) In air, $\eta = 377\ \Omega$, whereas in typical aircraft metals (which are good conductors), $\eta \simeq 0$. When the radar signal travels through one medium with an impedance of η_1 and strikes (at normal incidence) another medium with an impedance of η_2, the reflected portion ρ is given by

$$\rho = |\eta_2 - \eta_1|/(\eta_2 + \eta_1) \qquad (6.44)$$

For the typical air-metal interface, $\rho \simeq 1$ due to the large impedance mismatch at the interface. Hence, nearly all of the impinging signal is reflected.

For a material to be effective as attenuating RAM, it must reflect very little of the incident signal; hence, its electromagnetic impedance must be approximately that of air. Another requirement for attenuating RAM is that it rapidly absorb the energy in the radar signal as the wave propagates though the material. This can be accomplished using lossy (energy absorbing) dielectrics, or lossy magnetics or ferrites. The amount of absorption in a lossy material depends upon the particular properties of the material's impedance, the radar frequency, the thickness of the material, and the angle of incidence of the signal. For broad coverage over a wide range of frequencies, several layers of different lossy dielectric materials can be bonded together, making a dielectric gradient. Typical lossy materials are carbon or ferrite particles in a thin layer or mesh of synthetic rubber or plastic, foams, and hair mats.

Examples of RAM that work by interference absorption are the Dällenbach layer and the circuit analog. In the Dällenbach layer technique, a homogeneous, lossy layer is placed in front of a conducting ground plane, such as the aircraft skin. Absorption by destructive interference between the front face echo and the ground plane echo occurs when the radar wavelength (in the Dällenbach layer) is four times the distance of the layer front face from the ground plane.* As a consequence of the limited frequency coverage of the Dällenbach layer, circuit analog interference absorbers have been developed to broaden the frequency coverage. In the circuit analog, several thin sheets of material with specific surface impedances are separated by lossless dielectric layers. The Salisbury screen, consisting of a thin layer of lossy material (the screen) separated from a conducting ground plane by a lossless dielectric, is perhaps the simplest example of a circuit analog. The reflection from the front face of the circuit analog absorber is the net result of the reflections of the signal from the front face and the interfaces between the sheets and the layers. The behavior of this type of construction can be represented analytically by an electrical circuit analog consisting of impedances, resistors, and capacitors.

Typically, the lossy dielectrics are light and thick, the lossy magnetics are thin and heavy, and the circuit analogs, which may be the most effective RAM, are thick and expensive.

(3) Interference with the surface currents. The use of shaping and RAM is most effective when the radar wavelength is short compared with the dimensions of the target scatterer. A method that can be used when the radar wavelength is approximately the same length as or larger than the dimensions of the scattering surfaces is to interfere with the electric

---

*The radar wavelength in the conductive layer can be much shorter than the radar wavelength in air, particularly for ferrite loaded materials. Thus, the Dällenbach layer is usually much thinner than one-fourth of the wavelength in air.

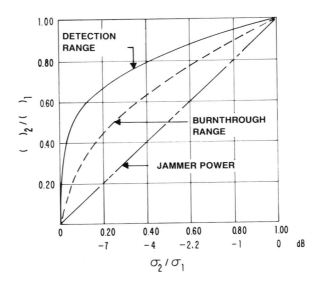

Fig. 6.25   Effects of a reduction in the RCS.

charge flow on the surface of the scatter. This is accomplished by introducing impedances at various locations over the aircraft surface, and consequently the method is referred to as reactive loading. Reactive loading cannot only modify the RCS, it can be used to actively control the RCS by opening and closing switches that alter the amount of interference.

(4)   Benefits of RCS reduction.   Reduction of the RCS of an aircraft reduces the range at which the aircraft is first detected by a radar system according to Eq. (6.5b). More importantly, however, is the impact on the burn-though range, Eq. (6.41), and the power required for a given jam-to-signal ratio, Eq. (6.40), for aircraft carrying a radar jammer. The reduction in these three parameters (for the same J/S ratio) is as follows: (a) detection range R_{max} varies as $(\sigma)^{\frac{1}{4}}$, (b) burn-through range R_B varies as $(\sigma)^{\frac{1}{2}}$, and (c) required jammer power J varies as σ. Figure 6.25 shows these three relationships. The baseline and new values are denoted by the subscripts 1 and 2, respectively. For example, if the controlled RCS is 60% of the baseline RCS, i.e., a 2.2-dB reduction, the aircraft with the controlled RCS is detected in free space at 88% of the baseline detection range, the burn-through range is reduced to 77% of the baseline burn-through range, and the jammer power required to achieve the same J/S ratio is only 60% of that required by the jammer on the baseline aircraft. It is easy to see from this illustration that the major advantage gained by a 40% reduction in σ is the reduced jammer power required to camouflage the radar echo. Although the example uses a 40% reduction, reductions by a factor of 5 or 10 may not be uncommon with present day technology, and the cost and other penalties

when the RCS is controlled early in the development stage of the aircraft may be relatively insignificant.

Careful attention to the radar cross section in the initial design stages can result in considerable savings in total weight and cost penalties due to the resultant reduction in the size and power of the jammer required to protect the aircraft. Figure 6.26 illustrates the relationship between the increase in weight due to the addition of RCS reduction techniques and the decrease in jammer weight required to achieve a specific J/S ratio. When the RCS is large, a relatively large, heavy, and expensive jammer may be required. Reducing the RCS adds weight and costs associated with the control technology, but also allows a lighter and less-expensive jammer to be used. The reduction in jammer weight and costs may be larger than the increases associated with the RCS control for certain levels of RCS. The designer should look for the optimum combination of RCS control and jammer size to minimize the weight and/or cost of the total system for the desired J/S value. In the example shown in Fig. 6.26, the minimum weight penalty occurs when the aircraft RCS has been reduced from 10 to 2 m^2. A 400-W jammer is required for this value of RCS, vs the 2000-W jammer required for the baseline aircraft.

The infrared signature. The principal sources of infrared radiation from an aircraft are the emitting surfaces and the reflecting surfaces. The emitting surfaces consist of the hot metal parts in the engine and on the airframe and of the engine exhaust plume. The reflecting surfaces are generally on the airframe. Control of the i.r. signature is required to degrade

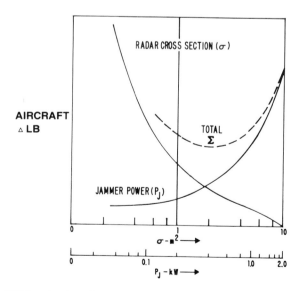

Fig. 6.26   RCS reduction/jammer power total weight trade-off for fixed J/S.

detection and tracking and to make viable i.r. countermeasures, such as the hot brick and expendable flares. The general method used to control the i.r. signature is to reduce the level of the signature. This is accomplished in the following ways: (1) reduction of the temperature, (2) reduction or masking of the observable radiating area, (3) reduction of the surface emissivity, and (4) reduction of the surface reflectivity. The specific application of these four techniques depends upon the particular source being controlled.

(1) Propulsion sources.   Cooling of the engine hot metal parts and the exhaust plume is a potentially effective technique for controlling the i.r. radiation level, since the level is at least proportional to T^4. The utility of cooling depends upon the type of engine, such as a turbojet, a turboshaft/turboprop, and a turbofan. Of these three types of engines, only the turbofan with its bypass air has an inherent available coolant source. The other two engine types must obtain ambient air for the cooling. The engine exhaust system components that may be cooled are the exhaust frame centerbody, the flame holders, the tail pipe, and the nozzle walls. Cooling air for these parts may be obtained by either external blowers or ejectors in the case of turboshaft engines or obtained from the fan flow in turbofan engines. The cooling air is generally applied to the surface through cooling slots that combine impingement and convective cooling. For components, such as the turbine blades, which remain hot, cooled shields that block the view of the component to an i.r. observer external to the exhaust system can be used. Another method of shielding the hot components from view is to incorporate a turn in the exhaust duct. Further i.r. radiation reduction may then be accomplished by coating the cooled surfaces with i.r. radiation absorbent materials.

Suppression of the engine exhaust plume i.r. radiation level is most efficiently accomplished by reducing the gas temperature either before it leaves the exhaust system or as soon thereafter as possible. One technique used on turbofan engines that have a hot gas generator or core stream and a much cooler surrounding bypass or fan airstream is to employ a mixer to bring the hot and cool streams into contact just downstream of the turbine discharge plane and to force these gases to mix in the duct prior to exit from the nozzle. A similar technique for turbojet and turboshaft engines is to use ejectors that pump either engine bay compartment cooling air or ambient ram air into a coannular stream surrounding the hot core gas stream. The ejector pump may utilize the residual energy of the engine exhaust gases to pump the cooling air into the exhaust plume. Still further plume radiation reduction can be obtained under flight conditions by turning the exhaust gas at an angle to the flight direction, which puts the plume in a cross flow. This cross flow will cause rapid mixing of the cooler ambient air with the plume as the exhaust gas stream is turned back into the direction of the cross flow. An additional advantage of turning the exhaust duct is that it may shield the hot engine parts from view. Another technique for reducing exhaust plume radiation is to make the exhaust duct transition from a round cross-sectional shape near the turbine discharge plane to an elliptical or rectangular (two-dimensional) shape at the exhaust exit plane. The two-dimensional exit shape gives more perimeter for the hot exhaust flow to mix with the surrounding ambient air, and the corners of the two-dimensional nozzle may cause turbulence to improve the mixing. One example of an i.r. suppressor is illustrated in Fig. 6.27. Note the two-dimensional nozzles and the turn in the duct path.

(2) Airframe sources.   Radiation from the airframe consists of the emission from the aerodynamically heated surfaces and the hot metal spots and of the reflection of incident radiation or sun glint. No efficient technique currently exists to reduce the aerodynamic heating effects. However, this source may be significant only for supersonic aircraft or for large aircraft flying low level at very high subsonic speeds. Infrared radiation from hot spots caused by other than the propulsion system and aerodynamic heating, such as oil coolers, heat exchangers, and rotary-wing aircraft main rotor transmissions and gearboxes, can be reduced by the use of insulation to reduce the emissivity, by masking, or by cooling flow techniques. The weight penalty associated with these techniques can be minimized by judicious placement of these hot components during the conceptual/preliminary design phase.

Sun glint off of the airframe opaque surfaces and transparencies may be a potential source of radiation for an i.r. tracker. If the surface is round, the glint can be observed from a wide range of angles, and this continuous i.r. source may be used by a seeker for tracking, even as the aircraft moves. The effect of the sun glint off of the aircraft transparencies can be reduced by using flat or nearly flat surfaces. The flat surface provides a specular return in a limited direction, and as the aircraft moves, any i.r. seeker will see a highly sporadic signal that either degrades tracking accuracy or eliminates tracking entirely. Reflection of sunlight off of the aircraft skin can be reduced by using a paint that has a very low reflectivity in the i.r. band of interest. This i.r. absorbing paint is referred to as IRAP. Because the paint absorbs the incident radiation, the surface temperature will rise. This could be a problem in surface areas that require a relatively cool environment, such as around electronic equipment.

Visual signature.   The control of the visual signature is based upon the method of minimizing the contrast between the aircraft and the background with respect to the four parameters, luminance, chromaticity, clutter, and movement. Those areas that require attention are the engine exhaust and glow, the glint off of the canopy and any rotor blades, the airframe signature, and the aircraft lighting.

(1) Engine exhaust and glow.   Engine exhaust contributors to visual detection include smoke, contrails, and, at night, exhaust glow. Until recently, chemical additives were used to catalyze the oxidation of carbonaceous particles, thus eliminating the carbon particles in the plume (the smoke), by lowering the fuel ignition temperature. The use of chemical additives has since been abandoned because it shortened engine life, was

ineffective at low altitudes of flight, and was toxic. Current emphasis is directed toward improved combustor design for a smoke-free exhaust. To minimize hot parts glow, an asymmetric or turned exhaust nozzle can be utilized. Hot parts glow reduction can be an inherent fringe benefit of an i.r. engine suppressor.

(2) Canopy glint. Canopy glint is most effectively controlled at the present time by the use of flat or relatively flat transparencies. The use of flat transparencies reduces the frequency of glint occurrence to the threat observer. Since the flat surfaces act like a mirror, the sun will be reflected at angles equal to the domain of incident angles, which is small. Curved surfaces, on the other hand, will reflect the sunlight into a much larger angle, thereby allowing the glint to be observable at many locations simultaneously and at one location over a large range of aircraft rotation. The objective of glint reduction is not to reduce it to zero necessarily, but to reduce it to the level of the next most dominant visual cue. Note that glint observability does not necessarily lead to glint detectability, and glint detection does not necessarily lead to target acquisition. For accurate weapon platform pointing and target tracking, the glint must be almost continuously (not momentarily) discernable to the naked eye or other sensor. Flat plate transparencies make this unlikely to occur.

(3) Rotor blade glint flicker. In rotary-wing aircraft, rotor blade flicker detection has been found to be higher with two blade configurations than with four or more blades. The blade frequency should be above 16 Hz to avoid the apparent brightness that is observed at lower frequencies. Helicopter rotor heads have also been found to be a significant source of reflected light. Consideration should be given to finishes or coatings that will minimize or subdue such reflective surfaces. Rotor blade tip markings may provide visual clues to the enemy, but elimination of such markings must be evaluated with personnel safety factors.

(4) Airframe. The technique to control the visual signature of a given airframe is the application of some form of paint or coating. Its effectiveness is dependent upon the successful suppression of any visible cues from the engine smoke and canopy glint. For in-flight visual signature control of aircraft, the paint application categories include glint suppression, luminance contrast minimization, countershading, pattern matching to structured backgrounds, searchlight suppression, and other concepts in paint schemes. When the aircraft's background is generally uniform, such as a clear sky, minimizing the luminous contrast of the aircraft with the background minimizes its detectability. Since the visual environmental parameters will usually encompass a range of luminous values, no one paint can be optimum. Therefore, the reflectance value of the paint should be chosen to minimize, on a frequency of occurrence basis, the possibility of large contrasts. For low-altitude flight profiles, generally associated with rotary-wing aircraft, other backgrounds should be considered. Most helicopter

flight profiles include either discernable terrain as the background or are so low as to preclude any significant illumination on the aircraft undersides. In such cases, paints with reflectances simulating foliated terrain should be used.

If the application of paints is insufficient to remove the luminance contrast between the various surfaces of an aircraft and a clear sky background, a further reduction can be obtained by lighting up the darker-appearing portions of the aircraft with "Yehudi" lights. If the intensity and location of the lights are properly controlled, the aircraft can be made more difficult to see.

In addition to matching the luminance of the background, contrasts over the exterior surface at such locations as the wing-fuselage intersection and around any inlet ducts should be eliminated through the use of countershading or Yehudi lights. Countershading is a painting technique for controlling the overall luminance (or brightness) of aircraft by removing internal contrasts while achieving the desired average apparent brightness of the overall surface. It consists, generally, of specifying paints darker than the overall paint for normally highlighted surfaces and lighter paints for surfaces normally in shadow. The dramatic contrast caused by the traditional insignias, identification markings, and safety/warning notices are strong visual clues that should be subdued or eliminated where possible.

Aircraft flying over cluttered background or parked on the ground should be camouflaged using pattern painting, a technique that has been used for many years. By using a disruptive pattern, the aircraft will be indistinguishable from the background clutter. The use of several different paints increases the likelihood that at least part of the aircraft will be of negligible luminance or chromatic contrast to its immediate background. However, the use of pattern matching can be disadvantageous if the aircraft is used in a different type of background. To reduce the nighttime detectability of aircraft encountering searchlight illumination, paints of low luminance reflectance should be used to reduce the high contrast relative to the night sky. Other paint concepts include paint formulations with seasonal features and paint schemes to give a false perception of the aircraft as to its type or its course of movement. One example of deception is the painting of a false canopy on the underside of a fighter aircraft. Enemy trackers trying to anticipate the heading of the fighter may be misled by the false canopy.

(5) Aircraft lighting. To minimize nighttime visual cues from the aircraft lighting system, exterior lights should be masked from ground angles to the greatest degree practical while maintaining adequate safety for formation flying. The capability of anticollision light installations to reflect moonlight or any other light source should be minimized. Care should be exercised to minimize the direction and intensity of instrument lighting as well as reflections from cockpit interior surfaces.

Aural signature. The aural signature is the only important signature that is not electromagnetic radiation. The aural signature can be very important to survivability on certain missions. The general approaches to controlling the aural signature are to reduce the level of noise and change the characteristics. The specific approaches include reducing the acoustic power in the audible frequency range; modifying the noise spectra (amplitude and frequency) of the radiated noise to increase the attenuation through the atmosphere, through any atmosphere-to-water interface, and through the ocean; and shielding and absorption.

(1) Acoustic power reduction.   Fan inlet radiated noise may be reduced by the use of an accelerating inlet with a high subsonic throat Mach number. Propeller and rotor blade radiated noise can be reduced by increasing the diameter and number of blades, by decreasing the tip velocity, by decreasing shaft horsepower, or by phasing the propellers of a multipropeller aircraft to minimize the noise through phase cancellation of the noise from each propeller. Since jet engine exhaust radiates noise to approximately the eighth power of the jet velocity, a small reduction in velocity results in a large reduction in acoustic power. With respect to aerodynamic noise, air turbulence and vibrations due to the motion of the wing and fuselage, rotating propellers, and air movement across a cavity or other airframe protuberances should be kept to a minimum.

(2) Spectrum shaping.   During the conceptual design phase, spectrum shaping of noise to where the human ear is less sensitive should be a consideration. Also, at the higher frequencies, additional reduction in noise is achieved through excess atmospheric attenuation, and at the very low frequencies, background noise levels may mask the aircraft noise. Another possible shaping concept is directing the engine exhaust through a number of small-diameter, remotely placed nozzles to produce a much higher noise frequency than that of a single exhaust pipe. Although no undersea detection criteria for the detection of aircraft by submerged vessels have been established, such criteria may allow high tone levels at some frequencies, while requiring very low tone levels at other frequencies. Therefore, it is important to consider trade-offs between amplitude and frequency of tones in the development of undersea detection criteria.

(3) Shielding and absorption.   The application of shielding techniques or absorbing panels can result in significant reductions in aural detectability. Shielding methods involve placing a physical barrier in the path of the noise so that a lower intensity of noise is propagated to the receiver. An example is the placement of engines or the engine exhaust nozzles above the wing. The effectiveness of shielding is greater for higher-frequency tones and when the shielding is located close to the noise source. Absorbing materials involve the use of sound absorbent materials or resonators that absorb the incident acoustic energy. These materials include fiberglass batting and open-cell polyurethane. The engine cowling can be designed to form a labyrinth for the cooling air and noise, and fan inlet radiated noise can be reduced by the application of acoustic materials. Likewise, exhaust noise

can be reduced by using acoustic materials and by the use of acoustic treatment downstream of the low-pressure turbine stage; and properly designed mufflers or resonators may be used as a combination mechanism for shielding and absorbing noise in duct walls of turboprop and turbofan engines.

Other signatures. There are other aircraft signatures that are potential sources for detection, tracking, and home-on-jam. These include the active electromagnetic emissions by the aircraft as it conducts its mission and those emissions that are inadvertent. Active emissions include radars for navigation and weapons, altimeter radars for height finding, communications, and active countermeasures, such as jammers and deceivers. Inadvertent emissions include emissions from equipment on standby status. These observables should not be overlooked. They should be examined to determine if they can be used by the enemy as a source for detection, tracking, and guidance.

Expendables

Expendables are materials or devices designed to be ejected from an aircraft for the purpose of denying or deceiving threat tracking systems for a limited period of time. As the name implies, they are not intended to be recovered after they are deployed. Because they are not reusable, they must be of low cost when compared to the cost of the aircraft they are designed to protect. Expendables can be used by an aircraft for self-protection or for mutual support between several aircraft. A dedicated aircraft can also deploy expendables to provide either a predeployed saturation screen or decoys for many aircraft. If the signature of the aircraft that the expendable is supposed to protect is too strong, it will be difficult, if not impossible, to design an effective expendable system.

Expendables come in many forms. Four of the simplest are chaff and retroreflectors (for radar), aerosols (for i.r. and visual systems), and flares (for i.r. systems). For radar, active deception jammers constitute more complicated forms of expendables, and it is conceivable that the future may see sophisticated, but relatively low-cost, drones in formation with a strike group to act as attractive decoys or jammers for potential radar threats.

Chaff. One of the oldest forms of expendables is chaff. Code-named Window by the British, it was first used in World War II to confuse German air-defense radars. It is still considered by many to be one of the most effective countermeasures for radar systems. However, the increasing sophistication of moving target indicator processing and other ECCM techniques may eventually render it ineffective.

(1) Chaff dipoles. A chaff cloud consists of a large number of dipoles. A typical dipole consists of a very thin strip of aluminum foil or a very thin glass fiber coated with aluminum or zinc. The fibers can easily be ingested by an aircraft engine with no adverse effects. Each dipole exhibits a radar

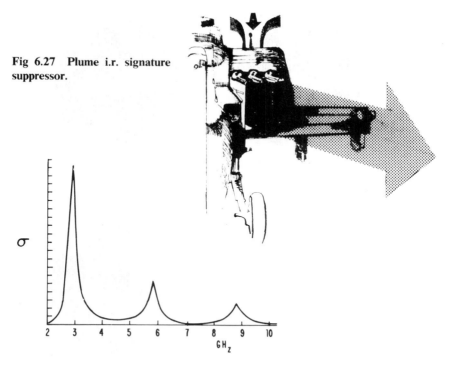

Fig 6.27   Plume i.r. signature suppressor.

Fig. 6.28   RCS of a single dipole.

return or backscatter cross section that depends on the radar wavelength λ. A typical example of the variation of σ with respect to λ is shown in Fig. 6.28. For dipoles with very large length-to-width ratios, the peak return occurs in the resonance region at the radar wavelength that is approximately twice the physical length of the fiber. Resonances also occur at higher integer multiples of the fiber length. The magnitude of the backscatter RCS of the dipole also depends upon its orientation with respect to the illuminating radar and the conductivity of the foil or coating. Viewed end on, the return is essentially zero, whereas from the side it could have a maximum RCS of approximately $0.866\lambda^2$. When averaged over all aspects, the return from a single dipole is approximately $0.16\lambda^2$ at the resonant wavelength.

(2) Chaff clouds. Aircraft dispensed chaff clouds generally leave a cylindrical shape along the flight path. When the chaff is dispensed from a fast-moving aircraft, the length of the cylindrical cloud along the flight path grows very rapidly. The composite echo received by a radar from the chaff cloud is the vector sum of the individual echoes received from each dipole within the radar range gate, accounting for the phase and polarization relationships between the return from each dipole. In order to affect a

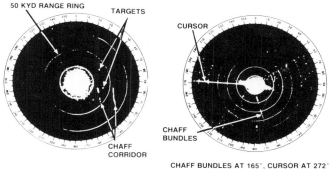

CHAFF CORRIDORS FROM 100° to 120°
AND TARGETS AT 50° AND 95°

CHAFF BUNDLES AT 165°, CURSOR AT 272°

Fig. 6.29 Appearance of chaff on a PPI.

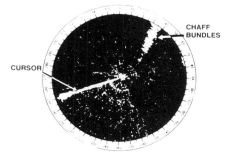

CHAFF BUNDLES AT 35° BEING DROPPED
BY INCOMING TARGET

particular radar operating at one wavelength, each dipole should be cut to one-half of that wavelength. For example, for a 3-GHz radar with a wavelength of 10 cm, the dipoles should be 5 cm long. When more than one radar frequency must be countered, the dipoles can be cut into several lengths, each length optimized to a particular frequency. The theoretical minimum number of dipoles required to give an average RCS of σ is $\sigma/(0.16\lambda^2)$. Thus, an average RCS of 100 m^2 at 3 GHz requires at least 60,000 dipoles. The actual number required is larger than the minimum number due to dipole shielding, uneven distribution, and breakage.

The effects of chaff on a surveillance radar PPI and a range scope are illustrated in Figs. 6.29 and 6.30. The radar return of a fully developed chaff cloud is not a constant value with time. The pulse-to-pulse variation of the RCS may be quite large. In general, chaff clouds at high altitudes tend to grow in physical size and RCS from several minutes to several hours after deployment, with most of the growth in the direction of the prevailing winds; whereas chaff dispensed from helicopters close to the ground may settle within a minute in calm air. The RCS of the mature cloud depends to a large extent on the geometry of the cloud to the radar, the cloud position, and the wind direction.

TARGET (INBOUND)

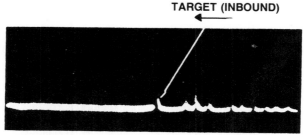

SELF-DISPENSED CHAFF, NINE CHAFF BUNDLES

TARGET BARELY VISIBLE

PREDISPENSED CHAFF CORRIDOR

TARGET CLEARLY VISIBLE

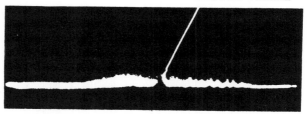

SAME CHAFF CORRIDOR AFTER DISPERSION

Fig. 6.30   Chaff on a range scope.

(3) Ropes. For the long radar wavelengths, the glass fibers and aluminum foil become impractical, and rope chaff is used. Rope chaff is metal or metal-coated fiber streamers that are very long compared with the frequency to be countered.

(4) Chaff dispensers. Dipole chaff is packaged and deployed in several ways. These include discrete rectangular or circular cylindrical containers, known as bundles or cartridges, and continuous rolls. The cylindrical containers are stored in a dispenser or block mounted on or built into the aircraft and are ejected by electromechanical, pneumatic, or pyrotechnical methods. A typical chaff cartridge and dispenser are illustrated in Fig. 6.31.

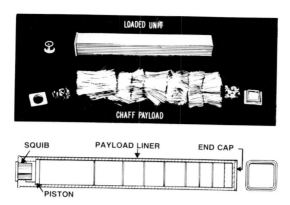

Fig. 6.31   Chaff cartridge, chaff dispenser, and flare dispenser.

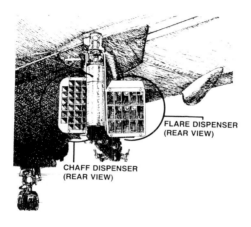

The rolled chaff can be precut fibers packaged between two sheets of plastic, or it can be a spool of continuous fibers that are cut to the desired length by the dispenser.

The location and orientation of the dispenser on the aircraft has a major impact on the effectiveness of chaff in the self-protection role. For self-protection, the chaff cloud must bloom very rapidly so that the radar sees both the aircraft and the chaff in the same range bin. Rapid growth is enhanced when the chaff is ejected into a very high turbulent flow. Consequently, forward of, but not in line with, wing roots and the engine exhaust are good locations for the dispenser. For a number of reasons, some chaff dispensers have been built to also carry and dispense i.r. flares and active jammers for decoying missiles. Smooth airflow conditions are desirable for the flares and jammers. This is, however, the least desirable environment for the chaff. Consequently, the location of the dispenser is often a compromise. The chaff is typically deployed under the control of a programmer unit according to the settings on a control panel. The most recent counter-measures dispensing systems connect the dispensing unit with a warning receiver.

(5) Uses and effectiveness. Chaff can be used against the long-range early warning radars, ground-controlled intercept radars, and acquisition radars in the predeployed saturation mode or the mutual support mode. Against airborne weapons systems and ground-based weapon-control radars, these two modes and the self-protection mode can be effective. Chaff can also be used as a countermeasure for radar proximity fuzes. Figure 6.32 illustrates three techniques for chaff deployment. The flight path of the aircraft subsequent to the ejection of chaff will influence the effectiveness of the chaff in breaking the radar lock-on.

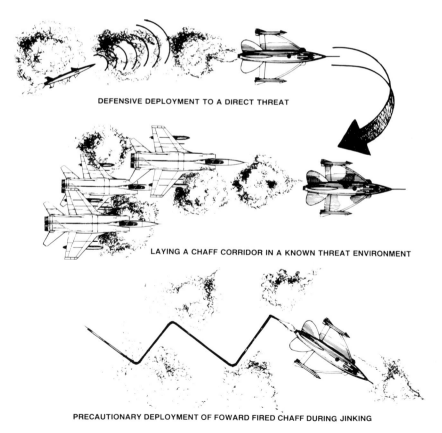

DEFENSIVE DEPLOYMENT TO A DIRECT THREAT

LAYING A CHAFF CORRIDOR IN A KNOWN THREAT ENVIRONMENT

PRECAUTIONARY DEPLOYMENT OF FOWARD FIRED CHAFF DURING JINKING

Fig. 6.32   Chaff deployment.

In general, chaff is effective when its echo masks the target's echo or when it decoys a radar tracker, causing a break-lock. However, if the radar employs ECCM against chaff, such as pulse-Doppler or MTI signal processing, the target aircraft echo, which is moving, may be identified by the radar in the presence of the relatively stationary echo of the chaff cloud. Skilled operators can track aircraft through the chaff, but the tracking accuracy will most likely be degraded.

Radar reflectors. In addition to chaff, other reflective devices are used, primarily in decoys, to create targetlike radar echoes. These reflective devices may be used either to make a small false target appear larger or to create clutter and confusion on the radar screen. The reflective device can be as simple as a corner reflector or as exotic and complicated as a Luneberg lens or Van Atta array. The main requirements are that the echo be the appropriate size in the band of the radar and that the extent of the viewing angle for the RCS decoy is appropriate. The corner reflector provides a relatively large return over a wide range of angles due to the multiple reflections of the incident signal off of the angled faces back in the direction of the receiver, as shown on Fig. 6.3d. Table 6.3 gives the formula for the maximum radar cross section for the triangular corner reflector. The triangular corner reflector is generally used because it can easily be manufactured and handled. When coverage wider than that provided by a corner reflector is desired, the use of a Luneberg lens or Van Atta array may be considered.

Aerosols. Mists, fogs, smokes, clouds, and similar atmospheric disturbances have been used in warfare since the beginning of recorded history. Until recent times, the main use of these disturbances was to provide a screen to prevent the enemy from seeing the friendly forces. However, aerosols can be used to hide aircraft from i.r. and other electromagnetic wave sensors, as well as visually. They can also be used to generate false targets and to modify the target signature.

An aerosol consists of many relatively small particles dispensed into the atmosphere to form a cloud. These particles will scatter, absorb, and transmit a portion of any incident electromagnetic wave. The amount of scattering, absorbtion, and transmission depends on the size and properties of the particles. When the aerosol cloud lies between the aircraft and the sensor, the amount of obscuration of the target signature will depend upon the level of reduction in the transmitted intensity of the incident electromagnetic wave as it passes through the aerosol, which is known as the extinction. The extinction is caused by the absorption and scattering of the incident wave, and the larger the extinction, the more effective the aerosol is at hiding the aircraft.

In principle, a light ray or any similar electromagnetic wave passing through a medium is unperturbed so long as the refractive index of the medium is unchanged. When the wave strikes an aerosol cloud, the extinction of the wave by the aerosol particles depends upon the wavelength of the incident wave, the particle size, and the refractive index of the particle. The refractive index is a measure of both the scattering and the absorption properties of the particle. There are three ranges of particle sizes: small sizes, where the particles are much smaller than the wavelength; intermediate sizes, where the particles and wavelength are of comparable magnitude; and large sizes, where the particles are much larger than the wavelength. The amount of scattering by a particle for a given wavelength is not a simple function of the particle shape and size, and the angular intensity is very variable and depends on the particle size and refractive index. An aerosol cloud designed for optimum performance must use particles matched to the physical and electromagnetic constraints of the application. Aerosol generation is ultimately a process of generating particles from a liquid, or separating discrete particles that tend to cling together, and dispersing them into a cloud of the right size, using various explosive or depressurization techniques.

Infrared flares. An i.r. flare is a self-protection device, designed to be ejected from an aircraft, that emits a large amount of radiation in the sensor bandwidth of an i.r. homing missile. It is supposed to be a more attractive target to the i.r. seeker. The seeker on an approaching i.r. missile will detect the presence of both the flare and the aircraft and hopefully will home in on the flare due to its i.r. signature. Because the flare is moving away from the aircraft, the missile will be decoyed away from the aircraft, possibly causing a miss distance sufficiently large to prevent a warhead detonation.

(1) Flare intensity. There are several factors to be considered in the design and utilization of flares. For example, the flare must be of sufficient intensity (relative to the target signature) in the bandwidth of the i.r. detector to be seen as a more attractive target. It must be launched at the right time, in the right direction, and must reach full intensity quickly if it is to draw the missile away from the aircraft. It must also burn long enough to prevent the seeker from reacquiring the aircraft. The fact that the flare is a point source of i.r. intensity, whereas the aircraft and exhaust plume are distributed sources, may have an influence on the effectiveness of the flare in decoying the missile. The amount of influence will depend upon the type of target tracker in the missile.

A typical flare energy spectra is shown in Fig. 6.33 for sea level conditions. Note that the flare emissions do not match those of an aircraft with respect to spectral energy content. Because the flare must be very hot in order to develop enough radiant flux, most of the flare energy is in the short wavelengths below 2 μm. This feature could be used by an i.r. missile to reject a flare as a target. The seeker could sample two wavelengths (a two-color seeker), and by comparing the relative intensity in each wavelength, it could make a decision as to whether it was tracking a flare or an aircraft. The flare intensity is affected by both the aircraft altitude and its velocity. There is a decrease in intensity for increasing altitude and a

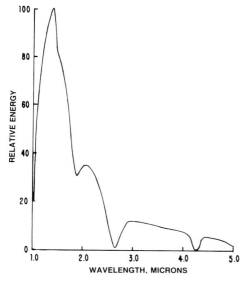

Fig. 6.33   Example of a flare spectra.

decrease in intensity for increasing velocity. The aircraft velocity has the most significant effect on the intensity, because the high-velocity air passing around the flare reduces the size of the fireball and cools the surrounding air, thus reducing the intensity of the radiation.

(2) *Flare ejection.* Flares, like chaff, are ejected from a dispenser. A flare dispenser is illustrated in Fig. 6.31. Attention must be given to the location, direction, and velocity of flare ejection. Whereas chaff should be ejected into turbulent airflow, flares should be ejected into nonturbulent airflow in order to minimize the decrease in intensity caused by velocity effects. Generally, flares are ejected down and slightly to the rear of the aircraft, as shown in Fig. 6.31. This allows gravity to maintain the flare at the ejected velocity away from the aircraft and also draws the missile down and behind the departing aircraft. Flare ejection velocity should not be so low that the miss distance is insufficient to prevent warhead detonation, nor so high that the seeker will not respond to the rapidly moving flare and the lock-on will not be broken as the flare transits the seeker's field of view.

Aircraft maneuvers after flare ejection must be considered in the development of a successful flare system. Sharp turns in the horizontal plane accompanied by reductions in power reduce the aircraft i.r. emissions in the field of view of the seeker, thus allowing the flare to be seen. The desire to use the engine afterburner for additional power after a missile sighting and flare ejection may be self-defeating due to the large increase in the i.r. emission.

Threat Suppression and Tactics

Threat suppression consists of actions taken by friendly forces with the intent to physically damage or destroy part or all of a threat system. The actions can be taken by supporting elements, such as a fighter escort, Wild Weasel, or artillery; or they can be taken by an aircraft in jeopardy for self-protection. For example, missiles and guns carried by utility helicopters, ASW aircraft, and bombers for self-defense are threat suppression weapons. Threat suppression can also occur through intimidation; the presence of armed helicopters escorting an airborne troop assault may discourage an attack on the troop carriers. Often the threat suppression does not have to destroy all of the threat elements. The use of an antiradiation missile (ARM) that homes in on the transmissions from a radar antenna can render a radar-guided threat useless. The concept of threat suppression has been around for a long time (get them before they get you) and is a major survivability factor in many scenarios. Quick destruction of the hostile air-defense systems is a primary goal in any conflict.

Tactics is the employment of units in combat, and the development of tactics is normally the responsibility of the operational and test units. Typically, the tactics consist of the flight profiles, operations, and formations used to accomplish the mission. The tactics employed in a particular combat operation are influenced by many factors, such as the intensity and lethality of the air defenses, the urgency of the mission, the type of aircraft for the mission, the availability of supporting elements (FE, SOJ, etc.), and the terrain and weather. Those in charge of choosing the tactics should take into account the susceptibility and vulnerability of the aircraft at their disposal and plan the operation accordingly. Usually, those tactics are selected that minimize the susceptibility of the aircraft, either by eliminating the threat or by reducing the exposure time to the various threat elements (threat avoidance). However, they must account for the aircraft's performance and weapon delivery capabilities. Some of the current tactics are high-speed and low-altitude penetration and egress, jinking maneuvers to defeat fire-control flight path predictors and cause large miss distances, evasive maneuvers to avoid approaching propagators, avoidance of known locations of threat sites, the use of stand-off weapons, nap-of-the-Earth flight, terrain masking, adverse weather operations, saturation attacks, and the use of every available friendly unit for support of one kind or another.

Selected Bibliography

"Aircraft Battlefield Countermeasures and Survivability," Field Manual No. 1-2, Headquarters, Department of the Army, Washington, D.C., July 1978.

Army Aviation, Monthly Publication, Army Aviation Publications, Westport, Conn. (Special Aircraft Survivability Equipment issues; June 1978, Aug.–Sept. 1981, Oct. 1983.)

Aviation Week and Space Technology, weekly publication.

Bachman, C. G., *Radar Targets*, Lexington Books, Lexington, Mass., 1982.

Barton, D. K. and Ward, H. F., *Handbook of Radar Measurement*, Prentice-Hall, Inc., Englewood Cliffs, N.J., 1969.

Blake, L. V., *Radar Range-Performance Analysis*, Lexington Books, Lexington, Mass., 1980.

Boyd, J. A., Harris, D. B., King, D. D., and Welch, H. W. Jr., Eds., *Electronic Countermeasures*, University of Michigan, Signal Corps Contract DA-36-039 SC-71204, 1961.

Constant, J., *Introduction to Defense Systems Radar Engineering*, Spartan Books, New York, 1972.

Crispin, J. W. Jr. and Siegel, K. M., Eds., *Methods of Radar Cross-Section Analysis*, Academic Press, New York, 1968.

Donatelli, G. A. and Fleeman, E. L., "Methodology for Predicting Miss Distance for Air-Launched Missiles," AIAA Paper 82-0364.

Electronic Warfare/Defense Electronics, monthly publication, EW Communications, Inc., Palo Alto, Calif.

Engineering Design Handbook, *Army Weapon Systems Analysis Part One*, U.S. Army Materiel Development and Readiness Command, DARCOM-P 706-101, Nov. 1977.

Fitts, R. E., Ed., *The Strategy of Electromagnetic Conflict*, Peninsula Publishing, Los Altos, Calif., 1980.

Fuhs, A. E., *Radar Cross Section Lectures*, AIAA, New York, 1984.

Hendon, G. B., "Aircraft Survivability Equipment—From the Lab to the Field," *Journal of Electronic Defense*, April 1982, pp. 46–53.

Hudson, R. D., *Infrared System Engineering*, Wiley-Interscience, New York, 1969.

International Countermeasures Conference, technical program, EW Institute, Limited, Los Altos, Calif., 1976.

The International Countermeasures Handbook, published biennially, EW Communications, Inc., Palo Alto, Calif.

International Defense Review, bimonthly publication, Interavia, S. A., Geneva.

Jamieson, J. A., McFee, R. H., et al., *Infrared Physics and Engineering*, McGraw-Hill, New York, 1963.

Johnston, S. L., Ed., *Radar Electric Counter-Countermeasures*, Artech House, Oedham, Mass., 1979.

Journal of Electronic Defense, monthly publication, Association of Old Crows, Arlington, Va.

Lake, J. S. and Hartman, R. V., "Air Electronic Warfare," *U.S. Naval Institute Proceedings, Naval Review*, 1977, pp. 42–49.

Military Electronics/Countermeasures, monthly publication, Hamilton Burr Publishing Co., Santa Clara, Calif.

Military Electronics Defense Expo, annual publication, Proceedings, Interavia, S. A., Geneva.

Military Microwaves '78, Conference Proceedings, Microwave Exhibitions and Publishers Limited, Kent, England.

Ruck, G. T., Barrick, D. E. et al., *Radar Cross Section Handbook*, Plenum Press, New York, 1970.

Schindler, J. K. and Mack, L. B., Eds., *The Modification of Electromagnetic Scattering Cross Sections in the Resonant Region, A Symposium Record, Volume 1*, AF Cambridge Research Laboratories, Special Reports No. 6, AFCRL-64-727(1), Sept. 1964.

Schlesinger, R., *Principles of Electronic Warfare*, Peninsula Publishing, Los Altos, Calif., and Prentice-Hall, Inc., Englewood Cliffs, N.J., 1961.

Skolnik, M. I., *Introduction to Radar Systems*, McGraw-Hill Book Co., Inc., N.Y., 2nd ed., 1980.

"A Soviet View of ECM and ECCM" (from the Russian translation of *Radar Anti-Jamming Techniques*, by M. B. Maksimov et al.), *Journal of Electronic Defense*, Jan. 1982, pp. 53–60.

Throndson, L. W., "Combat Survivability with Advanced Aircraft Propulsion Development," *Journal of Aircraft*, Vol. 19, Nov. 1982, pp. 915–920.

Vakin, S. A. and Shustov, L. N., *Principles of Jamming and Electronic Reconnaissance* (Russian translation), USAF Foreign Technology Division, FTD-MT-24-115-69.

Van Brunt, L. B., *Applied ECM*, Vol. 1, EW Engineering, Inc., Dunn Loring, Va., 1978.

Venttsei', Ye. S., *Introduction to Operations Research* (Russian translation), Soviet Radio Publishing House, Moscow, 1964.

Wadell, R. L., "Infrared Seeker Threats from Attack Missiles Can Be Reduced Significantly," *Military Electronics/Countermeasures*, Feb. 1983, pp. 31–33.

Wolfe, W. L. and Zissis, G. J., Eds., *The Infrared Handbook*, Infrared Information and Analysis Center, Environmental Research Institute of Michigan, 1978.

Don Jacobs - 85

7. SURVIVABILITY

7.1 THE SURVIVABILITY PROGRAM

The survivability program for US military aircraft has been described in Chap. 1. The requirements and guidelines for the general program are contained in MIL-STD-2069, and the program tasks specifically identified in that document are the:

(1) Mission-threat analysis.
(2) Aircraft geometric description.
(3) Flight and mission essential function identification.
(4) Failure mode, effects, and criticality analysis (FMECA).
(5) Vulnerability assessment.
(6) Susceptibility assessment.
(7) Survivability assessment.
(8) System cost-effectiveness analysis.
(9) Survivability enhancement trade-off study.
(10) Combat damage repair assessment.

The first six of these tasks have been described in detail in Chaps. 3, 5, and 6. This final chapter contains descriptions of the remaining tasks.

The remaining tasks of the survivability program for an aircraft are the assessment of the aircraft's survivability in the predicted threat environment to determine the survivability measures, the conduct of effectiveness analyses and trade-off studies to determine those specific survivability enhancement features that increase the effectiveness of the aircraft as a weapon system, and the combat damage repair assessment. The survivability assessment is the culmination of the quantification of the measures of survivability. It combines the results from the mission-threat analysis with the studies of the aircraft's vulnerability and susceptibility and provides measures that can be used in the effectiveness analyses. Because the design process normally involves competition between the various aircraft design disciplines for the limited allowable space, weight, and cost, the selection of the particular survivability features to be included generally involves trade-off studies that are based upon the survivability measures and their relationship to effectiveness. The combat repair assessment involves the determination of the man-hours, downtime, logistic support, and levels of repair for damaged aircraft under combat operational conditions.

7.2 SURVIVABILITY ASSESSMENT

The survivability assessment consists of the systematic description, delineation, quantification, and statistical characterization of the survivability of

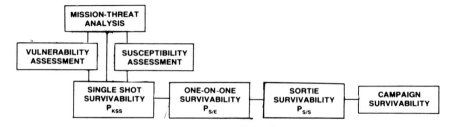

Fig. 7.1   Survivability assessment process.

an aircraft in encounters with hostile forces. It combines (1) the results of the mission-threat analysis, which include the identification of the specific threats to the aircraft and the scenarios describing the encounter conditions between the aircraft and the threats, (2) the results of the vulnerability assessment for the threat propagators, such as the vulnerable area tables and probability of kill given a detonation curves, and (3) the results of the susceptibility assessment, such as the aircraft signatures and propagator miss distances. There are several measures of survivability available that depend upon the scenario and the goal of the assessment. The three measures most often used are the probability the aircraft is killed given a single shot P_{KSS}, the probability the aircraft survives a one-on-one encounter with a single weapon $P_{S/E}$, and the probability the aircraft survives a sortie $P_{S/S}$. (In Chap. 1, $P_{S/S}$ is referred to as the survival rate S.) These measures can be used in a campaign analysis to determine the effectiveness of the aircraft for the given campaign. Figure 7.1 illustrates the overall survivability assessment process.

The Scenario

The scenario is a specific description of the many parameters that characterize an encounter between one or more aircraft and the hostile air defensive forces. Among these parameters are the aircraft flight path(s), the type, number, location, and operations of the threat, the environmental conditions, and the terrain. Examples of scenarios are illustrated in Figs. 7.2 and 7.3. Figure 7.2 presents a strike scenario in a very general sense, showing the full spectrum of threats and electromagnetic environment. The strike mission could consist of four aircraft carrying conventional ordnance [500-lb Mark 82 Snakeye (high-drag) iron bombs], antiradiation missiles, and ECM pods. The attack aircraft could be accompanied by an escort whose primary function might be to jam or disrupt the communications links at the missile sites. Figure 7.3 shows a portion of a ground-based air-defense system typical of those which might be deployed in a sector in central Europe and a possible flight path for a close air support mission that might be used in such an environment. The path shown in Fig. 7.3 is that of one aircraft attacking an SA-4 site and an SA-6 site and then exiting the

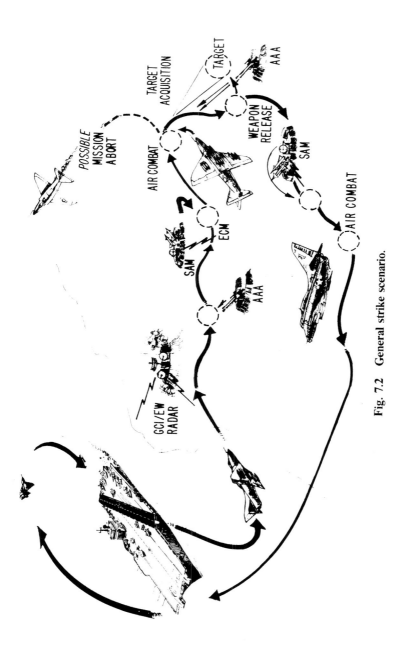

Fig. 7.2   General strike scenario.

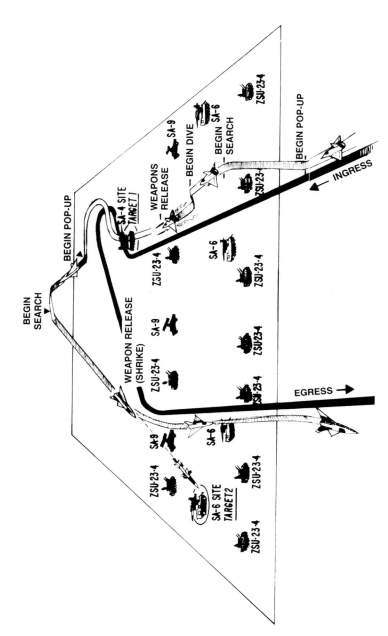

Fig. 7.3   Flight path for a close air support mission.

area. Conventional ordnance is used against the SA-4, and an antiradiation missile is used on the SA-6 site.

Survivability Measures and Equations

The assessment of aircraft survivability involves the computation of some measure of aircraft probability of survival (or kill) in a particular scenario. Aircraft probability of kill is a summary measure for the scenario that combines the aircraft's susceptibility (from initial detection and tracking through propagator launch to damage mechanism impact) with its vulnerability. Survivability may be expressed indirectly as the probability of kill per single shot, as the probability of survival per encounter or site, or as the probability of survival per sortie. Once the probability of survival or kill has been determined, other measures may be used, such as the losses per 1000 sorties, or the losses in a campaign, or the losses over the expected combat lifetime of the aircraft. In general, the assessment can be accomplished "by hand," or it can use small- or large-scale digital computer programs for an evaluation or analysis.

Probability of kill given a single shot. The probability of an aircraft kill given a single shot P_{KSS} is computed on the assumption that the aircraft has been detected and that a threat propagator has been launched or fired. Thus, the P_{KSS} depends on the ability of the fire-control/guidance system to direct the propagator to the vicinity of the aircraft, on the fuzing employed, if any, and on the aircraft vulnerability to the threat damage mechanisms. A P_{KSS} can be computed for gun projectiles, guided missiles, and the radiation weapons using the basic two-dimensional equation in the intercept plane

$$P_{KSS} = \int_{-\infty}^{\infty} \int_{-\infty}^{\infty} \rho(x,y) P_f(x,y) V(x,y) \, dx \, dy \qquad (7.1)$$

where $\rho(x,y)$ is the miss distance frequency distribution; $V(x,y)$ is the kill function that defines the probability the target is killed due to a propagator whose trajectory intersects the intercept plane at x,y; and $P_f(x,y)$ is the probability of fuzing for an HE warhead. Note the similarity between Eq. (7.1) for P_{KSS} and Eq. (6.33) for the probability the aircraft is hit P_H. The product of P_f and V is analogous to the hit function H. Thus, the evaluation of P_{KSS} is similar to the evaluation of P_H.

(1) Fire-control/guidance accuracy. The ability of the threat system to fire or guide a propagator to the vicinity of the aircraft can be expressed by the miss distance frequency distribution functions $\rho(x,y)$ or $\rho(r)$, given in

Chap. 6. These two functions are

$$\rho(x,y) = \frac{1}{2\pi\sigma_x\sigma_y}\exp\left(-\frac{(x-\mu_x)^2}{2\sigma_x^2} - \frac{(y-\mu_y)^2}{2\sigma_y^2}\right) \qquad (7.2a)$$

and

$$\rho(r) = \frac{1}{2\pi\sigma_r^2}\exp\left(-\frac{r^2}{2\sigma_r^2}\right) \qquad (7.2b)$$

(2) Fuzing. The functioning of a fuze can be represented by the probability P_f that may or may not be dependent upon the miss distance. For example, a proximity fuze that has an 80% probability of detonating the warhead within a miss distance range r_c of 100 ft and a 0% probability beyond r_c can be modeled in the form

$$P_f(x,y) = 0.8 \qquad \text{when} \qquad (x^2+y^2)^{\frac{1}{2}} \le 100 \text{ ft}$$

$$P_f(x,y) = 0 \qquad \text{when} \qquad (x^2+y^2)^{\frac{1}{2}} > 100 \text{ ft}$$

If the fuze is a contact fuze, the shape of the target $L(x,y)$ defines the outer limits for a nonzero P_f, and if the warhead does not have a fuze, P_f is unity. Note that the use of a two-dimensional analysis for P_{KSS} does not require a proximity-fuzed warhead to detonate in the intercept plane. A three-dimensional effect (detonation before the propagator reaches the intercept plane) can be accounted for in the two-dimensional analysis.

(3) Aircraft vulnerability and the P_{KSS}. For warheads that do not use a proximity fuze, such as small arms and HE warheads with contact fuzes, a hit on the aircraft must occur to cause damage. Thus, $V(x,y)$ becomes $P_{K/H}$ for random hits, and the integration is carried out over the extent of the aircraft. HE warheads with proximity fuzes only need to come close, and hence $V(x,y)$ becomes $P_{K/D}(x,y)$.

(a)   Contact warheads: There are two approaches to the evaluation of P_{KSS} for this type of threat. In one approach, the probability the aircraft is hit by the propagator P_H is computed and multiplied by the probability the aircraft is killed given the (random) hit on the aircraft $P_{K/H}$, or A_V/A_P. When the two-dimensional cookie-cutter hit function is used, the computation of P_H given by Eq. (6.32) is accomplished using tables of the standard normal distribution. For the two-dimensional Carlton hit function, Eq.

(6.35a) defines P_H, and hence,

$$P_{KSS} = P_H \left(\frac{A_V}{A_P} \right) = \frac{A_V}{\left(2\pi\sigma_x^2 + x_0^2 \right)^{\frac{1}{2}} \left(2\pi\sigma_y^2 + y_0^2 \right)^{\frac{1}{2}}}$$

$$\times \exp\left(-\frac{\pi\mu_x^2}{2\pi\sigma_x^2 + x_0^2} - \frac{\pi\mu_y^2}{2\pi\sigma_y^2 + y_0^2} \right) \qquad (7.3)$$

where $x_0 y_0 = A_P$ according to Eq. (6.34b). In the one-dimensional symmetric analysis,

$$P_{KSS} = \left[1 - \exp\left(\frac{-A_P}{2\pi\sigma_r^2} \right) \right] \left(\frac{A_V}{A_P} \right) \qquad (7.4a)$$

according to Eq. (6.37) for P_H with the circular cookie-cutter hit function, and

$$P_{KSS} = \frac{A_V}{2\pi\sigma_r^2 + A_P} \qquad (7.4b)$$

according to Eq. (6.38) for P_H with the circular Carlton hit function. Note that, with this approach, P_{KSS} is linearly proportional to A_V. Thus, any reduction in A_V will cause a corresponding reduction in P_{KSS}. Also note that P_{KSS} given by Eq. (7.4b) is reduced by increasing A_P; larger aircraft with the same vulnerable area are less likely to be killed given a shot. This surprising result is due to the fact that the vulnerable area in the larger aircraft is assumed to be spread out over the larger area and thus is less likely to be hit by a shot aimed at the center of the aircraft.

In the other approach, the aircraft vulnerability is represented by its vulnerable area A_V, centered at the aim point, and any hit on the vulnerable area causes a kill. Thus, with this approach, the equations derived for the probability of hitting the aircraft presented area A_P can be used with A_P replaced by A_V. Therefore, for the two-dimensional Carlton kill (hit) function, Eq. (7.3) can be used with $x_0 y_0 = A_V$. [The probability of killing the ith component on the aircraft due to a single shot also can be computed using Eq. (7.3) with $x_0 y_0 = A_{v_i}$, provided the miss distance means μ_x and μ_y are measured with respect to the location of the component rather than to the aim point.] In the symmetric analysis,

$$P_{KSS} = 1 - \exp\left(\frac{-A_V}{2\pi\sigma_r^2} \right) \qquad (7.5a)$$

according to Eq. (6.37) for the cookie-cutter kill function, and

$$P_{KSS} = \frac{A_V}{2\pi\sigma_r^2 + A_V} \qquad (7.5b)$$

according to Eq. (6.38) for the Carlton kill function. Note that P_{KSS} is not linearly proportional to A_V with this approach. When multiple shots are considered, the multiple hit vulnerability measures $A_V^{(n)}$ or $P_{K/H}^{(n)}$ should be used for each shot in place of the single hit or constant values.

(b) Proximity-fuzed warheads: The proximity-fuzed warhead, which does not have to hit the aircraft to kill it, requires consideration of the miss distance, the fuze, and the kill function, or $P_{K/D}$, in this analysis. A simple, one-dimensional expression for $P_{K/D}$, Eq. (5.38), was derived in Chap. 5. This expression for $P_{K/D}$, when combined with either the bivariate or the circular normal miss distance distribution function, does not lead to a simple analytical solution of Eq. (7.1) for P_{KSS} in closed form. Consequently, the $P_{K/D}$ is usually modeled with either the circular cookie-cutter or the circular Carlton kill function. In the case of the cookie-cutter kill function, the warhead lethal radius r_l can be used as the cutoff value. Thus,

$$P_{K/D} = 1 \qquad 0 \leq r \leq r_l$$

$$P_{K/D} = 0 \qquad r > r_l$$

When the circular Carlton kill function is used for $P_{K/D}$,

$$P_{K/D} = \exp(-r^2/r_0^2) = \exp(-x^2/r_0^2)\exp(-y^2/r_0^2) \qquad (7.6)$$

The scaling parameter r_0 can be related to the warhead lethal radius such that when $r = r_l$, $P_{K/D} = 0.5$. Collocating the one-dimensional Carlton kill function through 0.5 when $r = r_l$ gives $r_0 = 1.20r_l$. In another approach, the area under the actual $P_{K/D}$ function, known as the lethal area A_L, can be equated to the area under the circular Carlton kill function, $2\pi r_0^2$, and hence, $r_0 = (A_L/2\pi)^{\frac{1}{2}}$.

For two-dimensional miss distance distributions, the square box cookie-cutter kill function leads to

$$P_{KSS} = \int_{-r_l}^{r_l}\int_{-r_l}^{r_l} \frac{P_f}{2\pi\sigma_x\sigma_y}\exp\left(-\frac{(x-\mu_x)^2}{2\sigma_x^2} - \frac{(y-\mu_y)^2}{2\sigma_y^2}\right)dx\,dy \qquad (7.7a)$$

according to Eq. (7.1). This expression requires tables of the standard normal distribution for a numerical evaluation. On the other hand, when the probability of fuzing is assumed to be a constant, the circular Carlton kill function leads to

$$P_{KSS} = \frac{r_0^2 P_f}{\left(2\sigma_x^2 + r_0^2\right)^{\frac{1}{2}}\left(2\sigma_y^2 + r_0^2\right)^{\frac{1}{2}}} \exp\left(-\frac{\mu_x^2}{2\sigma_x^2 + r_0^2} - \frac{\mu_y^2}{2\sigma_y^2 + r_0^2}\right) \quad (7.7b)$$

according to Eq. (6.35a), where x_0^2 and y_0^2 are replaced with πr_0^2 according to Eqs. (6.34a) and (7.6).

For a symmetric miss distance distribution about the aim point, a constant P_f, and a fuze cutoff range beyond r_l,

$$P_{KSS} = \left[1 - \exp\left(-\frac{r_l^2}{2\sigma_r^2}\right)\right] P_f \quad (7.8a)$$

with the circular cookie-cutter kill function. If there is no cutoff range for the fuze,

$$P_{KSS} = \left(\frac{r_0^2}{2\sigma_r^2 + r_0^2}\right) P_f \quad (7.8b)$$

for the circular Carlton kill function. If the fuze has a finite cutoff range, the P_{KSS} for the circular Carlton kill function is given by

$$P_{KSS} = \int_0^{r_c} \frac{r}{\sigma_r^2} \exp\left(-\frac{r^2}{2\sigma_r^2} - \frac{r^2}{r_0^2}\right) dr$$

Hence,

$$P_{KSS} = \frac{r_0^2}{2\sigma_r^2 + r_0^2} P_f \left[1 - \exp\left(-\frac{2\sigma_r^2 + r_0^2}{2\sigma_r^2 r_0^2} r_c^2\right)\right] \quad (7.8c)$$

Table 7.1 presents a summary of the P_{KSS} equations for the cookie-cutter and Carlton models.

One-on-one survivability. The probability that an aircraft survives an encounter with a single threat is given as $P_{S/E}$. Note that survival does not mean that no damage has been suffered, only that the aircraft was not killed according to the specified kill level. The specific encounter conditions between the aircraft and the threat are defined by the scenario. In most scenarios, in order for the threat to have an opportunity to kill the aircraft it must first detect the aircraft. (Barrage fire in anticipation of the appearance of an aircraft and a missile that is launched during a search are examples of scenarios where detection prior to launch or firing does not take place.) The measure of detection is P_D, the probability that the aircraft has been

Table 7.1 Equations for P_{KSS}

Contact Warheads	
Cookie-cutter	
(x,y)	$\dfrac{A_V}{x_0 y_0} \displaystyle\int_{-y_0/2}^{y_0/2} \int_{-x_0/2}^{x_0/2} \dfrac{1}{2\pi\sigma_x\sigma_y} \exp\left(-\dfrac{(x-\mu_x)^2}{2\sigma_x^2} - \dfrac{(y-\mu_y)^2}{2\sigma_y^2}\right) dx\, dy$
(r)	$\left[1 - \exp\left(\dfrac{-A_P}{2\pi\sigma_r^2}\right)\right](A_V/A_P) \quad$ or $\quad 1 - \exp\left(\dfrac{-A_V}{2\pi\sigma_r^2}\right)$
Carlton	
(x,y)	$\dfrac{A_V}{\left(2\pi\sigma_x^2 + x_0^2\right)^{\frac{1}{2}}\left(2\pi\sigma_y^2 + y_0^2\right)^{\frac{1}{2}}} \exp\left(-\dfrac{\pi\mu_x^2}{2\pi\sigma_x^2 + x_0^2} - \dfrac{\pi\mu_y^2}{2\pi\sigma_y^2 + y_0^2}\right) \qquad \begin{array}{l} x_0 y_0 = A_P \\ \text{or} \\ x_0 y_0 = A_V \end{array}$
(r)	$\dfrac{A_V}{2\pi\sigma_r^2 + A_P} \quad$ or $\quad \dfrac{A_V}{2\pi\sigma_r^2 + A_V}$

Proximity-Fuzed Warheads	
Cookie-cutter	
(x,y)	$\displaystyle\int_{-r_l}^{r_l} \int_{-r_l}^{r_l} \dfrac{P_f}{2\pi\sigma_x\sigma_y} \exp\left(-\dfrac{(x-\mu_x)^2}{2\sigma_x^2} - \dfrac{(y-\mu_y)^2}{2\sigma_y^2}\right) dx\, dy$
(r)	$\left[1 - \exp\left(\dfrac{-r_l^2}{2\sigma_r^2}\right)\right]P_f$
Carlton	
(x,y)	$\dfrac{r_0^2}{\left(2\sigma_x^2 + r_0^2\right)^{\frac{1}{2}}\left(2\sigma_y^2 + r_0^2\right)^{\frac{1}{2}}} P_f \exp\left(-\dfrac{\mu_x^2}{2\sigma_x^2 + r_0^2} - \dfrac{\mu_y^2}{2\sigma_y^2 + r_0^2}\right) \qquad \begin{array}{l} r_0 = 1.2\, r_l \\ \text{or} \\ r_0^2 = A_L/\pi \end{array}$
(r)	$\dfrac{r_0^2}{2\sigma_r^2 + r_0^2} P_f\left[1 - \exp\left(-\dfrac{2\sigma_r^2 + r_0^2}{2\sigma_r^2 r_0^2} r_c^2\right)\right] \qquad \begin{array}{l} r_0 = 1.2\, r_l \\ \text{or} \\ r_0^2 = A_L/\pi \end{array}$

detected (at least once) from the start of a search up to the present time t. In most situations, this probability is directly proportional to the probability there is a clear line of sight from the detecting element to the aircraft. Given that the aircraft has been detected, the probability that a propagator will be launched or fired at the aircraft P_L can be assigned. Once the propagator leaves the firing platform, the probability it kills the aircraft is the single shot probability of kill P_{KSS}. Thus, the probability that the aircraft is killed in an encounter $P_{K/E}$ in which one propagator may be fired or launched at some time t is given by

$$P_{K/E} = \bar{P}_D P_L P_{KSS} \qquad (7.9a)$$

and the probability that the aircraft survives the single shot encounter $P_{S/E}$ becomes

$$P_{S/E} = 1 - P_{K/E} = 1 - \overline{P}_D P_L P_{KSS} \qquad (7.9b)$$

If the threat is a gun system, from several to quite a few shots at the aircraft are to be expected after detection, and each shot has a P_{KSS}. If the threat is a missile system, more than one missile could be launched at the aircraft, depending upon the circumstances, and each missile has a P_{KSS}. The probability that the aircraft is killed by the sequence of N gun shots or missile launches is unity minus the product of the individual probabilities of survival for each shot or launch. Thus, P_{KSS} in Eq. (7.9a) is replaced with

$$1 - \prod_{i=1}^{N} \left(1 - P_{KSS_i}\right)$$

where the subscript i denotes the ith shot, and Eq. (7.9a) becomes

$$P_{K/E} = \overline{P}_D P_L \left(1 - \prod_{i=1}^{N} \left(1 - P_{KSS_i}\right)\right) \qquad (7.10a)$$

Note that P_L in Eq. (7.10a) is the probability that a firing or launching sequence of N shots occurs, given that the aircraft is detected. The probability the aircraft survives the N shot encounter is given by

$$P_{S/E} = 1 - \overline{P}_D P_L \left(1 - \prod_{i=1}^{N} \left(1 - P_{KSS_i}\right)\right) \qquad (7.10b)$$

Sortie survivability. On a sortie, an aircraft can have multiple encounters with several different weapon types, as shown in Fig. 7.3. The probability of survival of the aircraft in a one-on-one encounter with each of the weapons in the scenario can be computed using the methodology described above. The probability an aircraft in a raid survives the sortie depends upon the number of threat encounters it experiences as it flies through any zone and point defenses.

The zone defense system is usually assumed to be composed of a number of weapons of several types distributed over the area to be defended. If T_z weapons or weapon sites of a particular type are located within a rectangular defense zone of length L and width W, the weapon density ω (the number of weapons of one type per unit area) within the zone is given by

$$\omega = T_z / LW$$

The weapon is assumed to have an effective radius R_{eff} within which it can engage the aircraft. Thus, a single aircraft flying straight through the defended zone will pass through the coverage of E_z weapons of one type, where the expected number of weapon encounters E_z is given by

$$E_z = 2 R_{eff} L \omega$$

If there is a total of A aircraft in the raid, the average number of encounters between any one of the aircraft flying through the zone and the threat weapons is given by

$$E_z = 2 R_{eff} L \omega / A$$

At a point defended target, defended by T_t weapons of the same type, each of the A aircraft will encounter E_t weapons, where

$$E_t = T_t / A$$

(The assumption is made that the number of aircraft in the raid remains constant.)

The total encounters with a particular threat for the sortie, E, is the sum of those encounters that occur as the aircraft flies through any zone defenses to get the target, those that occur near any point defended targets, and those that occur as the aircraft returns through the same defended zone. Thus,

$$E = 2E_z + E_t \tag{7.11}$$

The probability the aircraft survives the E encounters on the sortie, $P_{S/S}$, is given by the product of its survival probability for each encounter P_{S/E_i}. Thus,

$$P_{S/S} = \prod_{i=1}^{E} P_{S/E_i} = \prod_{i=1}^{E} \left(1 - P_{K/E_i}\right) \tag{7.12a}$$

If P_{K/E_i} is a constant value for all encounters, Eq. (7.12a) becomes

$$P_{S/S} = \left(1 - P_{K/E}\right)^{E} \tag{7.12b}$$

and if the individual encounter survival probabilities are approximately unity, Eq. (7.12b) becomes

$$P_{S/S} \approx \exp\left(-E P_{K/E}\right) \tag{7.12c}$$

When more than one type of weapon is encountered during the sortie, the sortie survival rate becomes

$$P_{S/S} = \left(\prod_{i=1}^{E_1} \left(1 - P_{K/E_i}\right)_1 \right) \left(\prod_{i=1}^{E_2} \left(1 - P_{K/E_i}\right)_2 \right) \cdots \left(\prod_{i=1}^{E_m} \left(1 - P_{K/E_i}\right)_m \right)$$

$$\tag{7.13a}$$

where $E_1, E_2, \ldots E_m$ refer to the number of independent encounters with weapon types $1, 2, \ldots m$, respectively, and $(1 - P_{K/E_i})_j$ refers to the probability of survival of the ith encounter with the jth weapon type. If the P_{K/E_i} are the same value for each encounter with a weapon type,

$$P_{S/S} = \left(1 - P_{K/E}\right)_1^{E_1}\left(1 - P_{K/E}\right)_2^{E_2} \cdots \left(1 - P_{K/E}\right)_m^{E_m} \qquad (7.13b)$$

where $(1 - P_{K/E})_j$ refers to the probability the aircraft survives each encounter with the jth weapon type. If the $P_{K/E}$ are all small compared with unity,

$$P_{S/S} \approx \exp\left(- E_1 P_{K/E_1} - E_2 P_{K/E_2} \cdots - E_m P_{K/E_m}\right) \qquad (7.13c)$$

Computer Programs for Survivability

During the past two decades, many computer programs were developed to assess aircraft survivability. Some of these programs were widely used, whereas others were used only by the developing organization. In developing the models and gathering the data, each organization used its own criteria as to how to model an element or event and what data were needed for a study. Thus, study results from different organizations were not directly comparable even though they were studying the same problem, and there were no accepted standards. As a consequence, the JTCG/AS has adopted a set of controlled standard models (and data) for use throughout the DoD survivability assessment community. The controlled models do not represent the only models of their type, rather, they represent a standard against which an analyst can compare his or her own model. The programs currently accepted as standards by the JTCG/AS are BLUEMAX, P001, SAMS, PACAM V, and SCAN. These programs are maintained by the JTCG/AS Aircraft Survivability Model Repository (ASMR), and additional information on the programs can be obtained by writing to: AFWAL/FIMB (Attn: J. Folck), Wright-Patterson AFB, OH 45433; or by calling (513) 255-5888.*

BLUEMAX. Most survivability assessment programs, such as P001 and SAMS, require the aircraft flight path and attitude as input data. Because these data are difficult to generate intuitively for any path other than straight and level, a computer program that simulates the maneuvering flight of a particular aircraft provides a much more realistic flight path than one obtained by estimation. BLUEMAX and BLUEMAX2 are such flight path generating programs. They generate three-dimensional flight path trajectories and aircraft attitudes, primarily for ground attack missions.

The BLUEMAX program provides variable-speed flight path descriptions which are suitable as input to AAA and SAM attrition models. The aircraft

*The model repository was incorporated with the CDIC into the SURVIAC (Appendix C) in early 1985.

modeled are limited to fixed-wing subsonic types operating between sea level and 20,000 ft altitude. A flight path is synthesized by the selection and combination of several segments from a series of available flight path maneuvers. There are five different types of maneuvers modeled: navigation, base-leg, roll-in-and-attack, pullout, and recovery. The roll-in-and-attack maneuver may be used only once in the flight path, but the other maneuver types can have as many as 30 flight path segments. The maneuvers can be entered and repeated in any combination to develop the desired path.

A new version of the BLUEMAX flight path generator has been developed under the sponsorship of Headquarters USAF/Studies and Analysis. This new version, called BLUEMAX2, has improved the basic model in four areas. It has added new segment control modes, improved the control logic, designed a more interactive user interface, and moved the aircraft characteristics data to an external file. Both an interactive version and a batch version of BLUEMAX2 are available.

P001.   P001 is a digital computer program developed by the Air Force Armament Test Laboratory at Eglin AFB. The model simulates one-on-one engagements between a target aircraft and a ground-based gun system. Several types of gun systems are available, and more than one gun or type can be arbitrarily located in one run. Computations are performed over an entire flight path for each gun, and probability of kill results due to multiple shots are accumulated for each increment of the flight path. The final output includes the probability the aircraft is killed in the encounter.

Since its creation, P001 has been modified by many organizations. The basic version includes the various error sources that occur in the encounters between an aircraft and a radar- or visually-directed gun. In addition to the basic capability, the controlled version of P001 incorporates the results of work performed by the Air Force Aerospace Medical Research Laboratory. This effort has led to a set of equations that permit the model to simulate gun operation with a man-in-the-loop. The gunner's tracking errors are modeled along with the other system errors, such as the lead angle prediction error and ballistic dispersion. All error sources that contribute to the projectile trajectories with respect to the aircraft are assessed by the program in order to evaluate the biases and standard deviations of the miss distance between the air targets' vulnerable area and the projectile. Equation (7.3) with $x_0^2 = y_0^2 = A_V$ is then used to predict the probability the aircraft is killed by each shot.

Gun types are described in terms of the numbers of barrels, projectile characteristics, system reactions, and tracking capabilities. The aircraft's flight path is entered into the model as a series of way points. The target aircraft vulnerability is described in terms of its single hit vulnerable areas, which are functions of 26 impact angles and the closing velocity. (Some versions of P001 allow the aircraft to be described by a number of separately located components, and the P_{KSS} of each of the components is computed.) Target flight paths may be calculated internally by P001 or entered from a data file. The internal flight path generator is capable of producing only straight and level flight paths. Other types of flight paths must be developed separately, possibly by a flight path generator such as BLUEMAX, and read into the simulation as an input file.

SAMS. SAMS is a restructured, completely documented successor to a family of computer programs called TAC ZINGERS that were developed by Headquarters USAF/Studies and Analysis. The SAMS model was developed to provide a standard surface-to-air missile engagement model to support survivability assessments of current and future Air Force weapon systems. The SAMS is a generic computer program that can be used to model the characteristics and capabilities of Soviet SAM systems. The characteristics and capabilities of the program include sensor lock-on and tracking parameters, missile flight dynamics and control, target vulnerability, and countermeasures.

The model simulates the interaction between a single airborne target and a specified SAM missile fired from a designated location. A launch/no-launch decision is based on the predicted target trajectory relative to the site and the SAM capabilities. The firing time is given by input, and the direction is determined by the geometry of the targets' approach. Since SAMS is basically a one-on-one engagement simulation, each engagement simulates a single mission, a single site, and a single target. Multiple sites or multiple launches from the same site are multiple executions of the SAMS simulation.

The target motion, derived from a table lookup of flight history data, consists of position, velocity, acceleration, and attitude of the target versus time. The postlaunch flyout consists of a boost-sustain powered flight phase, a glide phase, and an endgame phase. The forces acting on the missile center of mass are aerodynamic lift, aerodynamic drag, booster/sustainer thrust, and gravity. The navigational and guidance systems control the missile's flight path. Target and missile track sensor data are used to compute guidance commands for the missile. These commands, the pitch and yaw accelerations needed for intercept, are translated into fin deflections by the missile autopilot.

The SAMS endgame consists of a simulated warhead fuzing and subsequent detonation. When fuzing criteria are satisfied, the missile warhead detonates. SAMS models the subsequent motion of the warhead fragments and determines the target kill probability based on target attitude, presented areas, and vulnerability characteristics.

PACAM V. The Piloted Aircraft Combat Analysis Model (PACAM) is a simulation of encounters between friendly and hostile aircraft. PACAM V has been developed from a series of earlier versions in an evolutionary process. The original version, PACAM I, prepared for the Air Force Aeronautical Systems Division commencing in 1968, was designed to simulate one-versus-one aerial combat in three-dimensional space. Both sides used the same tactics, and both used the same policy: fully aggressive. A limited maneuver suite was available, and each aircraft fought unaware of weapon usage by his foe. The resulting flight path data for the two aircraft were stored on tape to permit the subsequent evaluation of weapon firing opportunities.

In developing PACAM II, the program was completely rewritten for efficient operation and ease of input. The major thrust of the development was in the area of tactics. Asymmetric tactics were permitted in that each side was allowed different decisions under various conditions, and a level of aggressiveness was incorporated. Nonaggressive (escape) tactics by reason of position, as well as for low fuel conditions, were included. Finally, and most significantly, the model was designed to permit multiaircraft combat. PACAM III efforts were aborted in favor of PACAM IV. The principal thrust of the PACAM IV development was to permit dynamic reaction to weapons firing.

The dynamic weapons provisions, plus the desire by the Laser Engineering and Application for Prototype Systems (LEAPS) office at the Air Force Weapons Laboratory (AFWL) at Kirtland AFB to use PACAM for bomber defense evaluation, led to another series of changes. First, size variations (from B-52 aircraft down to AIM-9 missiles) required that the detection range be made a function of target size and aspect, as well as the type of sensor. Second, this size variation, plus the requirement of a smaller time interval during missile flyout, led to a requirement for limitations in the vehicle response rate (roll, pitch, and thrust) that effectively permits simulation of 3-degrees-of-freedom movement. The ability of PACAM IV to handle bomber penetration and defense tactics against fighters led to the next major modification, PACAM V, which added surface-to-air missiles to the scenario.

SCAN. The endgame program SCAN is described in Chap. 5 in the section on computer programs for vulnerability assessment.

7.3 SYSTEM EFFECTIVENESS

In Chap. 1, the relationship between airborne weapon system effectiveness and aircraft survivability was examined. Two simple, conceptual measures of effectiveness, the offensive mission attainment measure (MAM) and the defensive survival rate, S, were defined there. Their product, MAM(S), defined an overall measure of effectiveness, the measure of mission success (MOMS). Values for these and other similar effectiveness measures can be determined by using the campaign analysis and conducting effectiveness studies. Because no effectiveness study is complete without the consideration of costs, a system cost-effectiveness analysis is usually a required part of the survivability program.

The Campaign Analysis

The campaign analysis typically consists of the mathematical generalization of the multiple encounters and outcomes between friendly aircraft and the hostile air defense for a specified number of raids or sorties. Each raid consists of one or more aircraft on a particular mission. The scenario illustrated in Fig. 7.2 is an example of the scenario for an interdiction mission. On this mission, the strike aircraft are engaged during ingress to the target area by AAA, SAMs, and AI that are spread out in a zone or area defense pattern. The target itself is defended by one or more point defense weapons located in the vicinity of the target, and the departing aircraft are again engaged by the zone defense weapons as they egress the combat arena. Some of the parameters usually of interest in this scenario are the probability an aircraft survives the sortie, the probability an aircraft is damaged, and the number of bombs dropped on the target. The raid is repeated, and those surviving aircraft that are undamaged (not requiring repair) go after the target again. This procedure continues for a specified number of raids. The campaign analysis can become extremely detailed in the simulation and may include such events as the return of damage-repaired aircraft to operational status and the attrition of the air-defense elements.

Computer Programs for Effectiveness

Two families of effectiveness programs are described here to give the reader a general idea of the typical capabilities of such programs. The two families are TACOS and EVADE.

TACOS. The Tactical Air-Defense Computer Operational Simulation (TACOS) program, is a large-scale air-attack/air-defense engagement simulation developed by Braddock, Dunn, and McDonald (BDM), Inc., Albuquerque, N.M. TACOS II, the current version, is the fourteenth distinct evolution of the family whose development dates back to 1962. TACOS II represents interactions which occur between a large deployment of air-defense systems and a large attack of aerial penetrator vehicles in a conventional setting over a field army. The air-defense deployment may consist of virtually any mixture of various SAM systems and AAA systems. The attack may consist of aircraft and missiles. The TACOS II output is composed of both the history listing and the summaries of outcomes of all engagements cross-referenced several ways.

The TACOS II utilizes a detailed, digitized terrain file to provide a realistic environment for the battle, and terrain masking and terrain following flight paths are represented. The ECM representation includes the effects of stand-off barrage and spot noise jamming, self-screening barrage and spot jamming, and various types of self-screening deception jamming. The effects of the ECM are simulated rather than the processes themselves. A "critical event" technique conserves computer time over a "time step" technique, and TACOS uses Monte Carlo decisions rather than aggregating probabilities. Any IBM System/360 possessing at least 512K bytes of core memory and capable of supporting the Operating System may be used for TACOS. A complete run takes between one-quarter and six computer hours on a 360/50. The TACOS has been constructed utilizing a highly modular approach allowing detailed submodels to be added with relatively little effort.

EVADE.   The Evaluation of Air-Defense Effectiveness (EVADE) program is an expected value simulation of engagements between aircraft and ground-based air-defense systems and was developed under the auspices of the Army Material Systems Analysis Agency, Aberdeen Proving Ground, Md. The current version is EVADE II. The program calculates the time history of the probability of kill for each participant in multiaircraft versus multi-ground-weapon encounters. Up to 20 simultaneous, independent flight path tracks against as many as 50 individual ground-weapon sites can be simulated. More than one aircraft can be flown on a given track, and more than one barrel can be located at one ground position. Thirteen different combinations of ground gun and fire-control system types from 7.62 to 57 mm are available. Aircraft can fire 7.62-, 12.7-, or 30-mm gun systems, or the TOW missile system, as appropriate. The surface-to-air i.r. missile systems are used in conjunction with, but external to, the model. Seven different weather and five different lighting conditions can be superimposed on the model scenario. These conditions affect visual target detection and acquisition from ground to air.

Extensive use is made oí digitized terrain maps, with small grid sizes. A 12.7-m grid is currently being utilized. A 40 × 47-km area of west central Germany, including approximately 13 million individual terrain heights, is stored on magnetic tape for use with the program's intervisibility subroutine. These "bare Earth" data with superimposed vegetation are used in conjunction with detailed three-dimensional, nap-of-the-Earth flight profiles. From this information, a realistic time history of intervisibility between all weapon sites and all aircraft is obtained. This "mask" history is then input to the base engagement model. Each engagement within the scenario follows a time-dependent sequence of events, such as target detection (either visual, acoustic, infrared, or radar), acquisition, unmasking, weapon system reaction time, target moving into maximum effective range, projectile or missile time of flight, arrival at the first intercept point, and subsequent accumulation of the probability of aircraft kill. This process continues until the target becomes masked, goes into a dead zone, is suppressed or killed, runs out of ammunition, or, perhaps, goes out of range. Six different criteria for rules of engagement and target selection can be employed. Weapons can be burst-fired, using any desired firing criterion, and up to 13 levels of critical component kill criteria, including redundant critical components, can be simultaneously evaluated.

Program output consists of the time history of air and ground systems suppressed or destroyed, ammunition expenditure, and the time history of all major events that occur. The location of events, such as detection, unmask, fire, remask, reload, and re-acquire, along each flight path track are also available. The program is useful as a means of obtaining a first-order estimate of the practicality of flight paths and the adequacy of weapon deployments. It can also be used as a relative survivability indicator when investigating tactics, techniques, equipment, environmental variations, and other systematic variations of input parameters to the engagement problem.

7.4   SURVIVABILITY DESIGN AND THE TRADE-OFF STUDY

The survivability design of an aircraft is that process in which those design features that have the potential to enhance the survivability of the aircraft are considered and are either incorporated into the design or rejected. If the enhancement feature does not cause weight, cost, maintenance, performance, or other penalties, it should be included as part of the design. If a feature does involve penalties, its inclusion is questioned. The decision to keep or to reject a particular feature should not be based upon whim or expediency, but instead should be based upon the results of the effectiveness studies. The methodology for the selection of those susceptibility reduction features (described in Chap. 6) and vulnerability reduction features (described in Chap. 5) that contribute to the effectiveness is briefly described in Chap. 1, and Fig. 1.4 shows the flow of the methodology.

The task of interest here is the trade-off study. The trade-off study is the determination and examination of the various peacetime and wartime effectiveness measures and penalties for each candidate survivability enhancement feature considered. Of particular interest are the payoffs and the penalties. The impact of each survivability enhancement feature on the system safety, maintenance, reliability, logistics, performance, cost, and weight, as well as on survivability and operational effectiveness, must also be determined.

The Other Disciplines

System safety.   Probable changes in system safety rates must be evaluated for the candidate survivability enhancement features. In most cases, they would be expected to lead to improvements in safety. For example, a lubrication bypass design that permits continued flight after damage to an oil cooler provides a greater probability of safe recovery of the aircraft and aircrew because of a material failure or maintenance error associated with the lubrication subsystem. However, some features can degrade the safety rates. A piece of ECM gear that unnecessarily distracts the pilot can increase the probability of a crash. The system safety rates that should be examined include (1) accidents per flying time and (2) aircrew survival per accident.

Maintenance.   Addition of survivability enhancement features as a modification to an existing aircraft may result in an increase of maintenance man-hours (scheduled and unscheduled) for the total system. For new designs, the penalties can be minimized and, in some cases, may result in benefits. Concentration and integration of a number of components in a subsystem to minimize its vulnerability may also require less maintenance effort and time to troubleshoot and repair. The maintenance factors are

(1) maintenance man-hours per flight hour (MMH/FH), (2) downtime per flight hour, and (3) mean task times (accessibility).

Reliability.   System reliability values also can be affected by survivability enhancement features. The addition of redundant subsystem circuits may affect the reliability requirements upon individual components within each of the redundant systems in order to attain the overall system reliability allocations. The reliability factors are (1) component reliability, (2) component redundancies, and (3) mission success reliability.

Logistics.   The operation of military aircraft requires logistic support in order to perform the designated missions. The major items that can be affected by survivability enhancement features include fuel consumed, spares required, and payload (munitions) expended to achieve a given level of combat effectiveness. For example, the addition of weight to a design for survivability enhancement may require more fuel to be used to achieve a given level of performance, and an increase in system complexity may affect the number of aircraft required for specific missions over a given time period.

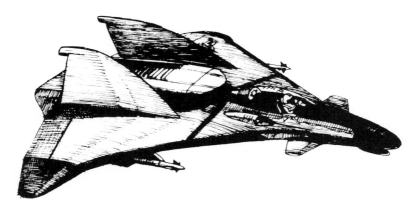

Performance.   Aircraft performance penalties are generally expressed in terms of mission range or radius loss or of a reduction in payload. For major subsystem additions to aircraft in design, the penalties may be expressed in terms of required aircraft weight and cost growth, with performance factors remaining constant. Modifications to the fuel system, such as the use of foam in the tanks and self-sealing, will result in a dry weight penalty as well as a reduction in available fuel weight due to fuel displacement. The combined effect of the survivability features may also affect the limitations on aircraft speed and maneuverability. For example, features which require the use of an external store station, such as an ECM pod, can affect aircraft performance, depending on the particular aircraft and store configuration. Aircrew performance factors refer to the effects that the survivability features have on the ability of the aircraft aircrew to perform their assigned tasks, such as flying the aircraft, navigating, locating the target, accurately delivering the weapon or payload, and observing the terrain flown over. This parameter also includes the effect on personnel mobility during emergency egress.

Costs. The final cost of the airborne weapon system may be the one factor to which all trade-off study values are ultimately related. It provides a basis upon which management may decide what combinations of survivability enhancement features will be the most effective for a specific design configuration, hostile threat spectrum, and length and intensity of the assumed conflict. Cost factors that may be influenced by survivability features are:

(1)   Development costs, including aircraft design, tests, and research.
(2)   Acquisition costs, such as production aircraft and spares.
(3)   Life cycle costs (LCC), including development costs, aircraft and crew acquisition costs (including peacetime and wartime replacement due to accidental attrition and wartime replacement due to combat attrition), peacetime operations and logistics, and wartime operations and logistics.

The inclusion of survivability enhancement features may increase the development and acquisition costs on a per aircraft basis. However, because the aircraft is more survivable, fewer aircraft need to be purchased to accomplish a specific operational goal because fewer aircraft will be lost in combat. This can lead to a smaller total cost over the lifetime of the system. For any assumed conflict, more of the more survivable aircraft will be left at the end of the conflict, and hence less aircraft will be required for replacement of the killed aircraft. The more intense or prolonged the conflict, the more important survivability becomes. For every aircraft that returns to base after a mission because of its enhanced survivability, one less aircraft has to be purchased and one less crew has to be found and trained. The cost of survivability enhancement can be greatly exceeded by the cost of replacing killed aircraft and their crews in the next conflict. The loss of the Government's investment in acquiring and training the crew and the cost penalties for search and rescue operations, administrative costs, dependency costs, and death costs associated with a lost aircraft can be a significant fraction of the hardware cost of the aircraft and, consequently, should be included in the cost of losing an aircraft in combat.

The Mission Trade-Off Model

The Mission Trade-Off Model (MTOM) is a computer program that was specifically developed to assess the impact of survivability enhancement features on mission effectiveness and costs. The model calculates the life cycle costs associated with a group of aircraft necessary to accomplish a prescribed mission. Although the model can be used for any of several possible missions, the primary emphasis is on missions in the air-to-ground category, such as interdiction and attack. Each mission must have a fixed measure of effectiveness. For example, the effectiveness measure for an air-to-ground attack mission is the delivery of a required number of weapons on a given number of targets in a given time. The model determines the minimum number of initial aircraft required to accomplish the prescribed effectiveness measure and the costs. Interactions between the aircraft and various enemy defenses are simulated by following a flight of aircraft on the raid. Probabilistic calculations are made for the attrition of aircraft and the ability of the aircraft to find the targets and deliver the weapons. Expected value calculations are made for the ground turnaround cycle of the aircraft to determine the sortie rate.

The costs include all aircraft losses and damage repairs as well as life cycle expenditures, including research, development, testing, and evaluation (RDT&E), procurement, training, operations, and maintenance. Evaluations of the effect of survivability enhancement features on the number of aircraft required to accomplish the effectiveness measure and their costs are made by using the model to compute the total mission cost to accomplish the prescribed mission with and without the features. The model also can be used without considering costs to calculate the effectiveness of an aircraft, or its modification, for a given scenario. Parameters can be varied easily so that sensitivity analyses and investigation of the effects of uncertainties can easily be carried out. The model development is modular and can be extended or modified by addition or replacement of submodels. MTOM consists of two major submodels. The mission trade-off/effectiveness (MTO/E) submodel evaluates the number of aircraft required initially to do a fixed job, and the mission trade-off/cost (MTO/C) submodel calculates the LCC for the aircraft. Extensive use is made of probabilistic and expected value calculations. Maintenance damage repair and ground turnaround are treated, and their effects are extrapolated over the length of the war. The primary emphasis in the model development is on a fairly short war; accordingly, killed aircraft are not replaced until after the war.

An Example Trade-Off Study

For an example of a trade-off study, consider the survivability design of an attack aircraft whose primary mission is the delivery of 10,000 lb of ordnance at low level within a combat radius of 600 miles. The mission-threat analysis has identified a ground-based AAA and a SAM as the two major threats to the aircraft. The AAA detects and tracks the aircraft using either radar or electro-optics and fires an HE warhead with a contact fuze at 1200 rounds per minute. The SAM threat also detects and tracks the aircraft using radar, and the missile is command guided and carries an HE controlled fragmentation warhead with a proximity fuze with a cutoff range of 50 m.

The vulnerability study has identified the critical components for an A level attrition kill. Among the nonredundant critical components are the wing and fuselage fuel tanks. The baseline design of the aircraft has no provision for suppressing the occurrence of a fire or explosion in the ullage of the tanks. The survivability enhancement design feature to be examined in the trade-off study is the use of a particular technique to suppress any fires and explosions within the wing tanks. The takeoff gross weight (TOGW) for the baseline design and for the modified design is assumed to be the same. The weighted average single hit vulnerable area of the baseline design with respect to the AAA threat, A_V, is 6 m^2 (only the single hit vulnerability will be used in this example), and the lethal radius with respect to the SAM, r_l, is 10 m. Suppression of fires and explosions within the wing fuel tanks reduces the weighted single hit vulnerable area and lethal radius to 5 m^2 and 9 m, respectively.

The susceptibility study has determined that the typical AAA platform will be able to detect the aircraft and to fire 20 shots, with a bias (μ_x, μ_y) of 6 m in both the x and y directions and a standard deviation (σ_x, σ_y) of 3 m in both directions. The typical SAM site also will be able to detect and track the aircraft, with enough time to launch two missiles, both with a CEP of 20 m. The fuze is assumed to properly function on all shots.

The P_{KSS} for the contact-fuzed AAA warhead is computed using Eq. (7.3) (with $x_0 = y_0$ and $x_0 y_0 = A_V$), and the P_{KSS} for the proximity-fuzed SAM warhead is computed using Eq. (7.8c), with $P_f = 1$, $r_0 = 1.2 r_l$, σ_r = CEP/1.177, and $r_c = 50$ m. The results for the P_{KSS} for both the baseline design and the more survivable aircraft are given in Table 7.2 for both the AAA and the SAM threats.

The probability of kill of the aircraft in a one-on-one encounter with both the AAA and the SAM, $P_{K/E}$, can be computed using Eq. (7.10a), with $N = 20$ for the AAA and $N = 2$ for the SAM. The probability of detection P_D and probability of launch P_L are taken as unity for this study. The results for $P_{K/E}$ for both designs and both threats are given in Table 7.2.

For the sortie survivability, the assumption is made that 100 aircraft will encounter five AAA platforms and two SAM sites during their raids. Thus, the typical aircraft on a sortie will have 0.05 AAA encounters with the AAA threat and 0.02 encounters with the SAM threat. The results for the sortie survivability $P_{S/S}$, obtained using Eq. (7.13b), and the associated sortie loss rates are given in Table 7.2 for both aircraft designs. Note in Table 7.2 that the loss rates are approximately 1%, which is comparable to the short-term loss rates of some recent conflicts. The number of threat encounters for the two threat types were specifically chosen to give this result. More encounters would lead to a higher loss rate, and less encounters would lead to a smaller loss rate. This loss rate of approximately 1% was selected based upon historical data. (A loss rate this high can only be sustained in a relatively short conflict. After 50 raids, only 61 of the original 100 aircraft are left, according to Fig. 4.1a.)

The weapon system cost-effectiveness measure used in this trade-off study is the sum of the peacetime 15-year life cycle cost of the total fleet of aircraft and the cost of replacing aircraft lost in combat. The flyaway or replacement cost of one baseline aircraft is $20 million. (This does not include the cost of replacing the crew, which can be significant, and should be considered in the trade-off study.) The peacetime LCC for 300 production aircraft and ten operational squadrons with 200 aircraft is $12,000 million. The more survivable aircraft flyaway cost is $20.05 million. The increase over the baseline flyaway cost is due to the cost of incorporating the suppression feature. The more survivable aircraft LCC is $12,020 million. The additional

Table 7.2 Aircraft Sortie Loss Rates

Parameter / A/C	AAA					SAM					Sortie
	A_V, m²	$\mu_x = \mu_y$, m	$\sigma_x = \sigma_y$, m	P_{KSS}	$P_{K/E}$ (N=20)	r_l, m	CEP, m	P_{KSS}	$P_{K/E}$ (N=2)	$P_{S/S}$	Loss Rate (per 1000)
Baseline	6	6	3	0.002579	0.05034	10	20	0.1996	0.3594	0.9886	11.4
More survivable	5	6	3	0.002059	0.04038	9	20	0.1680	0.3078	0.9906	9.4

Table 7.3 Trade-Off Study Results

Parameter / A/C	Δ Weight, lb	Payload, lb	Aircraft Launches Required	Loss Rate	Replacement Aircraft Required	Cost of One Aircraft, $M	Combat Replacement Costs, $M	Peacetime 15-yr LCC, $M	Peacetime + Replacement Cost, $M	Δ Cost, $M
Baseline	0	10,000	5057.7	11.4	57.7	20.00	1154	12,000	13,154	0
More survivable	150	9,850	5124.5	9.4	48.4	20.05	970	12,020	12,990	−164

LCC is due to the increase in the flyaway cost, the increase in the empty weight of the aircraft, the increase in maintenance requirements, and any decrease in reliability due to the incorporation of the suppression feature.

The total mission effectiveness measure selected for the study is the delivery of 50,000,000 lb of ordnance on the target. The weight of bombs dropped on the target per aircraft launch (normalized with respect to 10,000 lb) is selected as the sortie effectiveness measure. The optimistic assumption is made that the mission attainment measure (MAM) for the aircraft is unity; that is, every aircraft that is not killed delivers its 10,000 lb of bombs on the target. Thus, if no baseline aircraft are killed, 5000 sorties are required to deliver the total ordnance load. However, the sortie survival rate of the baseline aircraft is 0.9886. Thus, the measure of mission success (MOMS) of the baseline aircraft is 1×0.9886, or 0.9886. Assuming that all aircraft lost in combat are killed on their way to the target, the bombs delivered per aircraft launch by the baseline aircraft is 9886 lb. Thus, 50,000,000/9886, or 5057.7, aircraft launches are required to get 5000 baseline aircraft over the target, and 57.7 aircraft are lost in combat. The total replacement cost of these 57.7 aircraft is $1154 million.

The payload carried by the more survivable aircraft is reduced to 9850 lb because of the increase in the aircraft empty weight of 150 lb caused by the addition of the survivability enhancement feature. Thus, the MAM is 0.9850 for the modified aircraft, and 50,000,000/9850, or 5076.1, sorties are required when no modified aircraft are killed. The sortie survival rate for the modified aircraft is 0.9906. Thus, the measure of mission success is 0.9850 $\times$ 0.9906, or 0.9757; that is, 9757 lb of bombs are delivered per aircraft launch. Hence, 50,000,000/9757, or 5124.5, aircraft launches are required, and $5124.5 - 5076.1$, or 48.4, aircraft are lost in combat. The total replacement cost of these 48.4 modified aircraft is $970 million.

The major results of the trade-off study are presented in Table 7.3. The more survivable aircraft requires more aircraft launches and has a smaller MOMS (fewer bombs on the target per aircraft launch), but the significant savings in the replacement cost of nearly $200 million more than offsets the additional LCC caused by the fuel tank protection feature. The total savings in cost of $164 million, and in the lives of the aircrews, will increase for more intense or longer duration conflicts and will decrease for less intense or shorter conflicts. If no battles are fought, an extra $20 million have been spent for nothing. Survivability is somewhat like fire insurance on your house. If you do not have a fire, you are out the insurance premiums; but if you ever do have a major fire, the cost of the premiums is insignificant, and you will wish you had taken out more insurance. The same philosophy applies to survivability.

7.5 BATTLE DAMAGE REPAIR

The objectives of ACS are: (1) to attempt to avoid being damaged by the man-made hostile environment, and when that is not possible, (2) to withstand the damage caused by the environment. Aircraft that have been designed to take hits and survive are going to return to base with battle damage more often than less survivable aircraft. This damage must be repaired rapidly in order to turn the aircraft around and send it out to fight again. In peacetime, maintenance standards and repair criteria are devoted to maintaining a long operational life on the aircraft. Repairs are made to restore the structure to its original strength and to last for the duration of the aircraft's life. Carrying out repairs to these high standards in wartime would involve long periods of time and eventually could lead to a lack of operating aircraft. It is essential, therefore, that capabilities be developed for speedy repairs and the return of battle damaged aircraft to operational use in the shortest possible time. This program is known as the Aircraft Battle Damage Repair (ABDR) program.

The primary purpose of ABDR is to restore sufficient strength and serviceability to damaged aircraft to permit them to fly additional operational sorties, with at least partial mission capability, within time to contribute to the outcome of the ongoing battle. A secondary objective is to enable those aircraft damaged beyond unit repair capability to make a one-time flight to its home station, rear area base, or major repair facility. ABDR will involve simple repair techniques that eliminate most of the fatigue conscious methods used in peacetime. Rapid repairs can be performed on most types of damage, resulting in significant savings of time without compromising the safety or mission effectiveness of the aircraft.

There are four types of preparations that have the potential of minimizing delays caused by repair of battle damage and that will significantly increase the number of damaged aircraft returned to operational service. They are: (1) use design concepts and materials in the aircraft that will facilitate battle damage repair, (2) allow the use of time-saving temporary repairs on certain types of damage, (3) train maintenance personnel in the new skills and techniques required for rapid repairs, and (4) provide the tools and materiel required to accomplish rapid ABDR.

The contractor's responsibility in ABDR is to develop an easily repairable aircraft and to determine the man-hours, downtime, logistic support, and levels of repair for damaged aircraft under combat operational conditions. One design technique for repairability that should be considered is modular construction that allows easy removal and replacement of damaged components. (The Lancaster bomber of World War II had about 1000 extra pounds of structural weight in bolts and flanges that were added to allow rapid dismantling of damaged parts.) Interchangeability of major components allows the cannibalization of functioning components from severely damaged aircraft. Damage-tolerant and easy-to-repair materials should be used where possible, and provisions for airframe access should be made to allow quick damage assessments and repairs to be made. The contractor must also identify the appropriate repair activities, as well as the identification and description of quick turnaround fixes, long lead time items, and spare parts storage requirements.

7.6 CONCLUSIONS

The consideration of survivability in the design and utilization of aircraft has been important in past conflicts and will be more so in future conflicts. The cost of procuring and operating modern aircraft makes imperative a thorough study of each system and feature to ensure that no Achilles' heel is lurking there, just waiting to be discovered in combat. If there is a next war, the battles will be fought with the aircraft on hand. There will not be time to build new aircraft and to train new crews to fly them. What we have has to survive.

Selected Bibliography

Arnold, R. J., "Survivability Design of Forward Air Control and Light Attack Aircraft," National Aeronautic and Space Engineering and Manufacturing Meeting, Society of Automotive Engineers, SAE Paper 690707, Oct. 6–10, 1969.

Atkinson, D. B., Blatt, P., et al., "Design of Fighter Aircraft for Combat Survivability," National Aeronautic and Space Engineering and Manufacturing Meeting, Society of Automotive Engineers, SAE Paper 690706, Oct. 10, 1969.

Dotseth, W. D., "System Engineering Process for Survival Enhancement of Military Aircraft," AIAA Second Aircraft Design and Operations Meeting, Los Angeles, AIAA Paper 70-893, July 20–22, 1970.

Foulk, J. B., "Survivability of the Army/Sikorsky YUH-60A Helicopter," 32nd Annual National V/STOL Forum of the American Helicopter Society, Washington, D.C., Preprint 1011, May 1976.

Larsen, H. C., "Considerations in the Design of COIN Aircraft," *Journal of Aircraft*, Vol. 5, May–June 1968, pp. 243–253.

McAllister, G. T., "Design of Helicopters for Survivability," *Proceedings on Aircraft Operational Experience and Its Impact on Safety and Survivability*, AGARD Conference Proceedings No. 212, May 31–June 7, 1976, pp. 14-1 to 14-22.

The Mission Trade-Off Model (MTOM) Part I, Model Description, JTCG/AS-76-S-001, Dec. 1977.

The Mission Trade-Off Model (MTOM) Part II, User's Manual, JTCG/AS-76-S-002, Oct. 1978.

Pruyn, R. R. and Windolph, G. W., "Survivability Tradeoff Considerations for Future Military Observation Helicopters," *Journal of the American Helicopter Society*, Vol. 24, April 1979, pp. 4–9.

Schmidtlein, H., Beisenherz, K., and Möhring, M., "Designing the Survivability of a Flying Weapon System," *Proceedings on Aircraft Operational Experience and Its Impact on Safety and Survivability*, AGARD Conference Proceedings No. 212, May 31–June 7, 1976, pp. 15-1 to 15-11.

Smith, R. B., et al., *A Review of Methodologies and Concepts to Measure and Evaluate Aircraft Survivability/Vulnerability*, JTCG/AS-75-S-002, Jan. 1978.

APPENDIX A. SURVIVABILITY FEATURES
OF SEVERAL AIRCRAFT USED IN WORLD WAR II

This appendix presents the development of the survivability features of
several of the most famous aircraft from World War II. Included are the
Boeing B-17 Flying Fortress, the Lockheed P-38 Lightning, the Republic
P-47 Thunderbolt, the North American P-51 Mustang, the Brewster F2A
Buffalo, the Grumman F4F Wildcat and F6F Hellcat, the Vought F4U
Corsair, the German Messerschmitt Bf-109, the Russian Ilyushin IL-2, and
the Japanese Mitsubishi Zero.

A.1   THE MOST FAMOUS BOMBER OF THEM ALL:
THE BOEING B-17 FLYING FORTRESS

The Boeing B-17 Flying Fortress is perhaps the most famous bomber of
the Second World War. Over 12,000 of these heavy bombers were accepted
by the US Army Air Corps/Force between July 1940 and August 1945.
However, as a result of considerable combat experience, the last production
version, the B-17G, was a far cry from the early models. Survivability
considerations played a major role in the evolution of the B-17 into one of
the classic bomber designs of all time.

The first B-17's were produced in the mid-1930's for the Army Air Corps.
The early models were the Y1B-17A, the B-17B, and the B-17C. The
original mission of the B-17 was that of coastal defense of the United States
against hostile ships, and the airplane was designed from the beginning to
deliver a bomb load with great accuracy from high altitude under daylight
conditions. The development of an improved bombsight, aircrew oxygen
supply, and engine supercharger eventually boosted the high-altitude performance to a service ceiling of 37,000 ft. The B-17C had a maximum loaded
weight of 50,000 lb, a top speed of 320 mph, a cruising speed in formation
of 160 mph, and range of 1100 miles with a normal internal bomb load of
6000 lb.

The all-metal fuselage of the Fortress was a circular, semimonocoque
structure with its strength evenly distributed throughout the entire length in
order to maintain integrity after combat damage. The circular cross section
of the fuselage was selected because of its efficient strength-to-weight ratio
and ease of manufacture. The flight controls were manually operated with
no power assist, except when automatic flight control equipment was used.
The flaps and landing gear were moved by electrical actuators with a
mechanical backup capability. Most of the other systems were also electri-

339

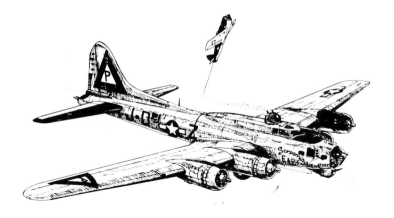

cally actuated. However, the engine cowl flaps, the wheel brakes, and the emergency brake were hydraulically actuated.

There were four 1200-hp Wright Cyclone air-cooled radial engines with a fire wall in each engine racelle, and the aircraft was capable of flying on just two engines. Yaw with one engine out was not a severe problem. The low-mounted wing had two main spars with one auxiliary midspar between the engines. The internal bomb bay fit between the front and rear spar locations. The wing loading was relatively low. All of the fuel tanks were located in the wings; no fuel was carried in the fuselage.

The pilot and copilot were protected by armor plate at the back of their seats and by armor placed on the No. 3 bulkhead (just forward of the windshield) and on the No. 4 bulkhead (leading into the bomb bay behind them). All other crew stations were similarly shielded by armor. Fire extinguishers were carried in the cockpit. The window glass throughout the aircraft was laminated and strengthened, but it was not bulletproof.

The self-protection armament carried by the B-17 went through a succession of increases. It consisted of either five .50 caliber or five .30 caliber machine guns on the Y1B-17A, two .30 caliber and three .50 caliber machine guns on the B-17B, and one .30 caliber and six .50 caliber machine guns on the B-17C, all manually aimed.

The first B-17's to engage in combat were those sent to the Royal Air Force under provisions of the Lend-Lease Act. Twenty B-17C's, modified to British standards and called Fortress I by the RAF, were delivered to England in May 1941. These modifications included replacing the small side blisters with flat, paneled gun positions and installing a bathtub-type gun position under the fuselage with its single machine gun oriented to the rear. More protective armor was added around the crew stations, and the fuel system was retrofitted with self-sealing fuel tanks. (The self-sealing compound was not particularly effective against the 20-mm cannon projectiles used by the enemy fighters.)

Misled by the airplane's nickname of "Flying Fortress" (a registered trademark), the British employed the B-17C during July 1941 in offensive, daylight raids over France, Germany, and Norway with only three to four aircraft per raid. Because the B-17C's operated beyond the escorting range of Spitfire and Hurricane fighters and during the daylight hours, they were highly susceptible to concentrated fighter attacks and consequently suffered heavy damage and loss. Eight of the original 20 B-17's were either lost or destroyed between May and September 1941, and after 22 missions, 18 planes out of 39 planes dispatched aborted due to mechanical problems. As the British quickly discovered, the B-17C was lacking in firepower and unable to defend itself under heavy daylight attack. The British pilots renamed the B-17 the "Flying Target," and the German Luftwaffe called it the "Flying Coffin." As a result of the poor initial performance, the British canceled the daylight raids, withdrew the aircraft from British squadrons, and sent them on coastal reconnaissance missions.

Boeing was aware of the potential survival problems of the B-17C prior to its use in combat by the British and was already making modifications to the C model in 1940. The B-17D, which was designed for the US Army Air Corps, became operational in February 1941. The B-17D was equipped with a better bladder-type self-sealing fuel cell system and additional crew armor. However, no changes were made to the defensive armament package.

The B-17D exhibited many of the same weaknesses as the B-17C, and it became obvious that an extensive redesign, including increased defensive armament, was vital. Consequently, Boeing greatly modified its earlier designs and introduced the B-17E in October 1941, two years after the start of the war in Europe and two months before the Japanese attack on Pearl Harbor. Boeing considered the B-17E to be the first "Flying Fortress" designed for offensive operations. The airplane had been lengthened by 6 ft to incorporate twin .50 caliber machine guns in a manually operated turret in the tail. The empennage was significantly increased in size to make room for the turret and to improve the directional handling. This change was particularly helpful during the bombing run and when the tail guns were fired. Twin .50 caliber machine guns were also installed in a Bendix electrically powered turret located in the top of the fuselage just behind the cockpit, and a Sperry electrically powered ball turret with twin .50 caliber guns was installed under the fuselage. Provision was made for .50 caliber guns to be fired upward from the radio compartment on the top of the aircraft and from a removable window on each side aft of the wing. In the nose of the aircraft, hand-operated .30 caliber guns were placed on flexible socket mounts on both sides of the aircraft for use by the bombardier and navigator when they were not engaged in their primary duty. (The flexible-mounted guns in the nose and waist, referred to as wobble-guns, were rumored to be ineffective due to the difficulties in aiming.)

The B-17F, introduced in May 1942, was an improved E model with more than 400 design modifications. It had additional protective armor, self-sealing oil tanks, and additional electrical power sources. Extra fuel cells in the wings, known as "Tokyo" tanks, were also added. These tanks added to the vulnerability of the aircraft because fumes tended to collect in the outer wing sections (these tanks were not vented), and an incendiary strike could cause an explosion that was capable of ripping off an entire wing. Only in the latter part of the war was a successful venting system incorporated to reduce the vapor hazard. Approximately 3,400 B-17F's were produced by Boeing, Vega, and Douglas.

Subsequent battle experience vividly illustrated the need for further improvement in survivability. The B-17E and F models were still susceptible to "head-on" fighter attacks. These attacks were nerve shattering to the bomber crews due to the possibility of a crash with a fighter containing a dead or crazed pilot. Consequently, numerous B-17F's were modified with a Bendix powered chin turret containing twin .50 caliber machine guns. The subsequent B-17G model, the final version introduced in September 1943, incorporated the chin turret and .50 caliber guns in place of the .30 caliber "cheek" guns. The G model was heavier (65,600 lb) and somewhat slower (290 mph) than the C model and typically carried 6000 lb of bombs. Over 8600 B-17G's were built by Boeing, Vertol, and Douglas.

An interesting variation of the B-17 was the YB-40, a "Flying Destroyer." The idea was to use a B-17 as a "fighter" escort to provide protection to the B-17 bombers on the longer missions. The program began in August 1942 with modified B-17F's, and the first model was completed in four months. The Bendix chin turret was added, as well as a second upper turret at the rear of the cockpit fairing, which was modified to give better coverage. This version had seven pairs of .50 caliber machine guns with over 12,000 rounds of ammunition available. Additional armor was also added. Unfortunately, the idea did not work out as planned. The plane, heavily loaded, could not keep up with the formation of B-17 bombers, even before the bombs were dropped. The idea was dropped, and the YB-40's were either reconverted to bombers or used as trainers.

The development of the B-17 into an effective daylight, strategic bomber was fraught with controversy. The British, as a result of their bad experiences with daylight bombing early in the war, confined their strategic bombing to nighttime in order to avoid what they considered an unacceptably high level of attrition. The Americans, on the other hand, were convinced that daylight precision bombing, flying at high altitude to reduce the effectiveness of antiaircraft artillery and in very tight formations for mutual protection and massed firepower against enemy fighters, was the most effective strategy in the European theater.

In early 1942, before the American bombing in Europe began, the British, including Prime Minister Churchill, were convinced that the accuracy gained by precision bombing using the Norden bombsight would be outweighed by the heavy losses that would take place as the unescorted bombers literally fought their way to the Ruhr and back home. Even if the bombers were escorted by long-range fighters, it was unreasonable to expect the fuel-ladened long-range fighter to cope with the short-range enemy defensive fighters operating over their homeland. They wanted the Americans to join them on their area bombing raids at night. Furthermore, they believed the United States should stop building the B-17 and start building the Lancaster, which they considered the world's best bomber because it could carry the heaviest load. (The Lancaster carried only .30 caliber machine guns, was not as tough as the B-17, and did not have a precision bombsight.) In their view, the B-17 was too dependent upon clear weather, was easy to detect because of extensive contrails, and carried an uneconomical bombload in relation to the crews and maintenance required. The Americans did not want to use the B-17 at night because the crews were not trained for nighttime operations, the simultaneous flights with the British would pose horrendous coordination problems, the Norden bombsight would be wasted, the engine exhausts would clearly be visible, and the entire design philosophy of the B-17 as a daylight bomber would become superfluous.

The Americans prevailed in their fight for daylight bombing, and consequently much of the bomb-carrying ability of the B-17 was used up by the addition of heavy armor plate, self-sealing fuel tanks, and all the manpower and equipment required to support as many as 13 heavy machine guns. Out of a typical crew of ten, eight men (four gunners and four part-time gunners) manned the machine guns during attack, often wearing heavy flak jackets and helmets for protection. The other two men were the pilot and the copilot, both capable of flying the aircraft, and thus providing an important redundancy.

Flying at 26,000 ft in the B-17 was not exactly the same as flying in today's intercontinental passenger jet. It was terribly cold; only the cockpit was heated. The temperature often dropped to 60 degrees below zero. The equipment was difficult to work with, the guns often jammed, and hands and feet froze. Gathering into formation for a major strike could take over an hour and was dangerous. The planes bunched into such tight boxes that sometimes the wings would nearly touch. It was a long trip, traveling at 170 mph, and a complete mission usually took over 6 hours. The flak (a word that denotes both bursting shells and the AAA itself) was heavy, the fighters many, and the straight-and-level bomb run took forever. There was always the fear that your airplane would be hit by a bomb dropped from an airplane overhead. The remaining bombers would be hassled again by the fighters on the way out. A standard tour for a B-17 crew was 25 missions.

Avoidance of early detection and confusion of intent were important to the survivability of the B-17. This was made difficult by the fact that the contrails from the hundreds of bombers in formation could be seen for hundreds of miles. The flight path to a European target was usually circuitous, avoiding known locations of AAA, and often one or more groups of bombers would depart on diversionary operations to draw the enemy fighters away from the main group or to delay their takeoff. Many different formations were tried. A staggered formation that was good for avoiding flak was bad for fighter defense, and vice versa.

The bombers were originally painted in a camouflage pattern to prevent them from being seen from the air when they were parked. Later in the war, when the danger of an airfield attack was reduced, the paint was removed to save weight and reduce drag. Fighter escort, which was not available on the longer missions until late 1943, had a dramatic effect on the survivability of the B-17. The losses were typically seven times higher on unescorted missions. The P-47 Thunderbolt was used on the shorter trips. The P-38 Lightning, which had a longer range, was in short supply in the European theater. Only the P-51 Mustang had the range to accompany the bombers on the longer missions without auxiliary tanks.

Electronic countermeasures were also used to enhance survivability. In order to reduce the effectiveness of radar-directed search lights and AAA, a few B-17's in each bomber group carried a pretuned spot noise jammer known as Carpet. Carpet was first used in October 1943, and over 7000 were built. The British experimented with several types of countermeasures, and an elaborate device that sent back amplified and extended radar echoes was used in August 1943 to divert nearly 150 German fighters from a B-17 attack on Rouen. Chaff, known by the code name Window, was also used, starting in 1943, to confuse the radar operators. When it was first introduced, it was very effective in reducing B-17 losses. However, within a few months, enemy counter-countermeasures began to reduce the benefits of the countermeasures. The British Bomber Command used several lend/lease B-17E's, F's, and G's as support aircraft whose role was radio and radar countermeasures in support of the main force. Painted black, they escorted the Lancasters and Halifaxes, or they made Window spoofs simulating bomber streams. This was the beginning of electronic warfare.

The B-17 was credited with the ability to absorb an amazing amount of battle damage throughout the war. Many of these rugged bombers limped back to base with engines destroyed and control surfaces shot away and were still able to make either safe landings or controlled crash landings. Early in the war in the Pacific, one B-17 was attacked by Japanese fighters and had all of its guns either shot out of action or jammed. Its radio was destroyed, the oxygen system put out of action, and one fuel tank was shot up. It eventually crash-landed near its home base and was found to have over 1000 bullet holes. Another B-17 had the misfortune of colliding with a German Bf-109. The Bf-109 sliced into the aft section of the fuselage of the B-17, nearly cutting the fuselage in half and destroying the left elevator. In a similar example, a Bf-109 collided with the aft end of a B-17, gouging out big chunks of the B-17's fuselage where the propeller sliced through. The bomber continued on its bombing mission. The tail gunner was not even aware of the collision until the plane had landed. The B-17 was also able to absorb large numbers of fragments from the high-explosive projectiles used by the German AAA batteries.

The combat data gathered from World War II indicates the intensity of the conflict. In the three and a half years of the war, 4700 B-17's were lost on combat missions out of a total of 12,700 built. More B-17's were lost than any other aircraft. Very few airplanes lasted a hundred missions. Those that did usually required many engine changes and major repairs. Loss rates on a raid were often as high as 10% and sometimes went as high as 25%. One such event was the infamous October 1943 raid on Schweinfurt, when 60 out of 280 aircraft failed to return and 17 were damaged beyond repair.

In the nearly three years of operations by the 384th Bombardment Group of the 8th Air Force over Europe, B-17's flew 9348 sorties on 386 missions. On these missions, 159 aircraft were lost for an average loss rate of approximately 1.5%. However, in the first six months of operations (June to November 1943), the loss rate for over 600 sorties on 38 missions was 8.7%. A crewman's chance of completing his required 25 missions was not good in those first months.

The British also suffered heavy losses during their nighttime bombing. Losses in the Bomber Command in late 1943 were nearly 4%, rising to 6% in January 1944, and 7% in February. On bad nights, it could go as high as 10%, and on March 30, 1944, 96 out of 795 aircraft failed to return from a raid on Nuremberg. A crewman's tour consisted of 30 missions, and his chance of surviving a complete tour in 1943 was about one in six.

In the European Theater, most of the B-17 losses were due to powerplant trouble, the inability to feather propellers, fires, and explosions. Fifty percent of the losses suffered engine damage serious enough to prevent the aircraft's return to home base. Also, any engine trouble that forced the aircraft to drop out of formation led to a much higher probability of loss due to the susceptibility of the lone aircraft to enemy fighter attack. The B-17 could maintain formation with one engine out if the propeller was feathered. Any other combination of engine problems caused the aircraft to drop out of formation. The B-17 had no backup feathering system; the B-24 Liberator did.

Fires were the major cause of about one-third of the bomber losses. The major areas for fire were the engine nacelles, the fuselage, and the wings. The early B-17's were equipped with nacelle fire extinguishers, but in the spring of 1943 the extinguishers were removed as part of a weight reduction program. The extinguishers were reinstalled by the summer of 1944. Fires in the fuselage sometimes resulted from hits which simultaneously punctured oxygen and hydraulic systems. Crew members using the portable fire extinguishers carried in the aircraft were unable to control the hydraulic fluid-oxygen fires in most cases. The wing fires usually resulted from hits on fuel lines or from holes in the fuel tanks that were too severe for the self-sealing compound to close. Fuel leaking from the wing tanks would flow the length of the wing and into the engine nacelles and the fuselage bomb bay.

The story of the B-17 is a heroic story of an airplane that evolved from an early reject due to its lack of survivability into a respected bomber that carried 40% of the bombs dropped on European targets. However, fighting its way to the target and back home took a heavy toll, and for every B-17 lost, ten crew members were potential victims. Nevertheless, the plane won international renown and was one of the few aircraft that saw continuous service throughout the war, despite having first flown in 1935.

A.2   SOME FAMOUS US ARMY AIR CORPS FIGHTERS OF WORLD WAR II

Lockheed P-38 Lightning

The Lockheed P-38 Lightning, originally designed as a pursuit or bomber interceptor, developed into a noteworthy fighter during the Second World War, and is credited with destroying more Japanese aircraft than any other

Allied fighter. The 1938 Lockheed twin-boom design was quite unorthodox for a pursuit, but resulted in a handsome, streamlined aircraft. The booms were used to carry the liquid-cooled Allison engines with their turbosuperchargers, radiators, and fuel tanks, as well as the main undercarriage. The relatively small center fuselage made an excellent gun platform. A pressurized cockpit was tested, but full-scale development was abandoned. The Lightning carried more and heavier armament than its contemporaries; one 20-mm automatic cannon and four .50 caliber electrically heated machine guns were installed in the nose of the center fuselage. At about 15,000 lb, it was heavier than a combat-loaded Bristol Blenheim I, Britain's standard medium bomber at that time, and its wing loading was nearly twice as high as that of other current fighters.

The early models of the P-38 saw initial combat with the British Royal Air Force. The design shortcomings (no self-sealing fuel tanks, lack of climb power, and poor protective armor) quickly became obvious to the RAF, and priority messages were sent to Lockheed requesting a redesign. The result was the P-38D, introduced in August 1941. The P-38D was the first model Lockheed considered close to being a true combat fighter. Self-sealing fuel tanks were added, a new propeller was installed, and heavier armor plating was installed in the cockpit area. This armor, placed directly behind the pilot's seat, protected the head and torso from the rear only. There was no armor on the sides or front of the cockpit. Consequently, many units produced their own armor plates and attached them to the sides of the cockpit.

The P-38 owed its combat ruggedness to the structural design. Its ability to absorb damage is exemplified in an incident where a P-38 and a Messerschmitt Bf-109, engaged in head-on firing passes, collided. The Bf-109 lost its wings and crashed immediately. The P-38, also a wreck, continued to fly. It had a prop torn away from one engine, its horizontal tail was severed, and one of its fuselage booms was reduced to rubble. The pilot was able to return the aircraft for a successful crash landing. In another case, a pilot flew his P-38 into a telephone pole. The wing sliced the pole in two and sustained severe leading-edge damage, but the aircraft returned to base safely. Another P-38 returned to base with one engine dead and riddled with over 100 bullet holes and five cannon strikes. In another extreme example, an overzealous pilot on a strafing run against a Japanese destroyer pulled up too late, and his wing tip sheared off the ship's foremast. A 3-ft section of the P-38's wing was missing, yet it continued to fly and eventually landed safely at its home base.

Even with its ruggedness, the P-38 had several shortcomings in combat. The turbosuperchargers produced a thick contrail at high altitudes that was visible to enemy fighters at great distances. The distinctive body design led to long-range recognition by the enemy fighter pilots and allowed them to prepare for engagement before the P-38 pilots spotted them. The contrail problem was eventually solved by using a water trap and enlarging the intake duct scoops. The P-38 was also extremely cold when used at altitudes above 30,000 ft, leading to pilot fatigue and many cases of frostbite during long bomber escort missions. The aircraft was difficult to maneuver at high altitudes, and the cold, damp European weather caused problems with the carburetor and the supercharger.

The twin engine design of the P-38 would seem to be a survivability enhancement feature. However, combat data from the European Theater of Operations on damaged P-38's returning to base indicated that only 10% returned after one engine was disabled. In most cases, the disablement of one engine led to a loss of the aircraft. This could be due to the fact that damage to the liquid coolant subsystem would put the engine out of action and often cause a fire, eventually resulting in the loss of the aircraft. Thus, the second engine probably increased the vulnerability of the aircraft rather than reduced it. The P-38 also had its dive speed limited due to compressibility effects near Mach 1. These shortcomings led many senior officials, including General Doolittle, the 8th Air Force Commander, to question the use of the P-38 in the European Theater.

Later production P-38J models had the curved windshield replaced with a flat bulletproof glass canopy, and the P-38L had an AB/APS-13 tail-warning radar installed. The radar warning system detected the presence of an aircraft in a cone-shaped area behind the P-38 and signaled the pilot with a warning light and ringing bell. The P-38J-25-Lo and subsequent variants were fitted with a hydraulic power boost system for the ailerons to increase maneuverability. This was one of the first applications of power-assisted controls to any fighter.

Although only 9923 P-38's were produced, the smallest number of the major USAAF combat fighters, it served on every battlefront in a wide variety of roles, including fighter escort, bombing with the Norden bombsight and with radar, photo-reconnaissance, casualty evacuation, smoke laying, and night fighting.

Republic P-47 Thunderbolt

The largest, heaviest (15,000 to 21,000 lb), and one of the most rugged single engine, single seat aircraft to be produced during World War II was the Republic P-47 Thunderbolt. The Thunderbolt's ability to absorb punishment was undisputed. With its two self-sealing fuselage fuel tanks, air-cooled Pratt & Whitney Double Wasp engine, cockpit armor, laminated-glass canopy, and rugged structure, the P-47 often survived the most damaging blows from 20-mm cannon fire, returning to base riddled with holes and with the majority of its control surfaces damaged or missing.

When the Thunderbolt was first introduced to the war in Europe in 1943, it was the only Allied radial engine, single seat fighter, and there was concern that it would be confused with the blunt-nosed German Focke-Wulfe 190 fighter. Consequently, to prevent Thunderbolts from being shot at by other Allied fighters, the engine cowlings were painted either white or a checkerboard white and black, and white bands were painted around the vertical and horizontal tail surfaces. Another survivability feature of the Thunderbolt, first introduced in the P-47D, was the use of emergency water injection into the intake manifold to temporarily increase the engine performance. In addition, conversion to a bubble canopy on some versions of the D model eliminated a 20-deg blind spot to the rear of the aircraft. Canopies that could be jettisoned were also added to the D model to help the pilot quickly get out of a damaged aircraft.

The major criticism of the P-47 was not its survivability, but its lack of range. The P-47 had been specifically designed to escort US daylight bombers over Europe. Although it was sluggish at low altitudes, its high-altitude performance was superior to that of the P-38, and consequently it was better suited to the escort role. However, even with external fuel tanks, it could only escort B-17 formations to the German border when operating from bases in England. As a consequence, the 8th Air Force suffered its greatest B-17 losses when attacking targets inside the German border. The Luftwaffe's favorite tactic was to wait until the P-47 escort was forced to return to England because of low fuel and then engage the bomber formations with overwhelming numbers of fighters. Sometimes they would make a feint at the fighters just as they crossed the English Channel, forcing them to drop their external fuel tanks in order to maneuver, thus limiting their range. Perhaps this sturdy fighter was too rugged for the escort role; its heavily weighted components too limiting to its operational range.

After forward bases were secured on the Continent, the P-47 was able to range over Germany and take advantage of its rugged construction, destroying both air and ground targets with its eight .50 caliber guns, bombs, and rockets. It became a very successful ground-attacker and dive-bomber. It was even used in formation on medium-altitude, bad weather, level bombing missions, dropping over half of a normal B-17 bomb load on command from a ground-based radar.

Over 15,600 P-47's were built, and 12,600 of these were P-47D's, the largest US production quantity of any one model fighter. It was operational in all active theaters except Alaska, and was used by the RAF, the Free French, and the Russian forces. Perhaps the most significant statistic regarding the survivability of the Thunderbolt is the fact that all ten of the leading Thunderbolt aces survived the war.

North American P-51 Mustang

The Mustang, considered by most authorities to be the best fighter aircraft of World War II, was originally ordered into production in 1940 by the British as an improvement over the Curtiss P-40 Hawk. The Mustang Mark I aircraft built for the RAF had a laminar flow wing, a low drag fuselage, and an Allison liquid-cooled inline engine. The distinctive air scoop for the radiator was located under the wing and behind the cockpit. With the Allison engine, the Mustang did not come near meeting the RAF's specifications for speed or rate of climb at altitudes above 20,000 ft. Although it had good performance qualities at 15,000 ft, it was outclassed by both the RAF Spitfire V and the Bf-109G at the higher altitudes. As a consequence, it was used as a close support/reconnaissance aircraft by the RAF in the early years of the war.

In the spring of 1942, a US test pilot suggested that a Rolls-Royce Merlin 61 supercharged, liquid-cooled engine be fitted to the Mustang. The first converted Mustang was flown by the RAF in October 1942; while in the United States, two RAF Mustangs were converted to Packard-built Merlin engines and were flown in November 1942. Since most of the US aircraft used air-cooled radial engines, there was a debate on the wisdom of using a liquid-cooled engine, with its increased vulnerability due to the radiator and the long coolant lines being located aft of the cockpit, over an air-cooled engine. Just when the limitations of the P-38 and P-47 as long-range, high-altitude escort aircraft were becoming apparent, the decision to mass produce the P-51 was delayed. The United States wanted to wait for a more powerful air-cooled engine that was being rushed into production. Eventually, the critical need for an improved escort fighter overcame the reluctance to use the liquid-cooled engine, and the P-51B with the Packard-Merlin engine was rushed into production. The first P-51B production aircraft were delivered in June 1943, and the first P-51 group joined the 8th Air Force in November 1943. The aircraft had a pressurized cockpit, weighed 6840 lb empty, and had a top speed of 453 mph at 28,000 ft. Its armament consisted of four or six 0.50-in. Browning machine guns.

The P-51 was equipped with two self-sealing wing tanks and one self-sealing fuselage tank behind the pilot. It had armor plating on the fire wall and on the pilot's seat back and had a laminated-glass canopy. As with most fighter aircraft, the P-51 had no onboard fire-extinguishing system. The early P-51's did have vulnerable coolant lines, but one of the last models had the oil cooling core in the aft radiator replaced by a heat exchanger located in the engine compartment. This eliminated the long oil lines back to the rear cooler.

In early 1944, when the German attacks on air bases in England diminished, the olive drab finish was abandoned in favor of a polished base metal finish to increase the top speed. To accommodate taller pilots and to improve rearward vision, a full bubble canopy was introduced on the P-51D, and some pilots got their ground crews to fit rear-view mirrors in the cockpit to help keep a watch out behind. (The physical resemblance of the early P-51's without the bubble canopy to the Bf-109 caused the loss of quite a few aircraft to US guns.) A tail-warning radar system was also installed, and the 8th Air Force P-51 pilots were among the first to wear the new anti-"G" suits.

A specialized dive-bomber version of the P-51 with the Allison engine was designated the A-36; and an interesting variant of the P-51 was the P-82 Twin Mustang, which had two P-51H's joined together at midwing. This twin fuselage design was prompted by the desire to use two pilots, thus reducing pilot fatigue on very long flights in the Pacific Theater.

Over 15,500 P-51's were built, and it was credited with nearly 5000 of the 10,200 air combat victories claimed by USAAF pilots in the European Theater.

Conclusion

The successful development of these three long-range fighters was totally unexpected by the German and Japanese forces. They did not imagine that such large and rugged aircraft could fly over long ranges for protracted periods of time and then effectively engage their short-range, maneuverable, defensive fighters on an even basis. They were versatile, handsome, loved, and sometimes cursed, and they will be remembered for a long time to come for their significant contribution to the Allied victory.

A.3 THE US NAVY AND MARINE FIGHTERS OF WORLD WAR II

The US Navy had a more difficult job than the Army Air Force in developing aircraft that could outclimb, outmaneuver, outshoot, overtake, and, if necessary, outrun both land- and carrier-based enemy fighters such as the Japanese Zero. For example, carrier-based aircraft must have very good slow-speed landing and touchdown characteristics and an ample fuel supply to ensure a return to the carrier from the combat area. The wings have to fold, a tail hook is required, and the structure and landing gear have to be rugged in order to absorb the shock at touchdown. These requirements usually add considerable weight to the aircraft and can degrade performance. As a consequence, the radial air-cooled engine was generally used on carrier aircraft because it was lighter, more tolerant to abuse and to landing shock, easier to maintain, change, and store, and less vulnerable than a liquid-cooled engine of equivalent power.

The two prewar Navy carrier fighters were the Brewster Buffalo and the Grumman Wildcat. When the war started, these two aircraft were almost totally outclassed by the Zero, particularly in range, climb, and maneuverability, and the need for better fighters became painfully obvious. The result was the appearance in 1943 of the Grumman Hellcat and the Chance Vought Corsair.

Brewster F2A Buffalo

In 1935, the Navy issued a design competition for the next-generation fighter. The most promising designs were Seversky's NF-1, a Grumman biplane, the XF4F-1, and a monoplane design from the newly formed Brewster Corp., the XF2A-1. The Navy canceled the Grumman biplane design in 1936, believing the biplane had passed its prime, and issued a contract for a midwing monoplane, the XF4F-2. The Brewster design continued, with many modifications, and had its maiden flight in late 1937. Officially known as the Buffalo (a fighter named Buffalo?), other names for this stubby, all-metal, stressed-skin, flush-rivet aircraft were Peanut Special and Flying Barrel. It had many new features for a Navy fighter, including an enclosed cockpit, split flaps, and hydraulically operated, retractable landing gear that unfortunately exhibited a propensity for collapsing during a hard landing. Its armament consisted of one 0.30-in. and one 0.50-in. machine gun located in the top of the cowling, with provision for one 0.50-in. machine gun in each wing outside of the propeller arc.

The Buffalo was considered by the Navy to have better potential than the Grumman XF4F-2 and the much slower Seversky design and, consequently, won the competition in 1938. The design of the F2A-2 Buffalo continued to change through 1939 and 1940 as the lessons of combat came in from Europe, where heavier armament, faster speed, and more armor were believed to be essential in a fighter. Consequently, the Buffalo got a new Wright Cyclone engine, a new variable-pitch propeller, increased fuel capacity, improved flotation gear, and an increase in armament to two 0.50-in. cowling machine guns and one 0.50-in. machine gun in each wing. Armor was added to the cockpit and around the fuel tanks. The additional weight totaled 900 lb, bringing the aircraft to over 7000 lb loaded, and causing a very high wing loading. The penalty for the increased weight was a decrease in service ceiling, maneuverability, and maximum speed, which was slightly better than 300 mph. This decrease in performance changed a marginally acceptable fighter into an unacceptable one. The F2A-3 model had increased armor protection for the pilot, self-sealing fuel tanks, a bulletproof windscreen, and a more powerful engine. In service, the Buffalo suffered from much faulty equipment that either performed badly or simply failed to work. About 160 Buffalos were eventually built.

The Navy eventually decided the Buffalo was unsuitable for carrier operation and relegated it to the Marines. Typically, inexperienced Marine pilots flying the Buffalo against experienced Japanese pilots flying the Zero had little hope for survival, let alone winning. In the Battle of Midway, on June 4, 1942, Marine squadron VMF-221 sent 19 Buffalo's and 16 F4F's to oppose 108 Japanese aircraft. After a brief engagement, the score was a kill of six Japanese aircraft for a loss of 13 Buffalos and two missing F4F's. The Marines were bitter, and one of the survivors said that any commander who ordered a pilot up in combat in an F2A should consider the pilot lost before he left the ground. As a result of this experience, the Navy withdrew the Buffalo from combat.

Although outclassed by almost all opposing fighters, the Buffalo saw service on a surprisingly wide scale from the far north of Finland to the Dutch East Indies. It is worth noting that it was Finland's most successful fighter. Kapt Hans Wind was credited with 38.5 victories against Russian aircraft, and the total Russian and German kills by Finns flying Buffalos was 477.

Grumman F4F Wildcat

Although the Grumman XF4F-2 lost in the Navy's design competition in 1938, it was regarded as a strong second, and, consequently, Grumman was given a contract for 54 F4F-3 aircraft in August 1939. The F4F-3 was rotund and rugged like the Buffalo; not sleek and feline like the Bf-109, RAF Spitfire, and Zero. It had a strong, retractable undercarriage, the Wright Twin Wasp two-stage supercharged engine, and two 0.50-in. machine guns in each wing. The French ordered 81 aircraft basically similar to the F4F-3, with the Wright Cyclone engine and six wing-mounted 7.5-mm guns. When France fell, the British took over the contract, changed the armament back to four 0.50-in. wing guns, and called them Martlet I's.

The F4F-4, which arrived in November 1941, was the first model to be produced in large numbers. This model was officially designated the Wildcat. A hydraulic wing folding system was initially installed, but the added weight and complexity were not felt to justify it, so the wings were folded manually. It had the Pratt & Whitney Twin Wasp 14-cylinder radial air-cooled engine and a variable-pitch propeller. Three 0.50-in. machine guns were installed in each wing, and the pilot was protected by a stainless steel fire wall, 25 lb of armored windscreen, and 94 lb of armor aft of his seat. A 45-lb armor plate was located directly in front of the oil tank. The empty weight of the aircraft was nearly 6000 lb, and it had a maximum speed of 320 mph and a range of 1300 miles with two drop tanks. By the end of 1942, all Navy carrier-based fighter squadrons were equipped with the Wildcat.

Against the Zero, the Wildcat was inferior in range, ceiling, speed, and climb above 1000 ft. It had equal or better dive speed, but the Zero had a much smaller turn radius. Only through tactics (a two-plane weave for mutual protection and diving down on the enemy from above), superior firepower, and the ability to withstand damage, was an experienced Wildcat pilot (and there were not many in the beginning) able to survive a fight with a Zero.

Early in 1942, production of the F4F-4 was transferred to the Eastern Aircraft Division of General Motors, and the aircraft was called the FM-1. A lightweight version of the GM-produced Wildcat, the FM-2, was developed in late 1942 for operation from the short flight decks of the smaller carriers. This aircraft had a new, lighter Wright Cyclone engine, some models of which had a water injection feature for temporary boosted performance. The armament was reduced to four 0.50-in. machine guns in the wings.

A total of over 7200 Wildcats were produced: 1060 FM-1's, 4777 FM-2's, 280 F4F-3's, and 1169 F4F-4's. The Wildcat was credited with the destruction of over 900 enemy aircraft in aerial combat, with the loss of only 178, during the period 1941–43. For the entire war, the victory-to-loss ratio was 6.7 to 1. The memory of the heavy losses early in the war tends to overshadow the excellent record of this portly little fighter that held the line in the Pacific until the arrival of the Hellcat and Corsair.

Grumman Hellcat

The Navy ordered Grumman to develop the F6F Hellcat in June 1941, and the first production F6F-3 flew in October 1942. It had a low-mounted three-spar wing and a single Pratt & Whitney R-2800 Double Wasp 18-cylinder air-cooled radial engine with water injection for an emergency boost of power. The Hamilton Standard hydromatic propeller replaced the original Curtiss electric fully feathering propeller. It weighed 9000 lb empty and had a maximum range of 1600 miles with a centerline drop tank and a

maximum speed of about 380 mph. It was armed with six 0.50-in. Browning machine guns and could carry two 1000-lb bombs.

The design of the Hellcat somewhat resembled that of the Wildcat, but it was considerably larger. The pilot was located at the highest position amidships, giving good all-around visibility. The design lacked elegance, but like that of the Wildcat it allowed for a very rugged structure.

Since the Hellcat design was proceeding during the early days of the war, there was some thought that perhaps the rugged, heavily weighted structure and armor plating should be sacrificed for more maneuverability and range, as was done with the Zero. However, the capability to absorb damage and to protect the pilot was eventually considered to be too important to sacrifice; improved performance had to come from a more powerful engine and good aeronautical design, rather than from a lighter-weight airframe. (In contemporary terms, vulnerability was not to be increased in order to gain a reduction in susceptibility.) Consequently, the Hellcat was designed to be tough. It had 212 lb of armor to protect the pilot, the oil tank, and the oil cooler. Initially, the armor plate located behind the pilot's head was shaped and sized for the head, but was not thick enough to stop the shrapnel from the Zero's 20-mm cannon shells from penetrating it. Its fuel tanks were located in the center wing section and were self-sealing, and it had an armored glass screen behind a curved plexiglass windscreen. Two variants of the F6F-3, the -3E and -3N, were developed for night fighting by installing a radar set in a pod attached to the starboard wing. In order to improve the poor night vision from the cockpit, red instrument lights were installed to cut down on cockpit glare, and the curved windscreen was replaced by a flat-faced screen.

The F6F-5 model appeared in 1944 and had a flat-faced windshield, red instrument panel lighting, a strengthened tail assembly, 242 lb of armor, racks for six 5-in. rockets, and a special smooth finish. The armor plate behind the pilot's head was expanded to provide protection over a greater area, and the thickness was increased to stop the 20-mm shrapnel. Its empty weight was 9238 lb and its maximum speed was 380 mph. Some late -5 models had a pair of wing-mounted 20-mm cannons in addition to four .50 caliber machine guns.

The Hellcat was famous for its ability to absorb damage and continue to fly. Retired Navy captain David McCampbell (with 34 air victories—nine of them on one mission), in an interview for *Wings* magazine, stated that on one mission in his Hellcat he was shot up badly by antiaircraft fire over Marcus Island. His Hellcat had a belly tank on fire, a hydraulic fire in the fuselage, partial loss of aileron control, loss of left rudder control, and loss of hydraulic power to lower the wheels and flaps. Nevertheless, the Hellcat brought McCampbell back to the carrier 135 miles away. McCampbell said that he never saw a Hellcat go down in flames or explode when hit. He attributed this to the superbly designed self-sealing fuel tanks.

The Hellcat was considered to be superior to the Zero in speed, dive, and altitude capabilities, but maneuverability and low-level climb rate were inferior. Thus, the Hellcat tactics were essentially the same as those of the

Wildcat; pilots would generally avoid dogfighting, with its tight turns and loops in which the Zero excelled, and would attack from above, diving down on the enemy. Once on the tail of a Zero, the Hellcat could usually stay with it in a turn long enough to get off a short burst from the six 0.50-in. guns, which was sufficient to destroy the highly vulnerable Japanese fighter.

The total number of Hellcats produced was over 12,000: 4402 -3's, and 7870 -5's, 3578 of which were produced from January to November 1945, when production was stopped. The Japanese pilots that encountered the Hellcat considered it to be the best US aircraft in fighter-versus-fighter combat, and at the end of the war, the Hellcat accounted for 4947 of the 6477 enemy aircraft destroyed in the air by US Navy pilots. Shore-based US Marine squadrons brought the total up to 5156 Hellcat victories. During the war, the Hellcat enjoyed a 19 to 1 kill-to-loss ratio.

Chance Vought F4U Corsair

The Chance Vought F4U Corsair was the eventual result of a Navy design contest of Feb. 1, 1938, for a single seat shipboard fighter with a particularly good service ceiling and speed. The F4U design was the most impressive of four designs and was built around the Pratt & Whitney Double Wasp engine, the largest and most powerful air-cooled radial, which drove the largest propeller ever considered for a fighter, the Hamilton Standard three-bladed, constant-speed, fully feathering hydromatic. The unusual inverted nonfolding gull-wing configuration solved the problems of accommodating the large propeller, while keeping the landing gear length and ground angle acceptable, and simultaneously providing a good angle at the wing root for minimum drag. The airframe consisted of relatively heavy frames and stringers and a thick skin, thus reducing the number of longitudinal members. A new spot welding technique was used, resulting in an

exceptionally smooth finish. The prototype had one 0.30-in. and one 0.50-in. gun in the upper decking of the forward fuselage and a single 0.50-in. gun in each wing. The F4U-1 first flew in May 1940, and was indirectly responsible for the US Army Air Corps allowing Pratt & Whitney to abandon their liquid-cooled engine program.

Extensive modifications were made to the F4U-1 prior to production based upon the British combat experience in Europe. The need for better armament was met by installing two, and later three, 0.50-in. machine guns with greatly increased ammunition capacity in each outer wing panel outside of the propeller arc, and removing the fuselage guns. The integral fuel tanks in the wing leading edges, which initially incorporated a carbon dioxide vapor dilution system for inerting the ullage, were removed, and a large self-sealing fuselage tank was installed near the aircraft center of gravity. This required the cockpit to be moved 3 ft aft, resulting in an extremely long length of fuselage in front of the pilot, obscuring his forward view, particularly during landing. One hundred and fifty pounds of armor were added around the cockpit and oil tank, rearward vision was improved, the canopy was made jettisonable, and IFF was installed. All Corsairs had a provision for automatically pressurizing the main fuel tank at altitudes above 12,000 ft. The pressure could be manually released in the event of a fuel tank puncture or prior to a crash landing, and all F4U models were equipped with an emergency landing gear extension system activated by a carbon dioxide bottle.

The early design of the Corsair did not prove to be suitable for carrier operations. The principal trouble was the restricted vision during deck landing caused by the long forward fuselage. The aircraft also tended to bounce and swing badly on touchdown. The cockpit was raised, and a frameless clear-view canopy was employed to improve the forward view. Several other changes improved the touchdown behavior, such as changing from a solid to a pneumatic tail-wheel tire. It was not until the end of 1944 that the Corsair was used operationally from a carrier.

In 1943, the water injection engine was added. At least one particular Navy lieutenant owed his life to the temporary boost in power provided by the water. According to the Navy, the 25-year-old pilot found himself in a position that is a nightmare to every combat pilot. He was only 50 ft over the water, and three Zeros were close on the tail of his plane, two on the right, astern, and one on the left. If he pulled up, he would be at the mercy of the Japanese Zeros, and he was in the same predicament if he turned right or left. It was then that the young lieutenant flicked the water injection switch. The resulting burst of speed took him out of the range of the enemy guns.

Some Corsairs were given a new armament consisting of four wing-mounted 20-mm cannons in place of the six 0.50-in. machine guns. However, only 200 Corsairs with the 20-mm cannons were produced, since most pilots preferred the machine guns. Several radar-equipped Corsair models were also developed.

The Corsair first saw action at Guadalcanal in early 1943. Like all US carrier fighters of World War II, the Corsair was found to be very rugged.

US Marine 1st Lt. Kenneth Walsh, a Corsair ace, was flying his Corsair over Guadalcanal on Aug. 15, 1943, when he encountered an overwhelming number of Japanese Val dive bombers and Zero fighters. He succeeded in destroying two Vals and one Zero before his aircraft was riddled by 20-mm cannon fire. His right wing was full of holes, his hydraulic lines were severed, the vertical stabilizer was shredded, and the right tire was blown. Lt. Walsh managed to elude his attackers and return home for a successful crash landing. Walsh was uninjured, but the Corsair was so badly damaged that it was declared a total loss.

The F4U-1 weighed nearly 9000 lb empty, had a maximum speed of nearly 400 mph, and had a maximum range of 2200 miles with a drop tank. In comparison with the Hellcat, a Navy evaluation board in May of 1944 concluded that the F4U is "...a better fighter, a better bomber, and an equally suitable carrier aircraft compared with the F6F." Over 12,500 Corsairs were produced by Chance, Vought, Goodyear (FG), and Brewster (F3A). The US Corsair destroyed 2140 Japanese aircraft with a corresponding loss of 189 aircraft in aerial combat. Further F4U losses included 349 from antiaircraft fire, 230 from other causes, 692 losses on nonoperational flights, and 164 in crashes on carriers or airfields. There were approximately 64,000 operational sorties, 54,500 from land and 9600 from carriers. The life of this spectacular aircraft, the last piston-engined fighter to be produced in the United States, was not to end at the conclusion of World War II.

Summary

At the beginning of the war, the Navy Wildcat and Buffalo fighters, at the hands of inexperienced pilots, were generally not survivable when matched against the experienced Japanese Zero pilot. The two new fighters, the Hellcat and Corsair, gave the United States a capability to match or exceed the performance of the Zero, without the vulnerability of the Zero. The Japanese did not intend to fight a prolonged war and consequently did not make sufficient plans for improving their aircraft. The US Navy pilot received more and better training (three to five times more flight hours before assignment to an operational unit) and had the opportunity for rotation for R&R, a luxury the Japanese pilot did not have. Consequently, as more US pilots survived and gained valuable experience, the ratio of experienced US pilots to experienced Japanese pilots began to grow heavily in favor of the US pilot. Thus, the combination of rugged aircraft with comparable or better performance, better crew training, experienced leaders, and improved communications and control gave the US Navy pilot a very good chance of surviving an encounter with his enemy.

A.4 WORLD WAR II AIRCRAFT FROM OTHER COUNTRIES

Messerschmitt Bf-109

The primary opponent of the Allies in the European Theater was the Bf-109, flown by the Germans, the Italians, and the Hungarians. (Several were also flown by the Swiss for neutrality defense only.) The Bf-109 was designed in 1934 by Professor Willy Messerschmitt for the Bayerische Flugzeugwerke to be an all-metal, lightweight, maneuverable, single seat, low-wing, cantilever monoplane fighter with a liquid-cooled engine. It had its teething troubles, but it was a highly successful combat aircraft in the early years of the war. In spite of its problems, the final version, the Bf-109K, was still in production at the end of the war. The K model weighed nearly 7500 lb fully loaded and had a top speed of 377 mph at sea level and 450 mph at 20,000 ft. It had a range of 350 miles at 20,000 ft and 6800 lb. It had a relatively thin wing and small wing area, resulting in a high wing loading compared to its contemporaries.

The armament on the Bf-109 underwent many changes. Originally designed to carry two 7.9-mm machine guns in the upper decking of the nose, the 1939 E model, the first true mass production version, also carried two wing-mounted 20-mm cannons. A third 20-mm cannon was installed in the nose of the 109E-3 to be fired through the airscrew boss, but the engine-mounted cannon was unreliable and consequently was seldom used. Later models carried a 15-mm cannon in the nose, and some had a 20-mm cannon mounted in a gondola under each wing. One heavily armed anti-bomber version of the G model carried a 30-mm cannon that fired high-explosive projectiles through the airscrew boss, two 13-mm machine guns above the engine, and two 20-mm cannons in the underwing gondolas. There were conflicting opinions among the German pilots concerning the armament. Some favored more of the lighter-caliber machine guns, while others preferred the more destructive cannon. However, the cannon pod, required because of the extreme thinness of the wing, adversely affected maneuverability.

There were many variants of the aircraft. For example, one of the E model versions was modified for low-flying, attack roles in North Africa. These aircraft had armor bolted beneath the engine and the coolant radiators. Many aircraft carried bombs weighing up to 551 lb and were the first land-based fighter bombers.

The Bf-109 Daimler-Benz engine was especially noted for its fuel injection system that prevented fuel starvation during negative g maneuvers, and the engine in the G-5 model incorporated a methanol and water injection system. The two agents were carried in a jettisonable tank under the fuselage and were fed to the engine in times of emergency to temporarily boost the power output. The G model was also the first to have a pressurized cockpit, a feature that had become necessary due to the increasing amount of combat at the higher altitudes. The Galland hood on the G model gave better visibility.

Even though constructed with weight savings in mind, the Bf-109 still had a rugged structure. (An isolated incident in 1937 in Spain in which a Bf-109 lost its tail in a high-speed dive led to the rumor that the aircraft would fall apart during high-stress maneuvers.) The aircraft typically broke into three parts when crash-landed. The cockpit area was one of these parts, and its tendency to maintain structural integrity saved the life of many pilots, as did the armor plating located behind the pilot's seat. The wings were of single-spar construction, and all of the internal fuel was carried below and behind the pilot. The windscreen was made of armorglass and was surrounded by an armored frame.

Although the Bf-109 was a popular fighter, the pilots were very uncomfortable in the cramped cockpit, and flying the aircraft was an exhausting occupation. It could hardly be maneuvered at speeds over 400 mph, and it was notoriously difficult to handle during takeoff and landing. Its narrow-tracked landing gear, high angle of incidence, and tendency to swing on takeoff and landing caused the loss of some 1500 fighters between the beginning of the war in September 1939 and the autumn of 1941.

From 1939 through 1943, the Bf-109 ranked as a superior fighter. Several fighter wings had 1000 victories before 1942, and some eventually exceeded 7000. However, toward the end of the war, the Bf-109, faced with P-51 Mustang and P-47 Thunderbolt opponents, the Luftwaffe's lack of trained pilots, the use of wood in place of aluminum due to material shortages, and construction by conscripted foreign laborers, suffered severe losses. No exact records are available on the total number of aircraft produced, but it has been estimated that more than 33,000 were built between 1935 and 1945, representing more than 60% of the total number of single-engined fighters produced by Germany. Czechoslovakia and Spain continued to manufacture the Bf-109 after the end of the war.

Ilyushin IL-2

The Russian-built Ilyushin IL-2 Sturmovik was possibly the most heavily used aircraft in World War II. Over 36,000 IL-2's and 6000 follow-on IL-10's were built between 1941 and 1945. It was designed in 1938 specifically for the purpose of destroying tanks, and in time would come to be known as the "Flying Tank" and the "Black Death." Its empty weight was somewhat over 7100 lb, and its maximum speed ranged from 260 to 310 mph. It carried underwing racks for rockets and bombs and internal wing cells for bombs. One 20-, 23-, or 37-mm antitank cannon was installed in each wing.

The Ilyushin design incorporated many features for reducing vulnerability. A single, compact, welded-steel armor cell weighing over 1500 lb encompassed the entire lower portion of the nose and center of the fuselage and provided protection for the pilot, the liquid-cooled engine and radiator,

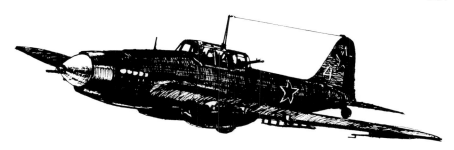

the fuel tanks, and other critical components of the aircraft. The armored cell was not parasitic, but was part of the stressed airframe. The rear section of the aircraft fuselage was wooden, but the wings and empennage were made from hard duraluminum. It had self-sealing fuel tanks that were made from hard aluminum sheets covered with a rubberized fabric. The engine exhaust gases were cooled and piped into the fuel tanks to inert the tank ullage, thus reducing the possibility of a fire or explosion.

The early versions of the IL-2 were single seat and, although well protected from forward ground fire, were highly susceptible to air attack from above and from the rear. They were also vulnerable from these aspects. This problem was solved by adding a rear seat that was equipped with a rearward-facing 12.7-mm machine gun. When the first IL-2's carrying rear-seat gunners appeared, a number of German fighters were shot down when they made their usual attack on the IL-2's previously susceptible and vulnerable tail. This modification led to dramatically reduced losses, and the IL-2 became almost indestructible. Yakolev, the famous Russian airplane designer, in his book on 50 years of Soviet aircraft production states that neither the Allies nor the Soviet Union's enemies had anything similar to the IL-2.

Erich Hartmann, the Luftwaffe's leading ace with 352 victories in World War II, said that the Sturmovik was the hardest aircraft to destroy once hit. He saw machine gun and cannon rounds bounce off the Flying Tank on countless occasions. Hitting the IL-2 was not very easy either. About the only tactic that was successful was to approach from behind and below and attempt to fire into the wooden fuselage.

The Flying Tank was also very effective in its mission of destroying tanks. When the German offensive at Kursk took place on July 5, 1943, IL-2's, armed with 37-mm cannons, destroyed 70 German tanks in 20 minutes. The aircraft played a central role in the Soviet effort in World War II and was described by Stalin to be as necessary to the Red Army as air and bread.

Mitsubishi A6M (Zeke) Zero

A contrast to the rugged designs of fighters from most of the other countries was that of the Japanese A6M Zeke, more popularly known as the Zero. The Zero was introduced in 1940 and quickly showed its superiority over its early opponents: the Chinese fighters, the Curtiss P-40, the Curtiss

Hawk, and the Brewster Buffalo. The Zero was even flying combat sorties of over 1400 miles in China, a feat considered impossible by all other aircraft producers. The Zero maintained its superiority until 1943, when the United States started introducing P-38 Lightnings, F4U Corsairs, and F6F Hellcats to the Pacific Theater.

The model A6M6, produced in 1944, weighed nearly 4000 lb empty and 6500 lb fully loaded. It had a maximum speed of 290 mph at sea level and 345 mph at 20,000 ft. Its maximum range with a normal fuel load was 1130 miles at 150 mph. It carried two 20-mm cannons and two 13.2-mm machine guns in the wings, and one 13.7-mm machine gun and one 7.7-mm machine gun in the upper decking of the engine cowling.

The Zero was famous for its range and maneuverability and was notorious for its vulnerability. Jiro Horikoshi, the lead aeronautical engineer for Mitsubishi during the development and manufacture of the Zero, said, "The Zero was a product of a given set of circumstances. The design answered specifically the unique requirements of Japanese pilots, who stressed the factor of unexcelled maneuverability. Much has been said of the Zero fighter's lack of pilot protection devices, such as armor plate and self-sealing fuel tanks. These items were omitted from the Zero at the insistence of our pilots. To them, fighting in the air meant only one thing: attack. They would not tolerate the encumbering weight solely for protective purposes. They felt that the gain in performance resulting from minimum weight more than compensated for a lack of safety features, which, to them, represented unnecessary luxury." A specific example of the Japanese philosophy is the fact that many Japanese pilots flew without parachutes because they found the harness irksome, and it prevented them from becoming an integral part of their aircraft.

In the initial stages of the war, the Japanese philosophy proved to be valid, based upon the loss ratios of Zero's to opponents. However, many of the best Japanese pilots were killed in the early years, and when eventually opposed by Allied aircraft possessing greater firepower, less vulnerable design, and increased maneuverability, the Zero lost its superiority. As happened to Germany, the lack of capable pilots and the material shortages contributed to severe loss rates as the war progressed.

Demand for a new and better aircraft led to the development by Mitsubishi of the A7M Reppu or Hurricane. However, production of the Hurricane was delayed, and the Japanese Navy was forced to make do with modifications to the Zero. After the Philippine Sea disaster, the specifications for the A6M5C included (for the very first time) protection for the pilot. Several survivability features were to be put in the A6M5C and the A6M6C models, including bullet-resistant glass for the cockpit windshield, a toughened-steel plate under the pilot's seat, automatic carbon dioxide fire extinguishers for the fuel tanks, water-methanol injection for a temporary boost in engine power, and self-sealing fuselage and wing tanks. However, the new and more powerful engines required to support the additional weight without loss of performance were not fully tested and ready for installation. They were also drastically overrated, as well as unreliable.

The Zero was still in production at the end of the war, and in spite of technical problems, a natural disaster in the form of an earthquake, and the devastation caused by the Allied bombing, the last version produced by Mitsubishi in 1945, the A6M8, was a very good aircraft. The airframe had been strengthened, a new engine manufacturer had been selected, and the survivability features of the A6M5 and A6M6 models were retained and improved upon. However, it still weighed less than half that of a Grumman Hellcat. It is questionable whether this new aircraft, improved as it was, could compete against the more massive, rugged, capable, and numerous American aircraft flown by skilled and experienced pilots.

Nearly 11,000 Zeros were eventually produced, more than any other wartime Japanese aircraft. The last version was first flown in May 1945, but no production aircraft had been completed by the end of the war. Had the war been short, as originally planned by the Japanese, the Zero would have reigned supreme. Instead, it suffered horrendous losses in the last two years of the war, and one of its final roles was that of a suicide aircraft.

Selected Bibliography

Air Force Historical Foundation, *Soviet Aviation and Air Power: A Historical View*, Westview Press, Inc., Boulder, Colorado, 1977.

Alexander, J., *Russian Aircraft Since 1940*, Putnam & Co., Ltd., New York, 1975.

Boeing Co., letters to the author, Feb. 27, 1980.

Caidin, M., *Fork-Tailed Devil: The P-38*, Ballantine Books, New York, 1973.

Coffey, T. M., *Decision Over Schweinfurt*, David McKay Co., New York, 1977.

The Encyclopedia of American Aircraft, edited by Anthony Robinson, Galahad Books, New York, 1979.

Fighter Pilot, edited by S. Ulanoff, Doubleday & Co., Inc., New York, 1962.

Freeman, R. A., *B-17 Fortress at War*, Charles Scribner's Sons, New York, 1977.

Green, W., *Famous Bombers of the Second World War*, 2nd ed., McDonald and James Publishers Ltd., London, 1976.

Green, W., *Famous Fighters of the Second World War*, Doubleday & Co., Inc., New York, 1975.

Gunston, W., *Aircraft of World War II*, Crescent Books, New York, 1980.

Jablonski, E., *Flying Fortress*, Doubleday and Co., New York, 1965.

Jackson, R., *Aerial Combat*, Galahad Books, New York, 1976.

Johnson, R. S. with Caidin, M., *Thunderbolt*, Ballantine Books, New York, 1959.

Jones, R. V., *The Wizard War: British Scientific Intelligence 1939–1945*, Coward, McCann & Geoghegan, Inc., New York, 1978.

Okumiya, M. and Horikoshi, J., with Caidin, M., *Zero!*, E. P. Dutton & Co., Inc., New York, 1956.

Owens, W. E., *As Briefed—A Family History of the 384th Bombardment Group*, Walter E. Owens, 1946.

Peaslee, B. J., *Heritage of Valor: The Eighth Air Force in World War II*, J. B. Lippincott Co., Philadelphia, 1964.

Price, A., "Magic Carpet to Survival," *Aviation Week & Space Technology*, Dec. 15, 1980, Vol. 113, No. 24, p. 40.

Price, A., "The Bomber in World War II," Charles Scribner's Sons, New York, 1979.

Ryan, C., *A Bridge Too Far*, Simon & Schuster, New York, 1974.

Toliver, R. F. and Constable, T., *The Blond Knight of Germany*, Doubleday & Co., Inc., New York, 1970.

United States Army and Air Force Fighters 1916–1961, edited by B. Robertson, Harleyford Publications Ltd., Arms and Armor Press, London, 1961.

VanIshoven, A., *Messerschmitt Bf-109 at War*, Charles Scribner's Sons, New York, 1977.

Willmot, H. P., *B-17 Flying Fortress*, Chartwell Books, Inc., New Jersey, 1980.

Yakovlev, A. S., *Fifty Years of Soviet Aircraft Construction*, NASA-TT-F-627, 1970.

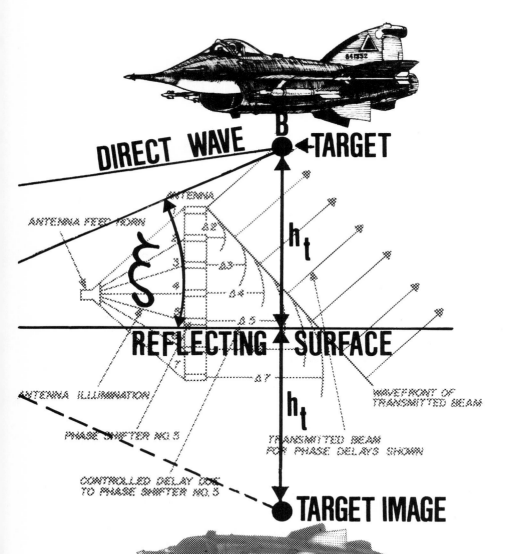

DIRECT WAVE ← TARGET

B

h_t

REFLECTING SURFACE

h_t

TARGET IMAGE

APPENDIX B.   AN INTRODUCTION TO RADAR AND INFRARED RADIATION FUNDAMENTALS

B.1   ELECTROMAGNETIC RADIATION

Radar, infrared, and visual detection, tracking, and guidance devices are designed to sense electromagnetic (EM) radiation that is either reflected or emitted by an aircraft. Electromagnetic radiation can be thought of as combined electric and magnetic fields (at right angles) that propagate through a medium as a harmonically oscillating, transverse wave, as shown in Fig. B.1. The EM wave has a frequency f, a wavelength λ, and a velocity of propagation c. EM wavelengths span the range from infinitely long to infinitely short. In the Earth's atmosphere, the radiation wave velocity is essentially the same as the speed of light in a vacuum.

The orientation of the electric field of the wave with respect to a reference plane defines the wave's polarization. When the electric field of the propagating wave remains in one plane, the wave is said to be linearly polarized. A linearly polarized wave in which the electric field is vertical with respect to the Earth is said to be vertically polarized. A wave with a horizontal electric field is horizontally polarized. The power of the EM wave is proportional to the square of the maximum electrical field strength.

Electromagnetic waves exhibit the phenomena of reflection, transmission, absorption, interference, diffraction, and refraction. Reflection refers to the scattering of an EM wave that impinges on an electrically conducting body. Transmission refers to the passage of the EM wave through a medium or body, and absorption is the process in which the energy in the EM wave is converted into heat within a medium or body. Interference is the vectorial addition of two or more waves, and diffraction is the bending or diffuse scattering of a wave around a relatively sharp edge. Refraction is the bending of a wave as it propagates across a boundary between two media with different velocities of propagation.

Electromagnetic radiation can also be thought of as the propagation of little packages of energy, known as light quanta or photons, whose energy is directly proportional to the "frequency" of the wave. The treatment of EM radiation as a wave appears to be more appropriate for the relatively long wavelengths, such as radar, whereas for the relatively short wavelengths, such as the infrared and visible portions of the EM spectrum, both the wave theory and the photon theory can be used.

Electromagnetic radiation is emitted by accelerated charges, such as electrons. Thus, harmonically oscillating electrons emit an EM wave, and electrons that move from a higher energy level orbit to a lower energy level orbit within an atom give off EM waves in the form of photons.

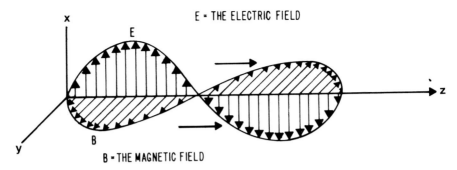

Fig. B.1   Electromagnetic wave.

B.2   RADAR

Generic Radar Systems, Operations, and Terminology

A typical radar (*radio detection and ranging*) system includes a transmitter, one or more antennas, and a receiver. The transmitter generates
electromagnetic radiation known as the signal, usually at a single frequency.
The signal is either a continuous wave (CW radar) or one or more short
pulses (pulse radar), with each pulse containing many wavelengths. The
signal is sent from the transmitter to a feed horn that illuminates the
antenna, much like an ordinary flashlight, where the antenna is the reflector
and the light bulb is the feed horn. The signal from the feed horn is reflected
from (reradiated by) the antenna and becomes focused in space in either a
fully focused "pencil" beam or a semifocused "fan" beam, depending upon
the shape of the antenna. The signal then propagates into free space at the
velocity of light. If the signal strikes an electromagnetically reflecting object,
such as an airplane, or a mountain, or rain, the incident signal can be
reradiated or scattered in many directions. Some of the scattered signal,
called the echo, will be in the direction of the radar receiver. (Echoes from
nonaircraft bodies are called clutter.) The antenna used by the receiver to
intercept the echo can be the same as that used to radiate the signal, or it
may be a separate antenna. (Radar systems in which the receiver is
collocated with the transmitter are called monostatic radars. Those systems
that widely separate the transmitter and receiver are referred to as bistatic
radars.) The return signal is then processed by the receiver to extract
information on the reflecting object, such as its relative radial velocity, and
its location in space.

For monostatic pulse radars, the slant range of an aircraft from the radar
R can be obtained by measuring the time delay Δt between the time a pulse
is transmitted and the time when the echo is received. The pulse travels a
total distance of $2R$ from the antenna to the aircraft and back at the speed
of light. Thus, the range to the aircraft is given by

$$\text{Target range} = R = c\Delta t/2 \qquad (B.1)$$

The general angular location of the aircraft with respect to the antenna is provided by the direction the antenna is pointing when the echo is received. As the radar continues to transmit pulses and receive echoes, the aircraft's flight path can be tracked. Additional processing of the echo can provide other information, such as the aircraft's radial velocity with respect to the radar antenna and the discrimination of a moving target from stationary clutter.

Air-defense radars fall into two broad categories: surveillance radars and weapon- or fire-control radars. Surveillance radars are used to detect the presence of aircraft at long ranges and to provide the general view of the overall situation in the air needed to control the defense. They are also referred to as search, acquisition, early warning (EW), or ground controlled intercept (GCI) radars. (The GCI radar is used to direct interceptors to hostile aircraft.) These radars normally operate as pulse radars at relatively low frequencies and long pulse widths and use large, rotating antennas with fan beams with relatively wide beamwidths. Figure B.2 is an illustration of a surveillance radar. The target's azimuth and range are usually presented in polar coordinates to the radar operator on a plan position indicator cathode ray tube (CRT), known as a PPI scope. Each time the aircraft is painted by the radar scan a bright spot or blip appears on the PPI. Target tracking can be accomplished by surveillance radars as they continue searching by following the location of the target echo or blip on the PPI. This is known as track-while-scan. When the decision is made that the target is a threat and is within the range of a weapon-control radar, the target track information is passed to the assigned weapon-control radar.

Weapon-control radars normally operate over a small volume of space and handle relatively few targets. They may be stationary, or they may be mounted on a mobile platform. Their function is to provide the information necessary to allow the weapon to be brought to bear on the target and to destroy it. The output from the weapon-control radar is used by the fire-control system to determine the target's flight path and to predict its future position so the weapon platform or propagator can be pointed in the

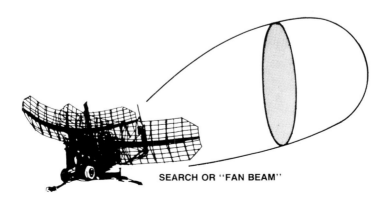

SEARCH OR "FAN BEAM"

Fig. B.2   Typical surveillance radar.

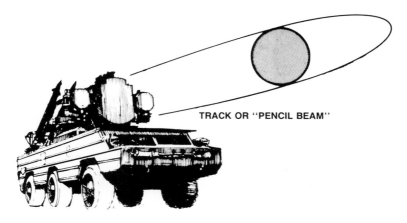

TRACK OR "PENCIL BEAM"

Fig. B.3   Typical weapon-control radar.

correct direction to cause an intercept. Consequently, these radars must provide accurate measurements of the target location in angle, and/or range, and/or velocity. Accurate measurements can be obtained using relatively short pulse widths, high signal frequencies, and narrow beamwidths. Figure B.3 is an illustration of a weapon-control radar.

Radar Signal Parameters

Some important parameters of the radar signal are the units of signal power, normally watts or decibels, the signal characteristics of frequency and wavelength, the parameters associated with pulse and CW radars, and the features of Doppler and pulse compression.

Decibels.   One common unit of measurement in radar is the decibel. The decibel is a term related to the common (base 10) logarithm of the ratio of two numerical values of the same quantity. The following example will serve to demonstrate the use of this system of measurement.

Suppose there are two radars whose output signal electric field voltages are $V_1 = 5$ V and $V_2 = 10$ V. The ratio of their output is 2. By definition, this ratio of voltages is expressed in decibels as

$$\text{Voltage ratio in dB} = 20\log_{10}(V_2/V_1) = 20\log_{10}(2) \simeq 6\text{ dB} \qquad (\text{B.2a})$$

This definition holds for both voltage and current ratios. It can be converted to a rule for power ratios, P_1/P_2. Note that

$$20\log_{10}(V_2/V_1) = 2(10)\log_{10}(V_2/V_1) = 10\log_{10}(V_2/V_1)^2$$

Since power is directly proportional to the square of the voltage, power can be measured with the decibel using the expression

$$\text{Power ratio in dB} = 10 \log_{10}(P_2/P_1) \qquad \text{(B.2b)}$$

Thus, the radar power ratio is

$$10 \log_{10}(10^2/5^2) = 10 \log_{10}(100/25) \simeq 6 \text{ dB}$$

Some common increments in decibels should be memorized to allow easier and quicker comprehension of the magnitudes involved. Since the base of the common logarithm is 10, the following relationships exist:

Power Ratio		Decibels
0.01	corresponds to	−20
0.1		−10
1.0		0
10.0		10
100.0		20
1000.0		30

Another value to memorize is the 3-dB increment. Three dB correspond to 1.995, which is nearly 2. Thus,

Power Ratio		Decibels
2	corresponds to	3
4		6
8		9

Another frequently referenced quantity in radar is the half-power point, or the point where the power has been reduced to one-half of its maximum value. Since twice the power is equal to $+3$ dB, one-half of the power is -3 dB, or

$$10 \log_{10}(1/2) = -3 \text{ dB}$$

The point at which power is reduced to one-half of its value is therefore commonly referred to as the -3-dB point.

The decibel unit of measurement is convenient to use in radar equations to compute numerical values, since the addition of decibels corresponds to the multiplication of numbers, and the subtraction of decibels is equivalent to division. Each number is first converted to decibels by using a reference level of unity. For example, the equation

$$2 \times 10 \times 4 \div 100 = 0.8$$

becomes

$$3 + 10 + 6 - 20 = -1 \text{ dB} = 0.7943 \simeq 0.8$$

in decibels.

In radar, the standard reference level for power is 1 W. However, in electronic countermeasure work, the standard reference level for power is not 1 W; instead, 1 mW is often used as a compromise value between the large transmitted power levels and the extremely small power levels of the radar echo. When a power level is compared to a standard of 1 mW (10^{-3} W), it is written with the units dBm, or decibels with respect to 1 mW. For example, a power level of 100 W would be expressed as

$$10 \log_{10}(100/0.001) = 10 \log_{10}(10^5) = 50 \text{ dBm}$$

Signal Characteristics

An important aspect of the operation of radar systems is the ability to compare, classify, and quantitatively discuss the differences and similarities in signals emitted from various radars. Each radar signal has a characteristic "fingerprint" that specifically identifies it and categorizes it as belonging to a particular group or radar type. The first characteristic is the signal or carrier frequency f, which is a measure of the number of harmonic oscillations in the signal within a specified time interval. The period of the signal frequency is T, the time interval for one cycle of oscillation, and is given by

$$\text{Period} = T = 1/f \tag{B.3}$$

The two standard terms commonly used to denote the carrier frequency are megahertz (MHz equivalent to 10^6 cycles/s) and gigahertz (GHz equivalent to 10^9 cycles/s).

Radar signals are electromagnetic radiation and therefore propagate at the speed of light. The speed of light is denoted by the symbol c and, in the Earth's atmosphere, is approximately given by

$$\text{Signal velocity} = c = 300 \text{ m}/\mu\text{s} \tag{B.4}$$

which is a good number to commit to memory early in any work with electromagnetic wave theory.

Another important parameter used in defining signals is the wavelength of the signal frequency λ. It can be defined either as the distance the radiated signal travels during one period of the carrier frequency or as the physical length of the wave at one instant in time. The wavelength can be computed from

$$\text{Wavelength} = \lambda = cT = c/f \tag{B.5}$$

Modern radars normally operate in a frequency range from 200 MHz to 35 GHz. The radar signals are commonly referred to as microwaves, where the microwave region is defined as that region of the electromagnetic spectrum with wavelengths falling between the limits of 1 m (300 MHz) and 1 mm (300 GHz). The microwave portion of the electromagnetic spectrum is presented in Fig. B.4. The specific frequency ranges or bands shown in Fig.

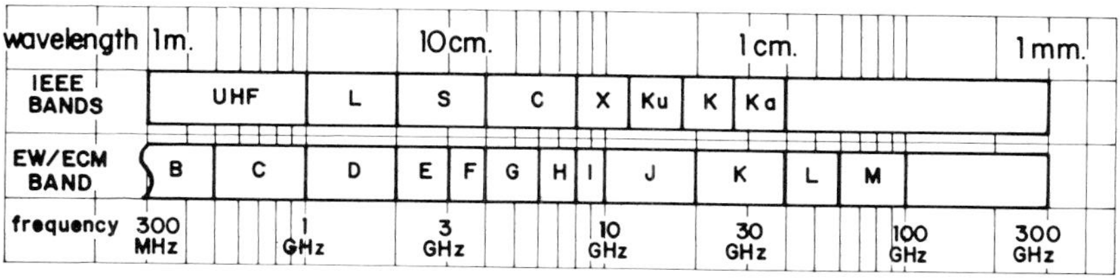

Fig. B.4   Microwave frequency spectrum.

B.4 can be denoted using either one of two standards of reference. Radar engineers use a standard developed and agreed upon by the Institute of Electrical and Electronic Engineers (IEEE). Separate electronic warfare band designations have been assigned by the military to facilitate the operational control of electronic countermeasures techniques. The military designations are the ones primarily used when discussing countermeasures and are the most recent of the two designation systems. Care should be taken when naming a signal by its band designator because certain letters of the alphabet refer to different bands, depending upon the system being referenced. This text will always utilize the countermeasures band designators.

Pulse and CW Radar

In general, radars can be divided into one of two general categories: pulse radars and continuous wave radars. Both types of radar have advantages and disadvantages. In order to compare these two types, some additional signal parameters for pulse radars must be defined.

The pulse from a pulse radar can have any type of a waveform from a simple single short burst, obtained by switching the carrier frequency on and then off, to multiple pulse patterns. Figure B.5 shows the time history of the output of a multiple pulse radar signal. Three parameters that apply to pulse radar signals are appropriately named the pulse repetition frequency (PRF) f_r, the pulse repetition time interval (PRI), where PRI $= 1/$PRF, and the pulse width τ.

When multiple pulses are transmitted, the pulse repetition frequency limits the maximum unambiguous range of the radar R_u. The first pulse echo that returns from a distant target after a second pulse is transmitted could be interpreted as the echo from the second pulse from a close target, hence the term maximum unambiguous range. Since the radar sends out a pulse of energy and then listens for the echo until a new pulse is sent out, the maximum time allowed for the first pulse to make the round trip from the radar to the aircraft and back is determined by the time interval between pulses, or the pulse repetition interval. This time can be expressed approximately as

$$\text{Maximum time for round trip} = \text{PRI} = \frac{\text{Round trip distance}}{\text{Velocity of propagation}} = \frac{2R_u}{c} \quad \text{(B.6a)}$$

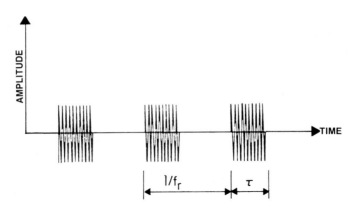

Fig. B.5   Typical multiple burst pattern.

Hence, the maximum unambiguous range is given by

$$\text{Maximum unambiguous range} = R_u = \frac{c(\text{PRI})}{2} \qquad \text{(B.6b)}$$

Fire-control radars that track targets at relatively close ranges use very high pulse repetition frequencies compared with those of the early warning and GCI radars, which normally operate at long ranges.

Pulse width is an important radar parameter for two reasons. First, it determines the amount of energy in the signal. If the output power of a radar is constant, the total energy in the signal can be increased by leaving the power on for a longer period of time, thus increasing the pulse width. For radars with very short pulse widths, a large power level is required to get sufficient energy into the signal in the short time that the transmitter is turned on. Conversely, the continuous wave radars normally operate at a much lower power level because they are transmitting continuously.

A second factor affected by the pulse width is the target resolution in range ΔR, or how far apart in slant range do two targets have to be in order to be resolved as two distinct targets? When the pulse of electromagnetic energy transmitted into space is returned from the target, it may be sampled in the receiver by an electronic circuit called a range or tracking gate. A range gate is a switch which opens at a time after the pulse is sent coinciding with a prescribed range and closes at a set time later corresponding to a longer range. The interval between the opening and the closing of the switch is called the range bin. Because the receiver wants to receive the entire pulse width, the sampling circuit must be divided by the range gates into range bins that will sample the echo for an equal length of time. This sample time is the target range resolution cell. The minimum range resolution cell size that can intercept an entire pulse width is $c\tau$. Now consider two closely spaced aircraft. Any pulse that strikes the two aircraft will cause two echoes.

The two echoes can be resolved as two targets provided that the leading edge of the second echo does not overlap the trailing edge of the first echo. Thus, twice the distance between the two aircraft in the direction of the radar must be greater than the pulse length, or

$$\text{Target resolution distance} = \Delta R = c\tau/2 \qquad (B.7)$$

for the minimum target resolution range. This equation also defines the minimum range at which a target can be detected. The equation shows that as the pulse width increases, the resolution in range degrades because the range bins must be proportionately larger. The extreme case is that of the continuous wave radar which theoretically has no range resolution capability because the pulse width is infinite. However, CW radars can be designed to give target range and resolution information by the use of special frequency modulation techniques.

Another pulse radar signal parameter is the duty cycle, which is defined as the ratio of the time the radar is transmitting to the pulse repetition interval. The duty cycle is expressed as a decimal, or as a percent, or in decibel measure. The duty cycle for a continuous wave radar is 100%. Normal fire-control radar duty cycles are on the order of 0.001. The average power level of a radar is defined as the peak power level, which is the level during the transmitting cycle, times the duty cycle. Thus,

$$P_{av} = P_{peak} \times (\text{duty cycle}) \qquad (B.8)$$

Doppler. When an aircraft is moving radially with respect to the radar, the frequency of the echo is shifted from the original carrier frequency by an amount that is dependent upon the relative radial velocity of the target with respect to the radar antenna, V_r. This change in frequency is called the Doppler frequency, or shift, f_d. Like the sound waves from the whistle of a passing train, the Doppler frequency increases for approaching targets and decreases for the ones that are receding. The Doppler frequency is given by the expression

$$\text{Doppler frequency} = f_d = 2fV_r/c = 2V_r/\lambda \qquad (B.9a)$$

Thus, the relative radial velocity of the target can be determined using

$$\text{Relative radial velocity} = V_r = f_d c/2f \qquad (B.9b)$$

when the Doppler frequency is known.

The Doppler frequency can be used to detect and track a target in angle. A radar Doppler or velocity tracker may use banks of frequency filters or velocity gates and a circuitry that indicates which filter "rings" when an echo is received. Continuous wave radars are theoretically able to determine the Doppler frequency most accurately because of their long sampling time and are therefore the type used when extremely accurate frequency shift measurements are required. In general, the ability of pulse radars to accurately measure the Doppler shift varies with the pulse width and duty cycle. In order to increase the Doppler processing time of a pulse radar, a multiple pulse waveform can be used to obtain the Doppler frequency. However, when the echo from more than one pulse is processed, an ambiguity in velocity can occur, just as in the case of range ambiguity. Also, blind speeds (velocities, and hence targets, not seen by the radar) can occur. For unambiguous velocity measurement

$$f_{d_{max}} \geq 1/\text{PRI} \tag{B.10}$$

Note that range ambiguity is directly proportional to the PRI, whereas velocity ambiguity is inversely proportional to the PRI. Thus, the designer of a pulse radar that tracks in both range and Doppler, known as a pulse-Doppler radar, must compromise between the two ambiguities. One technique to avoid this problem is to rapidly change, stagger, or jitter the PRF. However, this requires additional circuitry to transmit the pulses and process the echoes.

An important use of the Doppler frequency is for the detection and tracking of a moving target in the presence of strong echoes from stationary reflectors, such as ground clutter. Since the strong echoes from the stationary objects do not exhibit a Doppler frequency (with a stationary radar) and the weak echo from the moving target does, special circuitry can filter out the stationary clutter from the returned signal and reveal the moving target with its Doppler frequency. This capability is one type of a moving target indicator (MTI). Another type of MTI compares two consecutive echoes. The difference between the two echoes is due to objects moving with respect to the radar.

Pulse compression. Pulse compression refers to a modulation of the transmitted signal in order to obtain a relatively low-power, long-pulse-width signal with large radiated energy, without sacrificing the target range resolution. Normally this is accomplished using either frequency or phase modulation. In frequency modulation, known as chirp, the transmitted signal frequency is changed linearly from the leading edge of the constant amplitude pulse to the trailing edge. Upon reception of the scattered signal, the echo is passed through a pulse compression filter that slows down the leading edge of the pulse and speeds up the trailing edge. This procedure decreases the pulse width, and hence increases the peak power of the echo; and, by comparing the overlapping echoes from two targets with a stored replica of the transmitted signal, the targets can be accurately resolved.

Antenna Parameters

The antenna on a radar serves two primary purposes. First, it can direct and shape the radar beam, and second, it can provide a gain in power to the signal.

Gain. Antenna gain G_r is the ratio of the maximum power in the beam radiated by the antenna to the power that would have been radiated had the antenna been omnidirectional. The gain is related to the antenna size and signal wavelength by

$$\text{Antenna gain} = G_r = 4\pi\rho A / \lambda^2 = 4\pi A_e / \lambda^2 \qquad (\text{B}.11)$$

where A is the physical aperture or the total frontal (planar) area of the antenna, and ρ is the antenna efficiency factor. A nominal value for ρ is 0.6. These two quantities are sometimes multiplied together and called the effective aperture A_e. Two features that should be noted are that gain is directly proportional to the area and inversely proportional to the wavelength squared (or directly proportional to the frequency squared). Thus, to get appreciable gain, one of two choices must be made: either a very large antenna or a relatively high frequency must be used.

Beamwidth. An antenna does not radiate all of the signal power in just one specific direction. Small amounts of signal are radiated in nearly all directions, and the distribution of the radiated power around the antenna is called the antenna radiation pattern. A typical antenna radiation pattern in azimuth is shown in Fig. B.6. Note that the power measurement is in decibels, and the maximum power in the main lobe is the reference power level. Note also the presence of nulls and secondary lobes, called side lobes, in the pattern. Side lobes are undesirable because of the ambiguity in angle they cause; any echo taken in by a side lobe is interpreted as arriving in the main beam. The side lobe gain can be reduced by weighting or tapering the feed horn illumination pattern to reduce the illumination at the edges of the antenna. However, this also reduces the efficiency of the antenna.

The beamwidth of the transmitted signal is usually defined as the width of the beam between the half-power or -3-dB points. Thus, the beam in Fig. B.6 has a beamwidth of about 20 deg. In general, the beamwidth is inversely proportional to the aperture width of the antenna. The equation for the beamwidth of a parabolic dish antenna is

$$\text{Beamwidth (in degrees)} = b\lambda/D \qquad (\text{B}.12)$$

where D is the frontal diameter of the dish, and b varies from about 50 for a uniform feed horn illumination function to 80 for a cosine squared illumination.

Antenna types and shapes. Different antenna shapes are used to obtain beam patterns optimized to a specific function. Surveillance radar antennas are usually much wider than they are tall so that the radiated pattern is a vertical fan beam that provides narrow azimuth resolution while covering a large sector in elevation. Figure B.2 shows a typical search radar antenna with a fan beam. Some weapon-control radars use two separate fan-shaped antennas to create two (an elevation and an azimuth) fan beams.

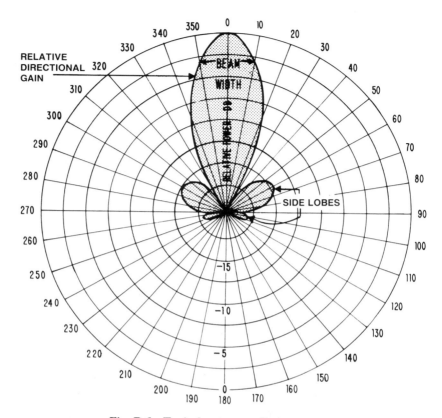

Fig. B.6 Typical antenna radiation pattern.

Weapon-control radars that use a symmetrical, dish-shaped antenna, similar to the one shown in Fig. B.3, have the narrow, high-resolution beam pattern referred to as a pencil beam. These pencil beams are so narrow they normally cannot be used to scan large areas for a target, but once "locked on" they provide accurate directional information. Occasionally, a symmetrical antenna will be used as a target illuminator rather than as a target tracker. In those instances, normally associated with semiactive missile guidance systems, the radar does not have to supply accurate guidance information, but it may have to maintain a continuous target echo for the missile to home in on. Consequently, a wider symmetrical beam can be utilized.

Another important type of antenna is the array antenna. This antenna consists of a multitude of individual radiating antennas or elements rigidly mounted in a regular one-dimensional (linear array) or two-dimensional (planar array) pattern. The elements themselves can be dipoles, open-ended

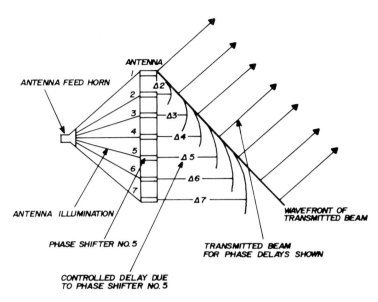

ANTENNA FEED HORN

ANTENNA I

ANTENNA ILLUMINATION

PHASE SHIFTER NO. 5

CONTROLLED DELAY DUE
TO PHASE SHIFTER NO. 5

WAVEFRONT OF
TRANSMITTED BEAM

TRANSMITTED BEAM
FOR PHASE DELAYS SHOWN

Fig. B.7   Planar electronically phased array.

waveguides, or any other type of antenna. One special type of planar array
is the electronically phased array antenna shown in Fig. B.7. By controlling
the phase shift and amplitude of the individual signals directed to each of
these elements, the radar beam can be electronically shaped and scanned
back and forth and/or up and down at speeds unlimited by the mechanical
inertia of the traditional scanning antenna. The beam shape and direction
can be changed so rapidly that the radar can track several targets, search for
other targets, and guide missiles simultaneously.

Polarization.   The electromagnetic waves radiated by an antenna are
polarized according to the antenna design. For example, conventional feed
horns radiate linearly polarized waves, and a combination of two orthogonal
feed horns will produce a circularly polarized composite wave when the
signals from each horn are equal in strength and separated in phase by 90
deg. The composite wave is elliptically polarized when the phase difference
is less than 90 deg and greater than 0 deg. When the polarized signal strikes
a scatterer, the polarization of the echo will be changed from that of the
signal according to the geometry of the body. This phenomenon is called
depolarization or cross-polarization. An antenna will effectively receive or
detect only those echoes that are polarized in the same manner as the
transmitted signal. For example, antennas that transmit horizontally
polarized signals will only effectively receive horizontally polarized echoes.
Thus, if the signal is horizontally polarized and the echo is vertically

polarized, the antenna will not receive the echo. By transmitting an ellipti-cally or circularly polarized signal, the antenna will be able to receive some portion of the echo from a depolarizing body.

Radar Cross Section

When a radar signal impinges on a body, a portion of the signal may pass through the body, a portion may be absorbed by the body as heat, and the remainder is reradiated or scattered in many directions. Some of the scattered signal will be in the direction of the receiver. The relative amount scattered in the direction of the receiver determines the radar cross section (RCS) of the body, σ. Thus, the RCS is the measure of the size of the body as seen by the radar. The RCS is an area and is usually measured in square meters or decibels, with a 1-m^2 reference level, and, except for the sphere, is aspect dependent. A formal definition of σ is 4π times the ratio of the signal power per unit solid angle scattered in the direction of the receiver to the signal power per unit area (the signal power density) that strikes the body.* In other words, the body intercepts the propagating radar signal and in essence becomes like a transmitting antenna whose power varies with direction. In general, the RCS of a body depends upon the relative sizes of the body and the signal wavelength, the body materials and shapes, and the signal polarization.

The Radar Range Equation

The basic relationship that determines the effectiveness of a radar is known as the radar range equation. This equation defines the maximum range at which a given radar can detect a given target. Figure B.8 shows the parameters that affect this relationship.

The hostile radar has a peak power output of P_r. If the power of the radar is radiated into space omnidirectionally, the power would be distributed evenly over the surface of a sphere whose center is located concentrically with the source of the power. At any range from the radar r, the surface area of the sphere is $4\pi r^2$. Dividing the total signal power by the surface area gives the power density at r for the omnidirectional antenna. However, most air-defense radar antennas have a gain factor G_r. Thus, the power density of the signal at the target, which is at the range R from the radar, is given by

$$\text{Power density at the target} = P_r G_r / 4\pi R^2 \qquad \text{(B.13a)}$$

The signal illuminates the target presented area A_t, creating a power at the target. The portion of the signal that is scattered in the direction of the radar receiver will either amplify or degrade this power by the gain factor G_t. The product $A_t G_t$ is the radar cross section σ. Thus, multiplying the

---

*The unit solid angle is the steradian, and there are 4π steradians in a sphere.

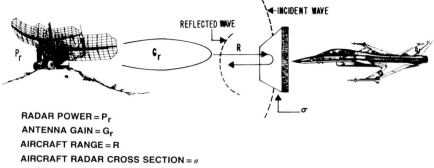

RADAR POWER = P_r
ANTENNA GAIN = G_r
AIRCRAFT RANGE = R
AIRCRAFT RADAR CROSS SECTION = σ
ECHO = S
ANTENNA AREA = A
ANTENNA EFFICIENCY = ρ

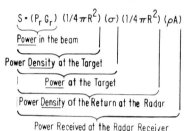

$$S = (P_r\, G_r)\ (1/4\pi R^2)\ (\sigma)\ (1/4\pi R^2)\ (\rho A)$$

Power in the beam
Power Density at the Target
Power at the Target
Power Density of the Return at the Radar
Power Received at the Radar Receiver

Fig B.8   Radar-target geometry and parameters.

signal power density at the target by $A_t G_t$, or σ, gives the echo power reflected at the target in the direction of the receiver, as if the target were a source of power itself:

$$\text{Power at the target} = \frac{P_r G_r}{4\pi R^2}(A_t G_t) = \frac{P_r G_t \sigma}{4\pi R^2} \tag{B.13b}$$

As the echo propagates away from the target and toward the radar receiving antenna, the density of the echo power decays inversely with the radius from the target squared, just as the original signal decayed as it propagated away from the transmitter. The power density of the echo of interest is that at the radar receiver, which is assumed to be located at the transmitter, so the radius of the echo sphere is given by R, and the surface area of the echo is given by $4\pi R^2$. The echo power density impinges on the receiving antenna, which has an effective receiving area of A_e, and the echo power density is converted to the echo power S. Thus,

$$S = \frac{P_r G_r \sigma A_e}{\left(4\pi R^2\right)^2} \tag{B.13c}$$

This is the basic radar equation, and it can be written in several different ways. By combining terms and using the relationship between the antenna gain and the effective area of the antenna, the following forms can be derived:

$$S = \frac{P_r G_r^2 \lambda^2 \sigma}{(4\pi)^3 R^4} \qquad \text{(B.13d)}$$

$$S = \frac{P_r A_e^2 \sigma}{4\pi \lambda^2 R^4} \qquad \text{(B.13e)}$$

Up to now, the effects of signal and echo power losses and extraneous noise have not been considered. The various signal and echo power losses that occur due to atmospheric attenuation, polarization losses, and signal processing can be accounted for by dividing the echo power at the receiver by a factor L, where L is equal to unity when there are no losses and is greater than unity when losses occur. The extraneous noise that appears with the echo can originate from outside of the radar system, such as from natural and manufactured sources, and from the electronic circuitry of the radar system itself. The power of the noise that lies within the signal bandwidth of the radar receiver N is an important radar parameter, and the ratio of the echo power to the noise power S/N is referred to as the signal-to-noise ratio. Thus, including losses and noise in the analysis gives

$$\text{Signal-to-noise ratio} = \frac{S}{N} = \frac{P_r G_r^2 \lambda^2 \sigma}{(4\pi)^3 R^4 L N} \qquad \text{(B.14a)}$$

During normal operations, the majority of the noise comes from the front end of the receiver, and N can be given in the form

$$\text{Receiver noise} = N = N_0 B \qquad \text{(B.14b)}$$

where N_0 is the noise factor per unit bandwidth, and B is the receiver bandwidth in Hz.

The signal-to-noise ratio plays a major role in the detection and tracking capabilities of a radar system. During the operation of any radar system, the goal of the radar operator is to be able to distinguish aircraft echoes from the noise. There are many signal processing techniques to assist him/her in this endeavor, such as designing echo thresholds so that most of the noise is below the threshold and is rejected, and using more than one echo pulse to determine whether a target is present. Ultimately, it is up to the operator to decide when he or she sees a target.

The maximum range at which the radar operator can detect an aircraft can be estimated using the S/N form of the radar equation. If $(S/N)_{min}$ is defined as the minimum signal-to-noise ratio for which a detection can be made, and R_{max} is defined as the range at which $(S/N)_{min}$ occurs, the radar

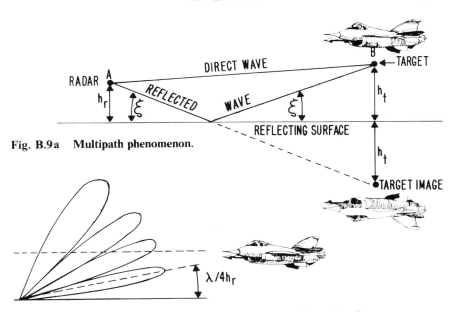

Fig. B.9a   Multipath phenomenon.

Fig. B.9b   Echo power vs target range with multipath.

equation can be solved for R_{max}, giving the radar range equation

$$\text{Maximum range} = R_{max} = \left(\frac{P_r G_r^2 \lambda^2 \sigma}{(4\pi)^3 L N (S/N)_{min}} \right)^{\frac{1}{4}} \qquad (B.14c)$$

The final modification to the radar range equation applies to low-flying aircraft and is due to signal reflections from the surface of the Earth as the signal travels from the transmitting antenna to the aircraft and back. Some of the outbound signal that is not propagating directly toward the aircraft may actually reach the aircraft and return to the antenna by an indirect path that includes a reflection from the Earth's surface, as shown in Fig. B.9a. This is known as the multipath phenomenon. The surface reflected signal travels a longer distance than the direct signal and hence interferes with the direct signal at the aircraft and at the antenna. The interference will either strengthen or reinforce the echo when the two signals are in phase or weaken or interfere with the echo when they are out of phase. As the aircraft travels along a path of constant altitude toward the radar, the echo will fluctuate in strength, growing stronger and then weaker, as the two signals differentially change in path length, and hence phase. Figure B.9b illustrates the peaks and nulls in the combined echo power. The change in the field strength F of the combined signals at the target will vary from zero when the two signals are exactly out of phase to a factor of 2 when they are exactly in phase, assuming the reflected signal and the direct signal are of equal strength and polarization. Because the echo power is proportional to the field strength squared, and because the path from the target to the radar is assumed to be the same as that from the radar to the target, the power of the combined echoes at the receiving antenna is given by F^4, where $0 \leq F \leq 2$. When no multipath echoes are present, $F = 1$. Including this multipath factor in the radar equation gives

$$\text{Maximum range} = R_{max} = \left(\frac{P_r G_r^2 \lambda^2 \sigma F^4}{(4\pi)^3 LN(S/N)_{min}} \right)^{\frac{1}{4}} \qquad \text{(B.14d)}$$

The drastic changes in the combined echo strength and the wandering of the apparent target elevation angle that occur because of the interference can make accurate tracking very difficult at beam angles less than one-half of a beamwidth above the surface.

B.3 INFRARED RADIATION

Infrared (i.r.) radiation, like radar, is a portion of the electromagnetic spectrum. The i.r. band lies within the optical band (1×10^{-3} m to 1×10^{-8} m) and encompasses wavelengths from 0.77 to 1000 μm (equal to 1×10^{-6} m). The i.r. band has been subdivided into four subbands, the near (0.77 to 1.5 μm), the middle (1.5 to 6.0 μm), the far (6.0 to 40 μm), and the extreme (40 to 1000 μm). The locations of the various i.r. subbands within the optical spectrum are shown in Fig. B.10.

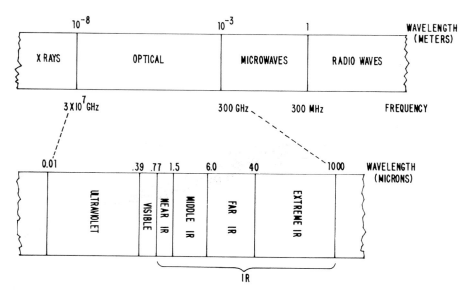

Fig. B.10   Optical spectrum.

Electromagnetic radiation in the infrared band is emitted by any body that has a temperature above absolute zero. This radiation is a form of power known as thermal radiation and is caused by the accelerations of electrons. Electrons can be accelerated by the rotation of molecules, by the vibration of atoms within molecules, and by electron transition. The radiation caused by molecular rotation lies in the extreme i.r. band and the high end of the far i.r. band. Vibration of the atoms within a molecule causes radiation in the middle and far i.r. bands, and the transition of electrons from a higher energy level to a lower one within an atom produces radiation in the near i.r. band and the visible and ultraviolet bands of the optical spectrum. As the temperature of a body is increased above absolute zero, the molecules start to rotate. As the temperature increase continues, atomic vibrations become important, and further increases in the temperature can cause electron transition radiation. The total amount of thermal power radiated by a body and the distribution of the power over the wavelength spectrum are functions of the body material and temperature. For solids, the power is smoothly distributed over a relatively broad band of wavelengths, whereas in hot gaseous mixtures, such as engine exhaust plumes, the power is radiated only within very small bandwidths centered at discrete wavelengths. The solids are known as continuum radiators or emitters, and the gaseous mixtures are called line radiators or emitters.

Continuum Emission and Absorption of i.r. Radiation

Consider a solid body at the temperature T K. The total thermal radiation or power emitted by the body over its entire surface is referred to as the radiant flux Φ and is normally given in Watts. The radiation emitted by the body over a unit area of its surface is called the radiant emittance, radiant exitance, or exitent radiant areance, M, and for a perfect emitter, called a black body, is given by

$$M = \sigma T^4 \quad (\text{W}/\text{cm}^2) \tag{B.15}$$

This equation is known as the Stefan-Boltzmann law, and σ (not to be confused with the RCS) is the Stefan-Boltzmann constant, whose value is

$$\sigma = 5.6697 \times 10^{-12} \quad (\text{W}/\text{cm}^2\text{-K}^4)$$

The radiation from the body is sometimes expressed as the power emitted over a unit solid angle and is referred to as the radiant intensity or radiant pointance I (Watts/steradian). Real bodies are never perfect radiators and consequently are called either gray bodies or selective radiators. The radiant emittance of a gray body is given by

$$M = \varepsilon \sigma T^4 \quad (\text{W}/\text{cm}^2) \tag{B.16}$$

where ε is the effective emissivity, which is equal to unity for the black body and is less than unity for the gray body.

The radiant emittance from a continuum emitter is composed of radiation in all of the wavelengths λ, but the amount of power contained in each wavelength interval is different. Consequently, the radiant emittance is given by the integral relationship

$$M = \int_0^\infty M_\lambda \, d\lambda \qquad (B.17)$$

where M_λ is known as the spectral radiant emittance (the radiant emittance per unit wavelength). The spectral radiant emittance of a general body is given by Planck's law

$$M_\lambda = \frac{\varepsilon_\lambda C_1}{\lambda^5 [\exp(C_2/\lambda T) - 1]} \qquad (\text{W}/\text{cm}^2/\mu\text{m}) \qquad (B.18)$$

where ε_λ is the spectral emissivity for the wavelength λ (in μm), and

$$C_1 = 3.74832 \times 10^4 \qquad (\text{W-}\mu\text{m}^4/\text{cm}^2)$$

$$C_2 = 1.438786 \times 10^4 \qquad (\mu\text{m-K})$$

For gray bodies, ε_λ is essentially constant. Bodies that have a widely varying spectral emissivity are called selective radiators. The black body spectral radiant emittance ($\varepsilon_\lambda = 1$) is given in Fig. B.11 as a function of wavelength for several values of temperature. Note that, as the temperature increases, the peak value of the spectral radiant emittance occurs at shorter wavelengths. For example, a body at room temperature (20°C or 293 K) emits most of its energy at about 10 μm, whereas an 800 K aircraft tail pipe emits the maximum radiation at about 3.7 μm. An estimation of the wavelength associated with the peak spectral radiant emittance is given by Wein's displacement law:

$$\lambda = 2893/T \qquad (\mu\text{m}) \qquad (B.19)$$

where T is in degrees Kelvin.

In general, many i.r. detectors can only sense radiation within a small band of wavelengths, λ_1 to λ_2. Thus, the radiant emittance in the detector bandwidth is given by

$$M(\lambda_1 \le \lambda \le \lambda_2) = \int_{\lambda_1}^{\lambda_2} M_\lambda \, d\lambda \qquad (B.20)$$

Note that, although the radiant emittance given by Eq. (B.16) is proportional to T^4, integration of the spectral radiant emittance over the small band of wavelengths that an i.r. sensor can detect could lead to a proportionality much higher than the fourth power. The amount of power radiated

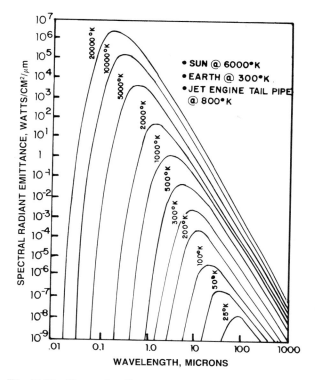

Fig. B.11   Spectral radiant emittance from a black body.

within the detector wavelength band and the specific proportionality with respect to T depend upon the temperature and the location and size of the interval of wavelengths considered.

The infrared radiation from a body is made up of the radiation emitted by the body due to its temperature and any incident radiation reflected by the body. In general, given any incident radiation from an external source, such as the sun, a fraction of the radiation α is absorbed by the body, thus raising its temperature, a fraction ρ is reflected at the incident surface, and a fraction τ is transmitted completely through the body. For metals and opaque materials, there is no transmission. Thus,

$$\alpha + \rho = 1 \tag{B.21}$$

That is, the relative amount of incident radiation absorbed plus the relative amount reflected is equal to unity, the relative amount of incident radiation. For a black body, $\rho = 0$, whereas for gray bodies, $\rho \neq 0$. Under isothermal equilibrium (steady-state) conditions, Kirchoff's law states that the ratio of the radiant emittance of a gray body to that of a black body is equal to the

Table B.1   Infrared Terminology and Notation

Physical Quantity	Term	Symbol	Unit
Power emitted	Radiant flux	Φ	W
Power emitted per unit surface area	Radiant emittance Radiant exitance Exitent radiant areance	M	W/cm^2
Power emitted per unit area per unit wavelength	Spectral radiant emittance Spectral radiant exitance Spectral radiant areance	M_λ	W/cm^3
Power emitted per unit solid angle	Radiant intensity Radiant pointance	I	W/sr
Power emitted per unit solid angle per unit area	Radiance Radiant sterance	L	$W/sr/cm^2$
Power incident per unit surface area	Irradiance Incident radiant areance	E	W/cm^2

absorbance. Thus, $\varepsilon = \alpha$, and bodies that are good emitters are also good absorbers; the black body being the perfect emitter and absorber.

When a body at temperature T is placed in a medium that has a background temperature of T_0, radiation will be emitted and absorbed by both the body and the surrounding medium. If the body is at a higher temperature than the medium, the radiant emittance from the body will exceed the radiant illumination or irradiance on the body from the surrounding medium, and the body will lose thermal energy. If no additional thermal energy is added to the body, the temperature of the body will decrease and approach that of the medium until thermal equilibrium is reached, when the emittance and irradiance become equal. If the body is cooler than the medium, the reverse process occurs.

To aid the reader in keeping track of the i.r. terminology presented here, definitions of the more common i.r. terms, symbols, and units are given in Table B.1.

Line Emission of i.r. Radiation

For gases, the intermolecular spacing is relatively large, and hence molecular rotation and atomic vibration are not constrained as they are for solids. Consequently, radiant energy is emitted and absorbed by the gas only at discrete wavelengths associated with specific rotation and vibration frequencies, called spectral lines, that depend upon the particular type of molecule. These spectral lines are clustered into very tightly spaced sets called bands.

The emissivity of the gas is essentially zero outside of these bands and is dependent upon the line spacing and intensity within the bands.

Atmospheric Transmission and Absorption of i.r. Radiation

When i.r. radiation propagates through the atmosphere (which is a gas), some of it will be reflected or scattered, some of it will be absorbed, and some of it will be transmitted. The first two processes cause an attenuation or extinction of the flux. For gases, the amount of reflectance or scattering of the incident i.r. radiation depends upon the molecules, haze, and fog in the atmosphere, but is generally small, whereas the transmittance and absorption are usually more important. Thus,

$$\alpha + \tau = 1 \qquad (B.22)$$

Both α and τ are very strongly wavelength and temperature dependent for a specific gas. Because gases emit radiation in discrete bands, they also absorb radiation only in those same discrete bands. Higher temperature and/or pressure in the gas causes the emissivity within the bands to increase and the bands to become broader.

Figure B.12 is an illustration of the percentage of radiation transmission over a 1-n.mi. path for a given sea level atmosphere and temperature as a function of wavelength. The absorbing molecules of the atmosphere are also

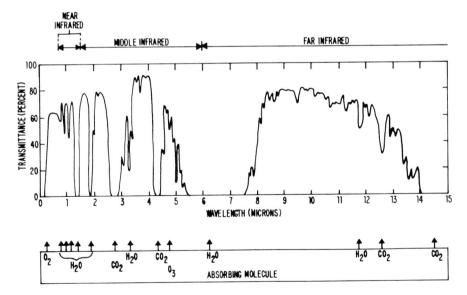

Fig. B.12 Atmospheric attenuation of i.r. radiation (Ref.: H.A. Gebbie et al., *Proceedings of the Royal Society of London,* Series A206, Vol. 87, 1951).

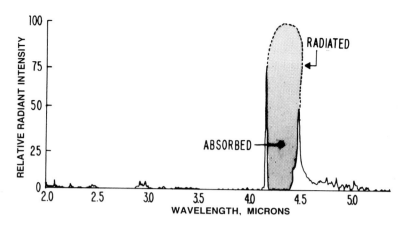

Fig. B.13   Exhaust plume i.r. radiation at 4.3 μm and the absorption by the atmosphere (Ref.: "Optical Radiation: Measurement and Analysis Capability," General Dynamics, ARL, Electro Dynamics Div., Pomona, Calif., 1975).

indicated in the figure. Those spectral regions where the transmittance is high are called windows. Note that the absorption bands that separate the windows are due mainly to the presence of carbon dioxide (CO_2) and water vapor (H_2O) in the atmosphere. The major absorption bands due to the water vapor occur at 1.4, 1.9, 2.7, 3.2, and 5.5 to 7.5 μm, and those due to carbon dioxide occur at 2.7, 4.3, and 14 to 16 μm.

Those CO_2 and H_2O bands where the greatest atmospheric absorption occurs are also the bands that have high emissivity. Thus, because these two gases are also present in the exhaust plume from an aircraft engine, a large amount of energy will be radiated from the plume in these bands. As this radiation propagates away from the plume and through the atmosphere, the CO_2 and H_2O molecules in the atmosphere will absorb it. However, the i.r. radiation from the carbon dioxide and water molecules in the hot exhaust plume will not be totally absorbed by the carbon dioxide and water molecules in the surrounding atmosphere, because the plume and atmosphere are at significantly different temperatures and pressures. Thus, their spectral radiant emittance and absorption values are somewhat different. This feature is illustrated in Fig. B.13, which shows both the radiation from the plume and the atmospheric absorbtion in the vicinity of the 4.3-μm carbon dioxide band. The exhaust plume will have a large spectral radiant emittance around 4.3 μm due to the presence of hot CO_2 in the plume. As this radiation propagates through the atmosphere, most of the center portion of the radiation will be absorbed by the cooler CO_2 in the atmosphere. However, spikes of radiation from the plume on both sides of the 4.3-μm band will continue to exist.

The altitude at which the radiation propagates also has a major effect on the amount of atmospheric absorption by the CO_2 and H_2O molecules. At sea level, the water vapor level is relatively high, and the attenuation is significant, as shown in Fig. B.12. However, as the altitude increases, the H_2O level decreases rapidly. At 20,000 ft, the amount of water vapor is less than 20% of the sea level value, and, at 40,000 ft, the i.r. attenuation due to H_2O is quite small. Fog and clouds, because they are heavy concentrations of water vapor, are strong absorbers of i.r. radiation. Transmittance of 1-μm i.r. radiation through a typical cloud is estimated to be only 1% for a path length of approximately 400 ft.

The absorption due to CO_2 also decreases as the altitude increases, but not as drastically as the change due to H_2O. The relative concentration of CO_2 molecules in the atmosphere remains essentially constant with respect to altitude. Thus, the absorption by CO_2 decreases only because the atmospheric density decreases. When the absorption by CO_2 is nearly total at sea level, it will be less than 20% per nautical mile at 40,000 ft.

Scattering of i.r. radiation occurs due to the presence of molecules, haze, fogs, and aerosols in the atmosphere. Rayleigh scattering is caused by atmospheric particles that are small with respect to the wavelength. The effect of these small particles on i.r. radiation scattering usually is small. Mie scattering refers to scattering by particles that are large compared with the wavelength, such as water droplets. This type of scattering is essentially independent of the wavelength when the particle is very much larger than the wavelength.

Infrared Detectors

An i.r. detector is typically a small, thin film or plate that is thermally isolated from its surroundings and whose electrical properties change when subjected to i.r. radiation. Detectors sensitive to radiation within the 1- to 40-μm band are the most common. There are two major categories of detectors: thermal detectors and photon detectors.

Thermal detectors. Thermal detectors require a change in temperature to function and include devices such as bolometers and thermopiles. A bolometer can be a semiconductor or thermistor that exhibits a change in an electrical property when it is heated by i.r. radiation. A thermopile consists of two dissimilar metals joined together. When the thermopile is heated by i.r. radiation, a voltage across the metals is produced. Thermal detectors are generally slower to respond and are less sensitive than the photon detectors. However, they are usually nonselective with respect to wavelength.

Photon detectors. Photon detectors do not require a temperature change to function. Consequently, they are more sensitive and are faster to respond than thermal detectors. However, their output is usually strongly dependent upon the wavelength of the i.r. radiation. They normally function in the 2- to 14-μm band. The photon detector is usually a semiconductor and works on the quantum effect. When the incident wavelength is sufficiently short, the photons in the i.r. radiation have enough energy to free electrons in the detector, causing a change in an electrical property of the

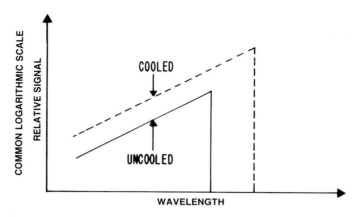

Fig. B.14   Idealized spectral responses of uncooled and cooled photon detectors.

detector. An idealized spectral response of a photon detector at room temperature is shown in Fig. B.14. There are several types of photon detectors, such as the photoconductors, photovoltaic detectors, charge coupled devices (CCD), and charge injection devices (CID). Some typical older photon detector materials that operate between 2 and 8 μm are lead sulfide (PbS), lead selenide (PbSe), and indium antimonide (InSb). Some photon detectors are cooled in order to lower the noise level in the detector. Furthermore, cooling the detector usually extends the sensor bandwidth into the longer wavelengths and increases the signal output, as illustrated in Fig. B.14. For example, uncooled PbS at 295 K is effective in the band from 1.2 to 2.8 μm. Radiation in this band comes mainly from very hot parts on the aircraft, from the solar reflection from the airframe and canopy, from the Sun, and from the solar reflection from clouds, trees, snow, Earth, etc. Cooling PbS may increase its effective bandwidth to 1.0 to 4.0 μm. Because of the increased sensitivity to the longer wavelengths, a cooled seeker may be able to detect the 4.3-μm radiation from the CO_2 in the exhaust plume.

Selected Bibliography

"Engineering Design Handbook on Infrared Military Systems, Part 1," AMCP 706-127, Headquarters, U.S. Army Materiel Command, 1971.

Hudson, R. D., Jr., *Infrared System Engineering*, Wiley-Interscience, New York, 1969.

Ridenour, L. N., ed., *Radar System Engineering*, McGraw-Hill Book Co., Inc., New York, 1947.

Skolnik, M. I., *Introduction to Radar Systems*, McGraw-Hill Book Co., Inc., New York, 2nd ed., 1980.

Toomay, J. C., *Radar Principles for the Non-Specialist*, Lifetime Learning Publications, Belmont, Calif., 1982.

Wheeler, G. J., *Radar Fundamentals*, Prentice-Hall, Inc., Englewood Cliffs, N.J., 1967.

Wolfe, W. L. and Zissis, G. J., eds., *The Infrared Handbook*, Infrared Information and Analysis Center, Environmental Research Institute of Michigan.

Zissis, G. J., "Fundamentals of Infrared—A Review," *Proceedings of the Society of Photo-Optical Instrumentation Engineers: Modern Utilization of Infrared Technology, Civilian and Military*, Vol. 62, Aug. 19–20, 1975.

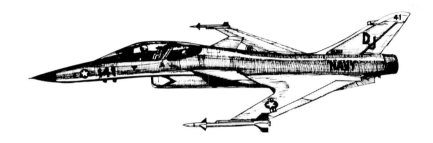

APPENDIX C. SURVIAC

SURVIAC stands for the Survivability/Vulnerability Information Analysis Center. It is a full-service DoD IAC, established in 1985, for the collection, storage, dissemination, and analysis of scientific and technical information, models, and data bases related to the nonnuclear survivability and vulnerability of US and foreign aeronautical and surface (excluding ships) targets. The SURVIAC objective is to increase the knowledge and productivity of scientists, engineers, and analysts engaged in scientific and engineering programs for the DoD. The SURVIAC will support users in the areas of survivability design, survivability technology, survivability assessment, and munitions effectiveness. The JTCG/AS and JTCG/ME are joint sponsors of the SURVIAC.

The initial core of SURVIAC consists of the merger of the Combat Data Information Center (CDIC) and the Aircraft Survivability Model Repository (ASMR) operations; the Center is expected to achieve full operational capability and will commence operations as a full-service DoD IAC by approximately mid-1986. Some of the user services that may be provided by the SURVIAC are:

- Report library.
- Vulnerability data base (including a component $P_{k/h}$ data base and standardized $P_{k/h}$ functions).
- Target geometric descriptions.
- Combat data.
- Susceptibility test and analysis data.
- One-on-one and M-on-N standardized and documented models and computer programs.
- Assessment methods.
- Vulnerability reduction design techniques and hardware.
- Susceptibility reduction design techniques and hardware.
- Systems survivability design techniques.
- Standardizations, handbooks, compendia of related R&D areas, specialist directories, newsletters, journals, workshops/symposia, and short courses.

The users of SURVIAC are organizations within DoD and their contractors. Information about the use of SURVIAC can be obtained by writing to AFWAL/FIES/SURVIAC, Wright-Patterson AFB, OH 45433-6553, or by telephoning (513) 255-4840/3956 or AV 785-4840/3956.

393

Index